Principles of Perception

Principles of

Perception

S. Howard Bartley
Michigan State University

Harper & Brothers, New York

PRINCIPLES OF PERCEPTION

To
those who most wish psychology
to be a science

Contents

Preface

This book is written on the supposition that psychology is first of all a science. As a science it is a form of biology and so developed as to take its place in a coördinate way among the other disciplines such as physics, chemistry, zoölogy, and botany. Much has been done in recent years to circumvent the forthright use of the word *biological* with reference to psychology. Terms such as life science, behavior science, etc., have been coined. With regard to each of these, the author suspects the inventor's lack of the appropriate appreciation for both psychology and biology.

The present volume is meant to be a decided step in getting away from the common persistent retention of mentalistic concepts and usages, while at the same time attempting to recognize the role of awareness (experience, consciousness, etc.) both as an object of study and as a factor in the activities of those who study it.

It is to be hoped that our criticism of the common use of the same words for both the stimulus and the response will be taken in good spirit and will thus result in the clarification of communication about behavior that seems so much to be needed.

There are many workers who have made decided and enduring contributions to our understanding of how the organism performs. We wish to express gratitude for what they have done. Some such workers will not find explicit reference to their work, largely owing to the fact that this is but a book meant for beginning students. They must be given only what they can handle in a single course which is all too short and too superficial at best.

All copyright owners and authors have been generous in granting permission to reproduce relevant material. We wish especially to thank the Munsell Color Company for the use of the plates for the illustration of their color scheme.

The most generous of all in use of time and abilities, and in the suffering of inconvenience, has been Leola Bevis Bartley, the author's wife. She graciously gave of her time in many ways when it was most trying and not at all convenient for her to do so.

S. H. B.

July, 1957
East Lansing

Principles of Perception

Chapter 1

INTRODUCTION

This is a book about perception. It is not solely a compilation of facts about perception but is also a development of a usable view of it and a description of the methods whereby it is studied.

Each of you brings to the reading of this book an idea of what perception is. You have used the word countless times, and may be quite satisfied with the way you use it. It is not likely that you have felt any need for revising or refining your understanding of it. The present call upon you to follow a discourse that examines the meaning of the term may, therefore, tend to be resisted. The resistance here is something that is not evoked in a field with which you admit you are totally unacquainted. You may receive the descriptions in such a field as a matter of curiosity and adventure. You act as though the author were competent to make positive statements, and you are quite prone to accept them. An open mind will be necessary here, too.

Our task is to show what kind of a definition of perception will best fit into a science of human behavior; how perception relates to other aspects of the behavior which psychologists study; how perception is dealt with in the laboratory and how it is involved in the social behavior of everyday life. The book will attempt to demonstrate that a technical understanding of perception is not simply something that experimental psychologists study, but something that anyone who aims at becoming a full-fledged psychologist needs to possess.

We shall first sketch for you the way the term perception was used in the early stages of experimental psychology, before and just after the turn of this century, and how it is generally used nowadays. As a consequence, it will be seen that although the term is not yet used as precisely as science would demand, it does refer to an aspect of behavior that can be singled out. Following this historical résumé, we shall consider what perception is according to the best understanding of the present day.

We shall suggest a usable definition of perception that deals with aspects of the problem left untouched. Such a definition must possess a reasonable degree of precision and must relate the group of facts subsumed under perception to other conventional subdivisions or aspects of behavior. This is the theoretical aspect of our task.

The second aspect will be to introduce you to a number of studies of perception that not only will acquaint you with the various sorts of findings in the broad area of perception, but also give you an understanding and a feeling for the ways perception is investigated. This is the factual and methodological aspect of the task.

Perception is an aspect of behavior that is rapidly undergoing a new appreciation among psychologists. You are entering psychology at an important period—a period of transition. To appreciate the subject properly, all aspects of the matter have to be dealt with.

APPROACHES TO THE UNDERSTANDING OF HUMAN BEHAVIOR

For some psychologists, their task is one of analyzing what they consider to be the basic mechanisms of behavior. These mechanisms are those of learning, perceiving, thinking, emoting, and so on. Some of these psychologists believe that any behavioral act is an example of *one* of these processes. Others believe that every instance of behavior potentially involves all of these processes as aspects, although only one can be studied very well at a time.

For a second group of psychologists, the organism[1] is made up of a

[1] In this text, several words are to be used for the human being, each of which in common usage conveys a little different shade of meaning. The first of these is *individual*. As we use it, the intent is to speak of the human being in more or less neutral terms, not stressing capacities or any other characteristics. The second is *subject*. This is the name for a human being who is placed under controlled conditions, and whose overt behavior is recorded. The third is *observer*. This, again, is the name for a human being who is placed under controlled conditions, but whose task is more especially that of using eyes or ears to report upon what is seen, heard, felt, etc. The fourth is *organism*. This term is one used for both animal or human being, and customarily carries certain quite definite connotations. It implies that the human being is biological, and studiable by all the methods used to study biological subjects. This implies that his observed behavior is a product of biological mechanisms. It implies that these mechanisms must be studied and understood if the subject is to be understood. The fifth term is *person*. This term is one that is meant to call attention to the unique characteristics of the human being, such as his ability to perceive, think, comprehend, plan, scheme, devise, love, hate, worry, hope, fear, and to do every other thing in the way that is unique to beings at the human level.

Contrary to necessity, but nevertheless by custom or habit, most people consider the term organism a little degrading when applied to the human being. It seems to imply that whoever uses it is forgetting the human characteristic of his subjects. One seldom, if ever, hears the terms person and organism used in the same sentence. Your author, group of traits called personality traits. The job for psychology, these psychologists think, is to define traits, or discover new ones. Some trait psychologists deal with traits that are operationally defined, and thus are not concerned with how many traits there are, or whether the list of traits which others propose corresponds to the traits they concern themselves with. For them, a trait is the characteristic of the behavior that is produced under a certain specified set of conditions. For all trait psychologists, traits are supposed to tell us what the organism is like, without our resorting to asking questions about perception, learning, and so forth.

A third kind of psychologist is devoted to dealing with people in accord with what is called their adjustments to their social surrounds. The psychologists in this group conceive of a limited number of broad ways in which the resources of the organism are channeled. The individual is described in terms of his evaluative and power relations to his environment. People are considered as being aggressive and expressing hostility toward something or somebody all the time. Part of this evaluative and power behavior is described in terms of the individual's appreciation (conscious or unconscious) of his own security. Analysis of the pervasiveness, the intensity, and the direction of the manifestations just mentioned is considered to be the exclusive job of psychology, as they see it.

There is still another group of psychologists. It does not focus its attention on the particulars of the relation *between* the organism and its surrounds, but rather deals with the patterns of activity *within* the organism itself, which can be described in energistic terms. This group is interested in how energy is mobilized and dissipated within the organism. For such psychologists, the bounds of their concern is the organism itself, and not the mechanisms through which the organism is acted upon by the environment. Hence they are not directly concerned with perception as such.

Thus it is that we find today four general categories into which psychologists have placed themselves, based upon what they consider psychology to be. These psychologists could be called mechanism psychologists, trait psychologists, power-relations psychologists, or energy-mobilization psychologists respectively. There are no men whom we could

---

however, disavows the incompatibility of the two words person and organism. It is one of the implicit tasks of this text to show something of how the organism achieves personality—the status of being a person. Or to put it in another way, to indicate the mechanisms that the person has at his command so as to be able to interact with his surrounds as he does.

well call general psychologists, unless they were to be those who make some pretense of using the techniques and ideas of these four groups in some kind of combination. Actually, it is difficult to see just how such combinations could be logically made without some alteration of the ideas that are appropriated.

In addition to these four groups just mentioned, there are *applied* psychologists, or psychological technologists, who occupy themselves with adapting the findings and ideas of these four groups to specific problems that emerge in industry, the healing professions, and the other civil and military affairs of the workaday world. Applied psychologists have found easier use of the ideas of some of the four groups than of others. In dealing with systematic views with regard to the human being, we are not concerned with applied psychology.

In the early days of experimental psychology, psychologists were virtually all occupied with the study of *mechanisms*, for they busied themselves with the processes that philosophers and other nonexperimentalists had discussed for centuries—sensing and perceiving being two of these processes.

Perceiving has been taken by all psychologists to be a process by which the organism relates itself to its surrounds. In perceiving, the individual interprets, discriminates, and identifies objects and conditions experienced to be existing in the environment. Can it be said that traits do the same thing in trait psychology; that adjustments do this for power psychology; and that energy mobilization does this for its psychology? If we could answer in the affirmative, then the excuse for the ultimate need of dealing with what is called perception would be greatly lessened, or possibly obviated.

The special appropriateness of retaining perception in a system of psychology lies in the fact that it concerns itself with *bodily mechanisms*. No other term or concept in psychology has taken on the task of carrying through the connection between what the individual does and the ways this behavior is related to the physical world which provides the "stimulus" in the first place. Mechanism psychology, through the use of perception (sensory processes), directs a portion of its attention to becoming acquainted with the literal physical energies through which the surrounds act upon the individual, upon the biological mechanisms whereby the organism is sensitive to those energies, and how these energies become code messages to the organism. Sense organs and neural pathways with all their physiological properties are studied, and the chain of events from those in the external environment clear through to the behavioral end results is traced. This procedure is the one providing the clearest understanding of the relation between environmental events and the behavior of the organism. It provides us with the most basic rationale for the acts and the abilities of the human subject.

SENSATION AND PERCEPTION

For a long time there were supposedly two processes involved in relating the organism to its surrounds. One of these was called *sensation* and the other *perception*. There was a time when these two supposed processes were described rather distinctly, but now the distinction between the two is less certain and more vague and difficult to conceive of. The information which we now have at our command leads us definitely away from the two-process idea. But to provide the reader with a basis for understanding this, and for possessing a clear basis for surmounting the confusion that still appears in many places in the literature, an account must be given of the matter.

Basis of All Knowledge

A couple of centuries ago, it became widely believed by the philosophers and other sophisticated people that all human knowledge comes through such senses as vision, hearing, and so on. There seemed to be two kinds of resulting experience. One was the simple irreducible kind represented by single colors, tastes, odors, touches, pains, temperatures. These were unit qualities, but they, in turn, became components of something beyond themselves. They became colors, tastes, for example, of *objects*. The experiencing of objects, activities of objects, and relations between objects were given a different name. They were called perceptions. Hence, although perceptions were called sensory experience, they were distinctly separated from sensations that were thought of as components of perceptions. Perceptions were seen to have reference to past experiences, previous attitudes, and even the activities which the individual was engaging in at the time. Thus it was said that sensations were simple and elemental, but that perceptions were complex and a result of elaboration and organization that occurred in the central nervous system. It seemed that as far as experimentation was concerned, sensations could be gotten at, whereas perceptions were elusive and the result of so many intangible factors that they could not well be studied. One could predict with reference to sensation, but not with reference to perception. To say the least, the distinction between the two classes of experiences was taken to be on solid ground. This attitude was not destined to prevail in full bloom for long. To those who were the most inquisitive and insightful, it became apparent that the category of sensation was not as tangible as might be hoped for. No one was actually able to isolate sensation in such a way as to show that sensations really exist. Irreducible experiences possessed at best a minimum of meaning, and thus seemed to partake of the quality of perception. Surely enough, conditions could be set up in which experiences of color, for example, were elicited from subjects who were trained virtually to ignore context and meaning. But this did not demonstrate the existence of sensations as elementary units literally devoid of all meaning.

Criteria for Distinguishing Sensation and Perception

It was not quite possible for one to show that a color was a sensation and an apple was a perception. The best that could be done was to set up rigid rules for experimentation in which "meaning" was to be kept out of subjects' verbal reports. Reports those days were generally introspective. Subjects were confronted with situations in which discriminatory reactions (verbal reports) were called for. The reports were descriptive of something that the subject experienced, and were not quantitative. Weights were lifted to determine the experiences that were elicited. Styli and other objects were used to contact the skin. From such procedures, two opposite possibilities existed regarding the introspective reports that were required. On the one hand, the report could center on the subject's identification of "what" it was that contacted the skin, or otherwise produced the experience. On the other hand, the report could be a description of the bodily experience itself, expressing no reference to a thing or agent that produced it. The latter form of report was the accepted one for experimentation in sensation. The former kind of report was ruled out, and was called committing a "stimulus error." The stimulus error was perceptual behavior. It contained "meaning" and was taken to be more than sensation. Even today, we can recognize these two forms of report and use them for different purposes, but in so doing we do not feel that we are unavoidably making a distinction between sensation and perception.

The second criterion for distinguishing between sensation and perception was a hypothetical one; namely, that a perception required an elaboration in the processes of the cerebral cortex of the brain, in addition to the processes required for sensation. It was as if sensations were produced shortly after the sense-organ input to the brain arrived there, and perceptions resulted only after certain secondary processes had had time to run their course, or to assemble. No one was ever able to demonstrate that sensations involved less brain activity than did perceptions. The difference was taken for granted, however, and became a part of the theoretical outlook of the day. Just so long as everybody could believe in these distinctions or took no active step in questioning them, or trying to see whether they could demonstrate them, all went very well. Psychology continued to be a matter of dictum, and that which was only purely hypothetical played the same role in psychological thinking as that which could be more concretely demonstrated.

If *elaboration* of brain activity is to be held as the second of the criteria for distinguishing between sensation and perception, one might expect perception to require more time to produce than sensation. One of the older reaction-time experiments seems to bear upon this problem. A comparison was made between lengths of reaction time for single letters and for short words, and it was found that the subject could react to short *words* more quickly than to *letters*. The significance of this difference in time needed to respond to the two kinds of presentation lies in the fact that the material with the more elaborate meaning (words) was responded to more quickly than the so-called units of which the word presentation was composed (letters).

It would have been expected that, if elaboration was a differential feature, it would have required longer to react to words than to letters. The word would have represented a presentation that had meaning and the letter a presentation evoking only about the same response as a color stimulus—something supposedly evoking a sensation.

Sensation—a Hypothetical Construct

Once it became apparent that to a large degree the sensation-perception distinction was artificial, and that sensations were not actually isolatable, sensation came to be admitted by some to be a *hypothetical construct*. It was still retained, however, to signify the solid and fixed core of the response process, or to label the more simple and stable experiential end results such as colors and sounds. The hypothetical construct, as it pertained to what was supposed to go on in the nervous system, designated the initial neural activities that preceded the supposed elaborations underlying the complex end result called perception.

"SENSORY RESPONSE." The word sensation was often changed to sensory response—sensory response that was fairly predictable, and largely determined by sense-organ characteristics. Perception was often classified, also, as sensory response, but was response that was flavored by detectable influences of learning and past experience, and manifested a kind of purposiveness.

Sensory responses tended to be chosen for study in formal experiments in laboratories. In such experiments, variables that ordinarily show up in everyday occasions were either controlled or eliminated. Subjects' responses came to be relatively predictable from the orderly findings of the experiments. This preserved considerable faith in the direct connection between stimulus characteristics and response characteristics. Sensory responses were said to be "stimulus-bound."

At the same time, it was freely admitted that many highly varied and quite unpredictable immediate responses could be elicited in everyday situations. These perceptions were highly personal, and tended to be called subjective.

The fact that two apparent classes of responses could be elicited led psychologists to group themselves. One group retained an interest in the fixed kind of response, which it tended to label sensory response, and the other group preferred dealing with the variable responses, which were called perceptions. Actually, many of the latter men even gave up dealing with perceptions and went to other considerations in psychology, such as have already been described in an earlier section.

As time went on, various men came to realize that the fixed "sensory" responses were not so fixed as they first seemed to be, and that perceptions were not so whimsical and lawless as first thought. This has led to the transition in which we find ourselves in psychology today. It is the embodiment of this realization that is one element of the position taken in the present text.

CURRENT DEFINITIONS OF PERCEPTION

Dictionary Definitions

Perception happens to be not only a term used in psychology but also a word with several meanings in common speech. We shall take a look at what the dictionary says perception is. Certain dictionary definitions are about as follows: (1) "Perception is any act or process of knowing objects, facts, or truths, whether by sense experience or by thought; awareness of objects; consciousness." (2) "Reference of sensation to an external object." (3) "An immediate or intuitive cognition or judgment;

an insight analogous to sense perception in respect of immediacy and the feeling of certainty accompanying it, and often implying nice observation, or subtle discrimination."

It will be seen that in common usage, as represented by these definitions, there are several diverse meanings of the term. In the first definition, perception is made to be a form of *knowing*.

The first definition makes perception a form of behavior not necessarily connected with sense-organ activity as well as behavior that is so connected. In other words, perception is made a form of thought as well as immediate behavior. The definition makes perception synonymous with consciousness itself. From this we can see that perception so defined is so broad a term as to have no established unique and restricted use. It is no wonder that the term is so variously and freely used.

But let us look at the remaining two definitions. The first of these makes perception a matter of sensation. In this definition, sensation is something psychic and a kind of copy process of externality. The third definition makes perception a judgment. The judgment may not only arise from sensory data but be sheer intuition.

These latter two definitions are no more appropriate for scientific purposes than the first. Thus, if we had to retain the breadth and variety of meanings given us by the dictionary, the term perception would have to be abandoned for our purposes. Our alternative is to restrict perception to some phase or aspect of the spectrum of meanings given in the dictionary. The situation with reference to perception is not different from that of many other terms which we want to employ so as to make psychology a science, and rescue it from being merely a de luxe form of parlor talk. In fact, at this point it might be well to state a rule with regard to technical language, of which scientific language is one form. In such language, a word must have no synonyms. Each concept must be labeled by only one word. Conversely, a word must refer to only one concept, no more. Thus shades of meaning and varied alternative connotations are not employed within a technical language so as to permit words to overlap one another. Each term has its domain, although words do relate to each other as genera and species. In a science or technology, a word used technically should obtain its meaning from a formal definition, and not from verbal context.

We wish to apply this rule in dealing with the subject matter that belongs to perception, and it is obvious that the dictionary approach is decidedly opposed to the requirements just stated.

Textbook Definitions

We may pass on from the dictionary to the field of psychology itself to examine a few definitions found in the literature. Here we should expect to find greater restriction in the usage of the term. But, to anticipate what will be found, it may be said that the restrictiveness is far from ideal, and incompleteness is the rule.

James' (128)[2] definition of perception, in 1892, was "consciousness of particular material things present to sense." He went further, saying that "sensational and reproductive brain-processes combined, then, are what give us the content of our perceptions."

In 1924, Seashore (224), in his *Introduction to Psychology*, stated that "sensation and perception together constitute sensory experience." Sensations are those elemental conscious processes that are ordinarily conditioned upon the functioning of sense organs. This implies that perceptions are something else—either that they are not elemental or else not dependent upon the functioning of sense organs.

According to this, sensations do not carry meaning, but mere awareness of sense quality. Perceptions, on the other hand, are the interpretations of sensations and convey meaning. "Thus, theoretically, we may experience redness, sweetness, fragrance, smoothness, and coldness as sensations in eating an apple; but when these qualities are interpreted as representing an apple, we have a perception." We may remind ourselves that these items involve the *concept* of an apple.

We come now to psychology texts that are in current use. Some of them give space to the discussions of perception without giving the reader a definition which he can carry away with him. Perhaps when the reader is finished with the section on perception, he is at a loss to put into a concise statement what perception was said to be. Some books operate on the basis of giving the reader general vague feelings with regard to various matters rather than verbal statements that can be carried away and reëxamined and put to use.

Perceiving is a process comparable with discriminating, differentiating, and observing. The term is customarily used to refer to relatively complex receptor and neural processes which underlie our awareness of ourselves and our world. This awareness is referred to as perception.

Although the term *perception* is usually restricted to aspects of experience, it has certain behavioral implications. Perception of objects, situations, and relationships is often correlated with particular overt reactions. If we are aware of a difference in the color of apples, we will very likely select the red ones for eating. If we see the detour leading off to the right, we will very likely take it.

[2] Figures in parentheses refer to References, pages 461–473.

If we do not see it, we are likely to continue and be forced to turn back later. Perceiving that a package is especially heavy, we use both hands to lift it; otherwise we use one hand. In general, when we perceive a difference between objects, we behave differently toward each of them, and when we do not perceive a difference, we fail to exhibit differential behavior.

Much of our information about perceptual processes is obtained without direct reference to their experiential aspects. Some of this information comes from experimental investigations of animal and infant behavior. Animals and infants can tell us nothing about their experiences, but they do respond differently to certain aspects of their environment. We can train them to approach one color and avoid another, to make one response to a triangle and a different response to a circle, and to differentiate various stimulating conditions. We can then reduce the difference between stimuli and observe the point at which discrimination no longer occurs. Differential responses tell us much about the stimulating properties of an organism's environment. This information may help us to understand receptor and neural development.[3]

We next turn to Boring, Langfeld, and Weld's (31) *Foundations of Psychology* of 1948. In it, it is said that "perception is the first event in the chain which leads from the stimulus to action." Also that "perception is the experience of objects and events which are here, now." Likewise, "perception is always a response to some change or difference in the environment."

Johnson (131), in his *Essentials of Psychology* of 1948, states that "The raw material delivered to the brain by the sense organs via sensory nerves is used and interpreted by the individual in accordance with his past experience and in furtherance of whatever activities he may be engaged in at the moment. The psychology of perception is an elaboration of this statement, which makes these generalities specific."

Stagner and Karwoski (232), in their *Psychology* of 1952, say that "perception is the process of obtaining knowledge of external objects and events, by means of the senses." They say, "William James put it well, when he wrote 'Perception is of definite and probable things.'" In other words, man takes his sensations (about which he is sure) and reaches conclusions about real objects (about which he is less sure if questioned)."

Summary of the Characteristics of the Definitions of Perception

Several conclusions may be distilled from what is to be found in current treatments of perception in textbooks and elsewhere. It seems that authors quite customarily act in accord with the following:

[3] Norman L. Munn, *Psychology: The Fundamentals of Human Adjustment,* 2nd ed., Boston, Houghton Mifflin Company, 1951, p. 400.

1. That perception may be dealt with by general description, without necessarily introducing a formal definition for the reader. It is as though it were taken for granted that most people know pretty much, in general, what perception is, and that any further discussion of it can be carried out simply by adding new illustrative material, or new anecdotal items.

2. That when definitions are offered, they need only be fragmentary, general, and need not place perception in relation to the other processes that go to make up the individual's overall behavior.

3. That sensation may still be looked upon as an elementary process underlying perception.

THEORIES REGARDING PERCEPTION

Nature of Current Perception Theories

Failing to find adequate definitions of perception limited to short statements, we can next examine certain more extended outlooks on various aspects of perception. Allport has called them theories of perception. Since most of them fail to cover the whole process called perceiving, they may be more appropriately called theories about certain *aspects* of perception. Allport (4) has listed 13 theories. Probably not all of them were even meant by their authors to be theories of perception, although they do specify something about the perceptual processes. We shall list 13 theories, but they will not be exactly the same 13 as designated by Allport. We do not believe that learning theories are, in any true sense, theories of perception; hence, learning theory will be omitted. Allport omitted a theory pertaining to visual space perception recently formulated by Gibson. We shall include it, and reserve our own outlook for the following chapter.

The Core-Context Theory

This is one of the classical theories of perception. It emerged in the days in which perception was thought of solely as an experiential or conscious response. According to the core-context theory, perception was not a single item but a group of interrelated parts. The elements consisted in simple sensations integrated with images and/or ideas left from past experiences. Conforming to the theory, sensory components do not, in themselves, have meaning; whereas perception, the aggregate, does. Sensations are combined into an aggregate under the laws of attention and certain principles of sensory connection. Images from past experiences are also part of the aggregate. The two (images and sensations) are often indistinguishable upon analysis. Some of the sensations form a *core* or focal group. The remainder of the constellation provides the context. From the aggregate, meaning emerges. Meaning is a contribution which the images and sensations provide each other. That is, meaning evolves out of *context*, or, more directly, context is thought to be meaning.

Texture-Gradient Theory

This theory has been formed to account for the spatial features of visual perception and, like other theories, has specifically to do with only limited features of perceiving.

The theory accounts for seeing the third dimension in space by the very same means as for seeing the two dimensions of a plane. It points out the orderly relations between the projection of the image of a surface on the retina and the orientation of that surface with reference to the line of regard. Surfaces at right angles to the line of regard provide for projections (images) of uniform texture. Tilted surfaces provide for images of graded texture. The portion of the surface nearer to the eye is represented in the image by coarser texture; portions lying farther away, by fine textures. This texture gradient, then, is the correlate of third-dimensional perspective. Artists and draftsmen have utilized this principle for centuries in their two-dimensional drawings. It remained only to translate this into a clear verbalized understanding for use in scientific circles. This was done only recently by Gibson (86).

According to this theory, perceived objects are not aggregations of sensations of pointlike units, but rather are constellations of surfaces and edges. Edges are formed by abruptions in gradients, and corners by vortices from which gradients extend. Perceptions are not copies of external objects, but certain kinds of correlates of them. Retinal images are neither replicas of the world nor pictures that perceptions copy, but patterns of variations possessing lawful relationships to externality.

The Cybernetic Theory

A cybernetic theory of perception is one in which the known facts of the nervous system and the principles used in the construction of electronic computing machines are brought together in the attempt to account for the organism's overall achievements we call perception. A major problem is how the experience of form is preserved despite differences of position of projection of objects on the retina, resulting from various eye movements. Another question dealt with pertains to how a pattern may be transposed; that is, how a melody can be recognized despite being played at various positions up and down the pitch scale.

The cybernetic theory of McCulloch and Pitts (181) employs the facts of accommodation (focusing of the lens of the eye), convergence, and adaptation (an analogue of volume control) in conjunction with other known or imputed processes in the nervous system to accomplish the essential tasks apparently performed in perception. Such mechanisms as negative feedback, scanning, and memory, or "storage of information," are used to bring about transformations within the nervous system of conditions lying outside. Thus external events are reconstructed within the organism and integrated with stored information derived from previous inputs. Since many features of perceptual behavior can be brought to enactment in electronic machines, the machines are used as models of the principles supposedly used by the organism.

Cell-Assembly-Phase-Sequence Theory

This is a view of how perception becomes what it is in the adult organism. Hebb (107), who is the author of this view, believes that there is convincing evidence to indicate that the initial response to visual targets is not nearly so complete and well integrated a process as the Gestalt psychologists seem to assert. While this theory is not one defining the nature of the process called perceiving, Hebb does indicate that perception is a product of learning. The idea of piecemeal building up of perception through the incorporation of various cell groups in the brain into larger and larger patterns of organized activity is somewhat opposite to the older idea of equipotentiality that had been advocated by Lashley (153) some years before to explain a number of experimental findings and common observations. Equipotentiality is the name given to the supposed interchangeability of various portions of the brain in bringing about the same behavioral end result, be it an experience or a motor end reaction. Hebb's theory attempts to whittle perceptions down to see what is initial and original, and what is the product of learning. It states that initial reactions to a visual presentation give rise to exploratory motor components that play the role of sequentially building up activities of small groups of brain cells into a larger sequence of activity—the neural bases for the activity which we know as perceptual in the adult organism. Certain forms of behavior of neural circuits (reverberating circuits) provide for prolonging the activity in the cell assemblies so that additional repetitions of the stimulus can become effective in the individual's attainment of a fuller response to it.

The experience of the figure-ground dichotomy is thought to be some-how primary in perception. This experience is very different from ex-periencing *identity* between objects. Identity comes only later on. Patient repetition is required to activate all the possibilities in the way things look. Separate attention to parts of figures is required at first.

Adaptation-Level Theory

This theory of perception, by Helson (*112*), is one that attempts to deal with the organism's response to configurations in accord with *di-mensional* or *quantitative* order. The adaptational process underlies the individual perception of sizes, distances, intensities, and other magni-tudes, or even qualitative properties such as beauty. The theory indicates that in order to behave this way the organism establishes a neutral or indifferent zone in the gamut of its encounters with the environs. This is used as the frame of reference. The evaluating process proceeds on the physiological as well as the psychological level, though generally it has its basis below that of conscious judgment formation.

Motor-Adjustment Theory

This outlook upon immediate response, typified in the thinking of Freeman (*78*), is one that emphasizes the motor posture or set of the organism at the time of stimulation. Hence, this outlook, too, centers on the character of the organism's contribution to its interaction with its surrounds. The description of behavior begins with postulating a covert pattern of tensions in skeletal muscles that precede the overt reaction of the muscles. This set, since it involves muscular tensions, provides a backlash input into the central nervous system by way of the proprio-ceptive pathways. This determines, to a large degree, the state of the nervous system at the time of receiving exteroceptive stimulation, that is, stimulation through eyes, ears, and so on. This tension consists in two components: a general background of diffuse and pervasive tension of all muscles, including the postural musculature; and a specific com-ponent, different in amount in various specific groups of muscles. Thus the tension, in general, is a pattern with a focus or foci. The percept, then, is the immediate overt action that takes place in relation to ex-ternal events, and is a part of the homeostatic regulation of the organism.

Sensory-Tonic Field Theory

This is an attempt to include in response to the environment certain motor aspects that are generally overlooked by other accounts of perception. We saw, in the two preceding theories, some recognition of the participation of muscular activity in perception, but neither of them included all of the possible motor aspects of perceptual response. The sensory-tonic theory is cognizant of one of the typically neglected features and attempts to bring it into the description of perception. The term tonic, in this theory, applies not only to the usual tonic feature of postural sets but also to the major aspects of phasic muscular activity involved in skeletal movement. Tonic seems to refer at times to the tonic *experience,* and at others to the physiological system in which tension conditions exist. Werner and Wapner (257), the proponents of the sensory-tonic theory, are concerned with how exteroceptive and interoceptive factors interact. Both factors seem to be involved, and neither can be neglected in understanding the organism's reaction to its surrounds.

To achieve this interaction, a process prior to both sensory and motor behavior was postulated. This was stated as a "total dynamic" process. Sensory and the tonic factors are contributing components by reason of their possession of "common dynamic" properties. The typical example of how this theory works is given in the following.

Stimuli that act upon the organism asymmetrically can be shown to set up unequal degrees of muscular tonus on the two sides of the body. This asymmetry is transformed into some tendency to perceive the positions of lines and other targets differently than when no asymmetry of muscular tone is involved. Thus, you see; that visual experience is partly regulated by the tonic asymmetry produced at the time.

Probabilistic-Functional Theory

This is a type of theory centering upon the phenomena of perceptual "constancy," in which "cues" form a considerable explanatory role. It is said that the organism, in line with the requirements of biological adaptation and using available data, tries to "reconstitute" the object, and is able to approximate it. The object it reconstitutes is an intermediate one having properties somewhere between those of the "*real*" object and the stimulus pattern *received* by the sense organ. Brunswik (46), the author of this theory of perception, calls it a probabilistic functionalism, for the object as perceived is never better than an approximation and represents a probability.

Transactional Theory

This theory, although developed quite independently of Brunswik's, also includes the idea that perception represents a probabilistic end

reaction. Perception is, as the theorizers Ames (5) and colleagues sometimes say, *prognostic*. This theory gives a central place to the purpose
or directionality of the perceiver and looks upon perception as a guide
to action. The action is for the furtherance of the organism's purposes.
The theory states that the organism infers the nature of the object by
an unconscious judgment[4] of what physical object would most likely be
required to produce the present pattern of impingement on the sense
organs. This theory has been built up largely on the study of physiological optics, in which it is recognized that a number of physical targets
are capable of producing the same pattern of retinal image. Hence, the
organism is confronted with a choice, and perception may or may not
be veridical.

This theory involves the recognition that past experience plays an
important role in perceiving. This pertains not only to specific objects
but to the nature of the world in which the organism finds itself. Certain
assumptions, as it were, result and perception occurs in accord with
these.

The Directive-State Theory

This is a theory of perception developed by Bruner and Postman
(44), and it is one of the earlier forms of social psychology's contribution
to perception. Perception is based upon two sharply contrasting factors:
the *structural* and the *behavioral*. These two factors are given the labels
of *autochthonous* and *behavioral* respectively. The determinants of the
first sort are the stimulus, the effects of the impingement on the receptors,
and the various pertinent parts of the nervous system. These factors are
the innate or fixed and unchangeable possession of the organism as a
mechanism for perceiving. They are those primarily dealt with by the
Gestaltists and those who apply psychophysics as a mode of experimentation. The factors can be said to be formal or formalistic.

The second set, or the behavioral determinants, stem from higher-
level processes, those having to do with other features of psychological
activity. These processes carry the effects of past experience in general
and include the organism's needs, tensions, value systems, and biases.
This theory indicates that the individual as a whole is represented in
his perceptions, whether this representation can be said to be synonymous to personality, or whether some more specific and tangible mechanism can be detected as being elicited by the given stimulus situation.

[4] This is quite reminiscent of the explanation used for certain features of perception
by Helmholtz in the nineteenth century. He called this process one of "unconscious
inference."

Be that as it may, the behavioral determinants form a central directive state making perception other than solely the often-described stimulus-bound end result.

The Hypothesis or Expectancy Theory

This theory, by Bruner (41), represents a later form of social psychology's contribution to perception. It recognizes the fact that perceptions do not arise from blank neutral ground, and states that the sets which the individual displays are what might be called hypotheses. As a rule, the subjects' sets are long established and firmly embedded. The theory points out that the stronger the hypothesis, the greater the probability of its activation in a given situation, and the less stimulus information that will be needed to activate it. The theory speaks of confirming and infirming the individual's hypotheses.

The Gestalt Theory

This is a view of organismic activity that disavows the very logic that was used to construct the core-context theory and all similar forms of associationism. It is a form of emergence doctrine in which the unit is not a building block but rather a complete product, a house itself. The theory specifies how the house comes into existence, but more especially how it operates once it exists. These formulations are generally known as "laws of Gestalten." One hundred and fourteen or more such laws have appeared in the literature from time to time, but later writers have attempted to reduce this number to a much smaller list, more or less comprehending the essentials of the longer list. One author, for example, reduced the number to 14 essential items, and more recently Allport (4) reduced them to six basic generalizations. The statements found in Gestalt theory are exemplified in the following:

Form is fundamental, and once it exists it tends to persist. There is parallelism or isomorphism between the form of underlying physiological processes and perceptual experiences, although the experience of form need not be correlative with the external stimulus.

The form of a percept is not to be explained by some adding or combining of prior elements.

Field forces are the interacting influences that pervade the state of wholeness. A field can be considered as a system of interacting influences maintaining an equilibrium, and thus maintaining a whole, or configuration. This field is viewed both at the physiological and at the experiential levels.

The relation between the stimulus pattern received by the organism and the fields or wholes of perception may undergo transformation. The following is an illustration of the retention of essential form while transformation is undergone. A picture that has been drawn on a rubber sheet may retain its identity even when the sheet is later stretched out of its original shape. The literal characteristics of the picture do not remain as they were; nevertheless, it retains an essential resemblance to its original self.

Topological Field Theory

Topological psychology has seemed to have been an attempt to develop a consistent and exclusively phenomenological psychology, but viewed critically it has intermingled physicalistic and phenomenological terms and concepts. The phenomenological field is one that is experienced as extending about the individual, the phenomenological self, but not lying within it. The individual's phenomenological experience of self and objects makes up the content of the field. The individual is treated as a point in space, and can migrate from one portion of this life space to another, thereby possessing a varying significance in the field. Perception has to do with the individual's comprehension of his positions in his life space.

Conclusions

It is not to be questioned that most, if not all, of these theories contain some truth. They assume properties that to some fair degree approximate the real nature of perception. They do in some cases, however, tend to overlap each other, and not all of them, in their present form, are necessary to complete a picture of perception. Certain of these theories, while not explicit about certain matters, seem to imply or take them for granted. It would be difficult to say that such theories did not possess features not explicitly mentioned. It could only be said that such theories did not make them explicit. For our purposes, then, it may be better to build anew, taking into account the contributions we find.

The present chapter, we trust, has provided a helpful orientation to the reader regarding what others have taken perception to be, and at the same time indicated the shortcomings in some of the uses of the word. The reader should be in a position to comprehend the more definitive usages of the term which we shall state, and which we shall adopt for the text.

The next chapter will be devoted to defining perception as it shall be used in the remainder of the text.

Chapter 2

PERCEPTION DEFINED

It is the task of this chapter to provide a working definition of perception. The reader must be so informed that he will know henceforth when he is dealing with perception and when he is dealing with forms of behavior that are not perceptual. This distinction is not customarily made clear, and this failure is responsible for many foggy ideas about behavior.

THE ENERGISTIC AND THE EXPERIENCEABLE WORLDS

The study of perception is not a simple direct task of accumulating easily obtained and easily understood data. Man is in the unique and peculiar position of having to lift himself by his own bootstraps. He needs to know about his environment and he needs to know about himself. He needs to come upon the principles that pertain to the interaction between the two. But, contrary to the logical necessity of the situation he faces, he has no absolute starting point. He possesses no absolute knowledge of his surrounds. What he does possess regarding his surrounds comes by way of his own limited facilities, that is, his own sense organs, his own nervous system, and his own effectors, the muscles. Yet it is these very mechanisms which he wants to test and understand. So what can he do? He can do no better than to use the facilities he has—his own abilities to experience and to conceptualize, and to make order out of his encounters. One group of men, the physicists, has used these capacities to construct ideas about the world outside. They, and all the rest of us, call it the physical world. But the psychologist has the problem of dealing with man. In other words, he is faced with studying himself. He must deal with man in terms of his reactions to the physical world, with the added supposition that he, himself, is wholly a part of the physical world, and not apart from it. The physicists talk about the physical world exclusively in terms of energy and the principles whereby energy is transformed into its several manifestations: thermal, electrical, mechanical, and so on. The world of the physicist is a nonexperienceable realm, but he must describe it in terms of the experienceable. Despite not knowing anything absolute about the physical world, the psychologist must use it as the basic system in his inquiry about human behavior. He must recognize the position he is in and make as consistent use of his materials as possible.

As has already been said, the psychologist regards man as a part of the physical world, and not apart from it. He obeys all physical laws just as though he were a substance in a test tube or retort. The psychologist is thus, even before he begins, presented with a paradox or a dilemma.

So the psychologist, in relating man to his environment, is obliged to start with the consideration of man as an energy system. What the psychologist understands stimuli to be must conform to the way the physicist would specify them, and what the psychologist understands as the lower-order body processes must be described as the chemist and the physiologist would describe them.

The psychologist must build up an understanding of man as a person by observing his interactions with his surrounds. His observations have to be worked into a conceptual scheme that makes a sensible and self-consistent picture. He must do just as the physicist—he must put his own interpretations on what he experiences. This, as was said to begin with, is a curious predicament, for it is his own ability to observe and perform which he is trying to analyze and understand. Because of the paradoxes and subtleties just described, he has been very slow in progressing toward his goal. He has made many blunders, and has had to backtrack many times, and take up new scents again and again.

IMMEDIATE AND PROTRACTED OR DELAYED BEHAVIOR

Some behavior of the organism can be seen to have a very close temporal connection with what happens in its surrounds. Such behavior follows closely the environmental event when brief, and is concurrent with environmental conditions when they are protracted. Other forms of behavior cannot so well be seen to relate to anything that is going on in the environment at the time. Such behavior, if it is to be related to anything outside the organism, must be connected with (stem from) what has already passed, or is yet to happen in the future. The difference between immediate and nonimmediate behavior is a natural and unavoidable distinction, and we are forced to take it into account in classifying behavior, although psychologists have customarily only loosely recognized it. We shall use the term perception only for the immediate form of behavior. Such terms as thinking, judging, remembering, will apply to the nonimmediate behavior, and to behavior that continues long after the transitory "stimulus" has come and gone.

Perception is the overall activity of the organism that immediately follows or accompanies energistic impingements upon the sense organs. The sensory apparatus mediates between the more internal ongoing activities of the organism and the events outside it. Mediation is a forerunner of utilization. Taken together, these consist in (1) the detection of impinging external energies, be they mechanical, chemical, photic, thermal, or otherwise; (2) transforming the quantitative relations of these energies into a set of quantity relations expressive of the organism (groupings of nerve impulses); and (3) relating the specific impingement patterns to "traces" of previous ones in terms of a code or system peculiar to the organism as a species and the particular organism receiving the impingement. The organism is not a simple mirror of externality, but rather a builder of a world of its own out of the nonexperienceable reality that the physicist calls energy.

Thus far we have indicated that perception is behavior that is immediately connected with energy patterns reaching the sense organs, and is to be distinguished in all cases from behavior that has less close temporal connections with external events. We have also pointed out that man in studying perception must do so in a way that recognizes that his world is one that is made out of ingredients that have no similarity to the finished product, perception. Perception does not copy anything. Perceived objects are not existent entities in the outside world that have the visual, tactual, thermal, and solidity characteristics which we experience in them. Hence, in studying perception, we are studying what it is that the organism experiences; not what the physical world contains, or is made up of.

Having come this far, we can designate an additional broad characteristic of perception which accompanies that of the *immediacy* already mentioned. It is *discrimination*. Immediate behavior in order to be called perception must be discriminatory. This is to distinguish it from pure physical and chemical interaction between the body and its surrounds.

IMMEDIACY

As we have already pointed out, perception is the immediate response of the organism[1] to the energy impinging on sense organs. What can be called immediate and what cannot may seem quite clear from the commonplace meaning of the word, but taking into consideration the specific kinds of response which we know the organism makes calls for defining the term "immediate" for our purposes. Can immediacy be defined purely by setting a time limit, or must something else be included?

Obviously, the perception of objects rapidly approaching the body or eye consists of brief avoidance reactions, involving only a second or less. With regard to these, there is no difficulty in calling them immediate. But there are many other occasions in which neither the external event nor the consequent behavior is limited to such short times. For example, when a person is asked whether two vertical strings suspended in front of him are equidistant from him, he does not typically react quickly and briefly. Even if the strings are actually equidistant, the observer may be far from sure. In fact, when such a question is asked, the observer generally attempts to be quite precise. Since he considers very small differences significant, he does not settle by a mere single glance how the strings look. He responds by taking several looks, and by moving his head and eyes, if allowed to do so. Even with very small amounts of motion, the strings may shift their apparent relative distances from him. The matter does not stop at that. Reverses in relative distance may continue for a number of seconds before the observer arrives at a report to give the questioner.

The changing behavior which we have just described is not to be considered a single unit of activity, or a single extended reaction, but rather a series of reactions, each of which can be taken as a unit, and called a perceptual response. Thus before the observer is willing to make his report (his terminal reaction), he has made a series of immediate reactions, each of which is to be called a perceptual response with respect to externality. When the observer comes to the terminal point, the reaction is called the expression of a judgment. Actually, the task given the observer was too exacting to be accomplished quickly by a

[1] When it is stated that the response is the response of the *organism,* it is meant that the response is directed from the central nervous system. Such responses adjust the organism to its surrounds. Other types of response are not those of the organism as a whole, but rather the activities that can be labeled in accord with the tissues involved. For example, they may be a sense-organ response. In such cases the "organism as a whole" is merely the context.

single perceptual response. The observer spontaneously began the process of "judging." The report given by the observer is called a judgment in conventional terminology, although it is also erroneously called a perception, as though the two words were synonymous. For us, the judgment is an integration of the several perceptions, and of certain concepts and possibly of certain memories.

Other occasions differ from the one just described. Let us say that a person is asked to look steadily at what he perceives as a card on the opposite wall and to observe its color for a period of a few seconds, or longer. If, when he does so, the color of the card remains constant in hue, intensity, and saturation, we can call the whole reaction a single perception. Since the experience, the crucial feature of the reaction, did not change, there is no reasonable means by which we could subdivide the reaction. Thus, in spite of its extension for a number of seconds in time, it is still an immediate reaction. It is a constant and continues during the life of the impingement. What we have then, in the color experience, is a steady and direct relation between an extended stimulus and response.

In dealing with response such as perception, the old problem arises whether perception is exclusively experiential or whether it may also be an overt form of activity. A careful look at what the human organism is capable of doing leads us to discard the sharp dichotomy between experiential and motor activities. Experience itself ranges from the clear and highly articulate to the unclear and only grossly differentiated. Part of what is experienceable is verbalizable, and part of it exists only in the form of a vague feeling state. Part of what the organism does in a motor way is describable as awkward fumbling, and part of it is the expression of highly organized systems of movements skillfully achieving certain ends. Feeling states and movements at times can be discerned to blend into each other more truly than is generally recognized. To say the least, one is not always compelled to make a distinction between feelings and movements in describing the behavior of the organism. The ranges and variables of the behavior just mentioned seem to express kinds of *relations* between the organism and its surrounds. To the extent we can tell what these relations are, we are accomplishing our task as students of perception.

Therefore, we depart from the older custom of applying the term perception to experiences, and experiences alone. The old outlook seemed to imply that experience always had to precede movement, solve the problem, and leave it to movement to carry out the indicated response.

It is not our purpose to discuss this matter at length. It is only that we are attempting a workable schematization to include all interactions of the organism with its surrounds in one class. The issue is not so much whether a subject talks, feels hopeless, or simply shakes his finger. What can be said about the interaction (response, reaction) as it signifies the subject's relation to his surrounds is the main thing. The development of a scientific understanding of organism-environment relations is the problem of the one who studies human activity regardless of its "kind." We must look upon the gross, incipient, halting processes as being the same in basic kind as those that are definite and articulate. We are interested in the role that processes play rather than in categorizing them in conventional terms. We attempt as much as possible to detour the mentalistic set of present-day language found both in the dictionary and on the lips of the people. When we use the terms assuming, guessing, judging, thinking, perceiving, we do not necessarily imply conscious acts, as is the case when the words are used in purely traditional contexts of everyday speech.

Freudianism has said a great deal about the unconscious and has made it a vast unknown and unknowable realm which most people fear and to which curious characteristics are ascribed. It is made a force with which the conscious is generally in conflict, and which requires a priesthood to appease. Biology provides us with a somewhat different view.

We shall look upon the unconscious not as a discrete realm governed by principles and driven by forces unlike the conscious, but rather as the human being in action in a less articulate fashion than when behavior can be said to be conscious. If one must make a distinction between the two, it is in degree rather than kind. Both the unconscious and the conscious draw upon the past. Naturally, "memories" may be forms of very inarticulate "reinstatement" as well as of the highly articulate kind.

What we have said in the foregoing paragraphs is that behavior is to be dealt with not only in terms of its phenomenology, but more especially in terms of its "expressiveness."

REFLEXES

Another problem in defining perception has to do with whether or not all forms of immediate motor responses are perceptions. It will be remembered in this connection that a very well-known form of immediate reaction is called a *reflex*. We therefore must ask about the connection between reflexes and perception. Are reflexes examples of perception, since they are forms of immediate reaction, or do they belong in the customary class by themselves? One of the chief characteristics of a reflex is that it is a *motor* response. Many reflexes are not accompanied by experiential concomitants. Classically, this, if nothing else, precluded their being perceptual responses. Since we are making no class distinction between experience and motor reactions, reflexes are candidates for the perceptual category.

We can say that reactions, then, which for many other purposes are called reflexes, are to be looked upon as instances of perceptual behavior, if and when they are forms of discriminatory behavior. It is thinkable that some reflexes are not discriminatory, and if so they would not be classed as perceptual.

DISCRIMINATION

Can we decide between acts that are and those that are not discriminatory? For our purposes, we can. To discriminate is to make a choice reaction in which contextual conditions play a deciding role.

The cerebral cortex is the best example of a system that discriminates. Hence, when we find behavior that involves cerebral cortical participation, we may arbitrarily class it as discriminatory. The determination of whether certain reflexes will occur, or to what extent, or in what contexts they will occur, often depends upon the cerebral cortex, hence such reflex behavior is certainly discriminatory.

As an example of a nondiscriminatory reaction, we can cite the behavior of the mercury column in a thermometer. It behaves rigidly in accord with thermal conditions impinging upon it, without regard to past history, present context, or any other such potential consideration. An example of a discriminatory reaction is that of human brightness perception, in which the apparent brightness of a disk of light depends not only upon target intensity but the luminance of the area around it, upon target area, and upon even other considerations.

PERCEPTION AND ITS INDICATORS

The description of the behavior of the observer and his communication with the second party, the experimenter, brings us to ask a further question in defining perception. The observer did two things in both experiments as mentioned in a previous section. He experienced objects, positions, colors, etc. Since these are what the experimenter wanted to know about, they had to be indicated to the experimenter by motor behavior, such as pressing appropriate keys, or by verbal description, using appropriate words. Thus, at times, a definite separation seemed to be involved between true perceptual response and the activity that communicated the nature of this response to the second party, the experimenter. This sharp separation need not always occur. Some tasks differ from our two illustrations.

We do not generally realize how varied the relation of the responses of the organism to the stimulus impingement may be, and how this depends upon the instructions or other arbitrary features of an experimental situation. Let us look at another experiment in which the instructions require the observer's delay in making the response asked for. It is the old attention "span" experiment, much used and made famous by Renshaw in his *recognition* technique. In this experiment, a row of letters or digits in random order is presented to the observer. The exposure time varies from something less than a thousandth of a second up to possibly one one-hundredth of a second. The problem for the experimenter is to determine how many letters or digits the given observer can produce from such a short exposure. The question is often thought of as involving how many letters the observer is able to see. This cannot be determined directly. The only way is to have the observer reproduce the series; and if he can, it is considered that he *saw* them. The criterion is thus the number of letters which can be written. Writing letters in this case is not synonymous with seeing them, or having seen them. Nevertheless, the experiment has some value.

The number of items written and the observer's verbally reportable experience have no direct correspondence. One of the specifications of the experiment is that the observer wait two or three seconds before beginning to respond. It has been found that the naïve observer will attempt to prompt himself during that time by trying to repeat the items to himself verbally, or trying to visualize them clearly. It has been found that doing this will lessen the number of items that can be written when the required two or three seconds have elapsed. Apparently the way for the observer to succeed best is to "do nothing" until the time of writing down the items, and then to begin to write without trying to experience the items in visual or verbal terms. It is as though the response was one that flowed right out into the motor behavior of the writing hand. It is only after the writing has been completed that the observer may look to see what he has done. The self-prompting or any of the spontaneous responses that occur before the writing down of the items seem to preclude the direct flow of the response into motor terms. To intellectualize and to perform the overt action required do not seem to be compatible. To do one is to alter or preclude the other.

REACTION-TIME EXPERIMENTS

There are still other perceptual experiments in which the subject is required to respond by pressing one of a number of keys in front of him. He is to do this as quickly as possible. The time lapse between the beginning of the presentation and the beginning of the reaction is usually somewhere between $\frac{1}{10}$ and $\frac{1}{4}$ second. The subject is likely to testify later that he did not have a clear-cut visual or auditory experience relating to the stimulus before pressing the key. Thus, although the stimulus was photic or acoustic, the reaction was largely motor. We therefore cannot only say that the reaction was mainly motor, but that the *perception* was largely in motor terms.

What we have attempted to say in the foregoing examples is that perception may be predominantly experiential, as when an observer stands and views a painting in a museum, or it may be predominantly motor when the subject is faced with reacting overtly, as in the experiment that was just described. In both cases, sensory channels are involved. The process includes seeing, hearing, touching, tasting, or the action of some other sense modality.

COMMUNICATING REACTIONS

If what the experimenter wants to get at is an experience, then a communicating reaction must represent it to the experimenter. This reaction may be either in the form of a predetermined motor response or a verbalization.

The degree to which the communicating response represents a perception may vary, and it is incumbent upon the experimenter to take this question into account in his experimental design. In fact, it is incumbent upon psychology to make a point of studying this very question directly, for it is of major significance.

This problem was involved in the two-string experiment given earlier. In it, we said that the overt indication which the observer gave the experimenter was a judgment. This terminal response stemmed from a number of perceptions. If we can accept the judgment in each trial as a mean representation of the perceptions leading up to it, then we can use the judgment to deduce what perception is like. If, however, such judgments contain biasing ingredients which the observer wittingly or unwittingly injects into them, then judgments do not very well represent perceptions. The discrepancy may very well vary from observer to observer. Extraneous factors are more likely to enter into the reactions of naïve observers. One of the greatest desires of a naïve observer is to be "right"; that is, to act in such ways as not to come into conflict with physical externality, or with custom. This is a natural and understandable tendency, since being "right" is required of him in all his everyday encounters, if he is to survive. For example, when a fan is revolving at a high rate, the blades are not observable as such. They may be perceived as a color film. Color films may look as though one could extend one's hand through them, since they do not seem to be solid. In such cases, it is important to utilize all possible criteria for determining whether or not to extend the hand. Hence, a number of factors are taken into account, in addition to the mere visual appearance of the film area itself. Thus it is that the attempt to be "right" is injected into laboratory behavior and often runs counter to laboratory instructions and invalidates the experimentation.

We are not without concrete information regarding the difference between perceiving and judging. The following experiment is an illustration. It is an illustration of how the outcome may differ when exposure time is varied. In the experiment, two different exposure durations of tilted circular targets (stimuli) were used. They were .01 second and 1 second. Obviously, the one is quite short, not allowing for much, if any, eye movement, and the other is reasonably long. It would be expected that the reaction or response could be called perceptual when the shorter exposure was used, since the observers were given no opportunity to utilize more than one relation between themselves and the target. That is, they could not, as it were, take several "looks" at it and use them in a combined way to arrive at a conclusion. They had only the single brief encounter. When the target exposure was more than .01 second in length, considerable more time was allowed, and during this more than one "look" could occur. That is, eye movement was provided for. When eye movement occurs, this is equivalent to saying that more than one kind of contact between organism and its surrounds can and most always does take place.

Leibowitz, Mitchell, and Angrist (157) found that with the shorter exposure the responses were such as to indicate one thing, and with the longer exposure they were such as to indicate a very different organism-target relation. More specifically, the reaction to the short exposure followed the law of the retinal image, and the reaction to the long exposure followed the law of shape constancy. With long exposures, the tilted circles looked like tilted circles; and with the short exposures, they looked like ellipses. Hence, not all experiments in which judgments are provided for bring out what perception is like. Thus, if the longer reaction was a judgment and the shorter one a perception, it can be said that we have an example in which they radically differ.

A LIMITATION OF FORMAL EXPERIMENTS

Certain kinds of experimentation often contain repetitive elements. This may make them learning situations, or situations in which the observer develops concepts or guesses as to what it is that is being presented. These "constructs" of the observer may enter into his reactions, and either distort or totally invalidate the experiment.

Let us take an example. Suppose a set of luminous cardboard disks is presented to an observer in a dark room for the purpose of determining their perceived shapes, or of determining the positions in which the seen objects seem to lie. Let us say that there are three different-shaped ellipses and one circle. Let us say that each of the disks is presented in one or the other of three positions of tilt in random order.

This is a limited set of variations and must be repeated several times to gain the information the experimenter wants. In part the experimental trials are like a natural set of conditions, and in part they are not; for, in the common run of everyday life, disks may vary a great deal more than these in shape and position. Outside the laboratory, the individual has to take each case as a case by itself, but in the experiment the limited number of variations just specified are repeated over and over many times. During this repetition, the observer may detect similarities in trials, even though random variation is employed. Hence he begins to stereotype his responses. He may say to himself, "Ah! This presentation is like one I had a moment ago. How did I respond to it? I must be consistent. I'd be foolish to respond differently to the same disk from trial to trial." This reaction would run counter to the instructions and intentions of the experimenter. The experimenter desires a response solely determined by what the observer can immediately make out of the limited sense material of the moment, rather than one that stems from an attempt to conceptualize or guess about the plan of experimentation used by the experimenter.

THE CONCEPT OF "TARGET"

Since it is assumed that we have two domains with which to deal in the study of perception, certain consequences follow: (1) Neither domain can be ignored and left unused. (2) The same terms should not be used to label the items in both domains. We cannot talk in the descriptive language of one when we are describing the other. (3) We must realize that our task is to relate the two domains, and that this is not to be attempted by trying to *reduce* one to the other, as when we say that human consciousness, for example, is simply complex group activity of neurons.

The domains to which we refer are (1) the physical world that provides the energies that excite sense organs, and that lead to the organism's interaction with the physical world; and (2) the experiential world in which the organism is aware of itself and of objects, of certain properties and activities of both, and certain relations between them. The latter is the world—the "real" world to most human beings. Our job is not to perpetuate "common sense" but rather to arrive at a workable scheme that will relate us consistently with the various sciences outside psychology.

Although it has been customary not to make consistent distinctions in terminology between the two domains mentioned above, we believe it is only logical to make as many terminological distinctions as possible between them. To do so would clear up many presently existing ambiguities and avoid confusion in thinking and communication regarding behavior.

To carry out the distinction as best we can, the experimenter should try to avoid describing his stimulus presentation in the same terms as are used by the subject in describing the experiences that are evoked by the presentations. It is for this purpose that we have resorted to "target" to denote, in general, the experimenter's presentation in visual experiments. The subjects do not report seeing targets, but rather colors, lights, and so forth. The use of true stimulus terms is easy in some dimensions and, as yet, impossible in others. In one dimension, for example, the stimulus is described in intensity units, such as candles per square foot, millilamberts, etc. The response is described in lightness and brightness. In such cases, no one need be confused by ambiguities of terminology.

But in using Euclidean geometry, which is in itself a perceptual system—a common-sense experiential system—one uses the terms square, triangle, circle, etc. These are at one and the same time items in a supposedly technical domain (a metrical system) and in everyday nontechnical conversation relating to perceptual experiences. For our purposes, it would be better were our geometry to have one set of terms and our everyday language of perception to have another set. Since this is not the case, when we have to use geometry in describing targets, we can do no better than perpetuate the ambiguity.

The word target is intended to be a generic term and thus neutral, since it is not, in itself, a description of the properties of the stimulus or of the response. It is rather a term simply to indicate a visual stimulus presentation. The target's properties are left to further description that should, of course, avoid being in the subject's response language, if possible. A target is an experimental situation toward which the subject or observer is made to direct his attention—that to which he is to react. In visual experiments, it is the arrangement whereby patterned photic radiation is sent to the subject's eye. This arrangement is sometimes simple and sometimes complex. It would be ideal if in all cases the target could be described in intensity, spatial, and temporal terms that would exclude conversational language. As was already stated above, intensity is dealt with in terms outside of direct experience (i.e., in energistic terms). Time, likewise, is dealt with in terms that are not clearly those of experience, though some of the words, such as second and minute, are used in daily nontechnical conversation. It would not be hard to get away from confusion here by a substitution of terms. But the matter is not so easily solved in the case of space. Space is still described in a set of terms which people would greatly resist giving up either for the stimulus or for the response. The description of space, as already alluded to, is still confined to Euclidean terms such as square, triangle, and so on. Terms such as angle and right angle are also the same in both domains.

In trying to pursue the study of perception, we shall have to bow to ingrained convention in the more difficult situations; but to the extent that we can, we shall try to be logically consistent and make distinctions between stimulus (energistic) and response terminology. Such an effort can be counted as a step ahead.

RELATIONAL PROPERTIES OF PERCEPTION

In previous sections, we have indicated the broad class of response to which perception belongs, but now certain properties of perceptions must be dealt with. The characteristics which we shall list and describe are to be called relational properties, for they tell of how perceptual response is the embodiment of the relation of the organism to its surrounds. These relationships are so subtle that no list of adjectives can do justice to them without definite overlapping. In the English language, many shades of meaning are supplied by a group of words. To select a term from the group is, generally, to leave some meaning untouched. To use all of the terms is to be needlessly redundant.

Actually, there seems to be no strict limit to the number and kind of words that might be used to describe perceptual response. We must be aware, then, in listing properties of perception that the terms we use are useful only in pointing out a few of the major aspects.

The properties we have in mind are the following: symbolism, classification, evaluation, prognosis, and field determination. These are not internal descriptions of the behavior which we call perceptive, but rather, as was indicated earlier, are terms to signify how perceptual behavior is related to the organism's environment.

There are other sorts of terms, however, which we could add. Some of these would describe what perceptual behavior itself is like. For example, perception is self-consistent. Not only do perceptions have relational properties but they represent something about the organism. Perception is purposeful.

Symbolism

Perception is symbolic. This is to say that it is a kind of behavior manifesting an abstract relation between the organism and its surrounds. A person, for example, receives photic radiation ("light") on the retina. In energistic terms, this is measurable by the physicist as so much radiant flux. Sometimes he measures it in quanta. But, when we tell what the person does when radiation strikes the retina, the description is in terms which the physicist does not use. We describe what the person sees. Even what is seen is not always in terms of what people call concrete objects. The person may see sadness, delight, or any one of a number of "conditions." Thus it is that we can say that the reaction of the person is a symbolic one. The literal energies convey to the person something that is not literally inherent in them.

Classification

This is the name of the property expressed when the reaction to the immediate situation is not as if to a totally isolated and unique one, but essentially to it as an example of a class of situations. Just what class of situations it is, is dependent upon the organism itself. This process by which the organism develops classifications is called concept formation.

To name an object is to put it into a class. To recognize (perceive) anything is to do likewise. Persons perceive objects, and whole situations, as examples of classes of these. Brunswick's probabilistic-functional theory brings this property out most explicitly, whereas other theories may more or less imply classification.

Whereas the classificational implication in perception may not appear to be news to the reader, it is, nevertheless, an important one, and to know the mechanisms whereby the organism behaves this way would be extremely enlightening.

One of the chief lines of inquiry that bears upon or, at least, borders upon this property is the study of the *constancies*. This is the study of the principle involved when a sheet of paper is identifiable as white, even in dim or slightly tinted illumination.

Evaluation

Whereas the term evaluation is much used in common speech, we are applying the word to a specific aspect of perceptual behavior that is generally overlooked.

All immediate response carries in it a very broad bias of the individual. We shall call the aspect the *evaluational*. This is to say that everything is reacted to in terms of a broad spectrum, at one pole of which is the *harmful*, and at the other the *beneficial* and *acceptable*. In the middle is the region of *indifference*. If we look closely enough, we can detect this evaluative aspect involved in every immediate response. When the situation evokes avoidance, or an "as if threatening or harmful" reaction, we are, in essence, dealing with what is called emotion. This is true also for reactions that elicit the extreme opposite. Most energies elicit neither of the more extreme sorts of reaction, but rather one of relative indifference. If we define emotion as the peculiar pattern of properties of behavior that represent its evaluative aspect, then perception is emotional.

What is to be called emotion can either be the behavior at two ends of the spectrum or else the term can be broadened and liberalized to be synonymous with the term *evaluation* and include also the middle of the spectrum. This would mean that all behavior is emotional, in the sense of being evaluative. Such a use of the term would be quite different than the customary one that singles out behavior that is disruptive (that is, at either end of the spectrum) to call emotional. We shall hold that emotional aspect of behavior is the expression of the *value* of the stimulus situation to the perceiver, including the evaluation of indifference as well as benefit and harm. It can be said, then, that the emotional property of perception is one of the aspects that is not stimulus-bound, and may be almost anything depending upon who the perceiver is and what he has encountered in the past.

Prognosis and Interpretation

We have already given an example in which the prognostic aspect of perception may be illustrated. It was the case of the revolving fan blades. The visual conditions presented by this situation contain some degree of ambiguity. It is common for the same perceptions to be producible by any one of several sets of conditions. Inasmuch as the observer is confronted with alternatives, the perception may be said to be prognostic. It is as though it were a bet on the nature of externality with reference to possible consequences of action. If in the present case of seeing a colored film it is simply the usual conditions that give rise to it, then the observer can safely put his fingers through what he takes to be the film. If it is some other set of conditions that is giving rise to the perception of the film, possibly the observer cannot put his fingers through it. The film might be something manufactured into a plate of glass, or it might be produced by revolving fan blades. Inasmuch as the perceptive property to which we have been alluding here could be said to represent the process of interpretation, we may speak of perception being interpretative. Furthermore, this same aspect could be called selective. All perception is potentially selective in this way.

Internal Self-Consistency

This is a significant property and an obvious one in examining many forms of perceptual behavior. As a principle, self-consistency applies only *within* perception, and not to the sequence from one perception to another. Self-consistency is one form of lawfulness, and in supposing behavior to be lawful, the student of perception should not stop until he can understand perception in such a manner as to see consistency between its various aspects.

In the dark-room situation described above, all the organism is given is the retinal image of the cardboard target. If the target is near, the image is larger than if it is farther away from the eyes. This varying-sized retinal image is, in itself, not enough to determine the nature of the perception. For an object to exist, it must have both position and size. Objects may vary in size and position. The same target will produce a larger image if near than if far away. This is a form of lawfulness, and through it the organism can make some sort of a self-consistent response. The convincingness of an object's properties, such as its size and position, is not always equally great. Lack of convincingness leads to further effort and to further testing activity on the part of the organism. The same stimulus evokes the perception of an object at a given distance, but as perceived distance changes the perceived size changes concomitantly with it, so long as the visual field is not structured so as to preclude it. This is a form of self-consistency. But there is another form that has been called *constancy*. Objects seen in structured fields—that is, in surrounds in which there are seen other objects (generally, three-dimensional)—tend to retain a relatively constant perceived size. This matter will be dealt with at length in a later chapter. Let it be sufficient for it to be said here that constancy is one type of self-consistency.

One of the very most fundamental matters to study in perception is the question of what principles the organism uses to provide self-consistency. What one might expect to be the basis for self-consistency may not be used by the organism in the perceptual behavior it manifests.

Field Determination

To say that an end result is field-determined is to say that a system of interrelated forces or activities produced it—that the total pattern of the forces produced it. This is different than saying that some one part of the pattern produced some aspect of the end result, and still other parts of the pattern produced other aspects of the end result. All aspects seem to stem from the system as a whole, and not from isolatable features of it.

In a field, the phenomena emerge as an expression of mutually interacting forces (vectors). One of the most easily understood examples of a field is the constellation of meteorological conditions existing over a continent at any given time. The air currents are accounted for by a system of high- and low-pressure areas, that is, by a system of differences in potential. No pressure at any point is high or low in its own right, but rather only in relation to the pressures around it, and even throughout the field. Thus pressures come and go, and are to be accounted for by the features of the field as a whole rather than by description of any restricted portion of it.

What has this to do with perception? It is simply that perception is a phenomenon that emerges from a system of interrelated events, first in the individual's surrounds, and then within the neuromuscular system of the individual himself. To understand perception, one must possess means whereby such interrelations can be grasped and dealt with. This implies a different outlook on the matter than is used when the perception of something is explained by *cues* in the customary manner.

DESCRIPTION OF THE STIMULUS

One of the primary and most crucial questions that is involved in dealing adequately with perceptual behavior is that of how to describe the features of externality that affect the organism—in other words, how to describe the "stimulus." We shall try to show that field concepts are applicable when this problem is considered. The organism reacts to external events as to *things*, and *actions* and *relations* between things. To the man on the street there is nothing else in the universe to consider unless we include spirits.

We know, however, that it is not "things" or objects that impinge on sense organs, the mediators between ourselves and our environment, but rather various forms of energy. Energy manifestations, as such, are describable only in the way the physicist describes them, and this is very different from talking about perceivable objects. A watt or a kilowatt is very different from the incandescence of the electric light we experience.

In describing visual "stimuli," nevertheless, it has long been customary to describe them as objects with perceptible properties. In audition, the stimuli are called sounds, just as the resulting experiences are called sounds. In gustation, both the experiences and the stimuli are, for example, often called tastes. The same principle is true for all the senses.

The student of perception should realize from the very beginning that he is confronted with a decision whether to describe stimuli in energistic terms or in perceptual terms. He should be aware of what the possibilities in this matter seem to be, and what the consequences are of attempting the task the one way rather than the other.

We may name the use of perceptual descriptions as *phenomenology* and the use of energistic descriptions as *dynamics*. Phenomenology deals with things—items that are directly perceivable. Dynamics describes events in terms of field action. To portray perception as field-determined is to use a dynamic account of it rather than the more usual account that is not fieldlike. We may call the two descriptions theories. The one is *field theory,* and the other is *cue theory.*

Cue theory attempts to explain, by using *cues,* why the stimulus situation is reacted to (perceived) in the way it is. The cues are aspects of the perception collateral to the perceptive item to be "explained." For example, one may ask why a certain presentation is seen as a house. The answer will be that certain cues are responsible. If we ask what these cues are, we shall likely be told that the result in question was produced by some other part of the visual experience, such as a tree, a road, or a sky. In each case, it will be something described in perceptual terms rather than being information about the stimulus, or about neural processes underlying perception. We can characterize such a procedure as that of using one perception to explain another. This implies that the observer had to perceive the cue first. For if it did not exist first, how could it account for the perceptual aspect in question?

As a really concrete example of cue theory in operation, we can mention the use of conventional monocular cues for depth or space perception. Among these are aerial haze, "color perspective," elevation, overlay or interposition, linear perspective, etc. Let us examine some of them. What is aerial haze? It is a perceived aspect of an outdoor situation. It is not a stimulus property. Certain stimulus conditions are involved, of course, in producing it. So are certain contributions of the organism. Aerial haze, then, in being used to account for distance of some item in the viewed scene, is an aspect of the perceived situation that is used to explain another aspect of the same situation. Color perspective, too, is a perceived feature of the scene in question. Color perspective is an imputed relation between seen color and seen distance. There is no denying that some kind of relation between the two may exist, but the relation is not causal. The two properties (color and distance) stem from the same stimulus complex. Shift the stimulus complex a bit, and the two factors, the one of which was supposed to be the "cause" of the other, will differ in their relation.

PURPOSE

One of the most significant things we can say about perceptual response is that it is oriented in all cases. The learning theorist, in describing immediate response, would call this *set.* This orientation has been spoken of in other ways as well. Some terms have to do with a description of the way energy is mobilized.

The word *drive* is one such term. Some of the terms pertain to the selectivity of the behavior, and so we have words like *bias*. Then there are still other terms, such as *directionality, continuity, stance, attitude,* and *purpose,* though not all of these terms have to do with the organism's internal organization on the same level. Purpose is a term, for example, having to do generally with processes of the very highest order. In fact, for a long time purpose was reserved for situations in which it could be said that the individual was definitely aware of his own directionality, and furthermore possessed the experience of having planned the direction of the activity to be engaged in. Consequently, the word purpose was not widely used, for it did not fit many situations, or was not reachable by the operations performed by scientists. Nowadays, there are broader and more liberal connotations given the word, and it is a factor that is being studied.

Granting the existence of orientation of some sort, we may assert that, whatever it is, it is expressed in the immediate responses the individual makes to his surrounds. The statements of the nature of this orientation as expressed in immediate response, or perception, are of various sorts, as is evidenced particularly in several of the theories listed in the previous chapter.

PERCEIVING, THINKING, AND KNOWING

It is one of the objectives in defining perception to indicate its relations to other forms of behavior. All of the behavior of the individual in which we are interested, whether it be perception or not, has to do with his relations to his surrounds. The individual's relating activities possess various names—perception, cognition, cogitation, thought, memory, and so forth. Out of all the terms that could be assembled, there are three which we wish to compare at this time. They are perceiving, thinking, and knowing. Both the dictionary and everyday usage indicate that there are many shades of meaning for each of these terms. In some ways they even overlap. In the preceding chapter, it was pointed out that we could not construct a scientific treatment of perception were all common meanings of perception to be retained. This is also true for the other two terms with which we are now dealing.

To *think* is "to form a judgment or opinion of, to center one's thoughts on, to mediate, or reflect upon." A little different meaning would be involved in stating that thinking is a major form of problem-solving activity. Whatever meanings of thinking we use, they seem to imply an ongoing active process—an activity evolving or unfolding in time, and not having a close temporal connection with a definite external event or series of events.

To *know* is "to apprehend as true, to have direct experience of, to have experiential ('mental') certitude of, to discern the character of." Some of the dictionary definitions of the word *know* use the word perceive in them; i.e., to know is to perceive directly—to perceive as true. Knowing would, thus, be a form of perceiving. Some of the objects of knowing are external, and some have to do with oneself. The unique characteristic in knowing is the experience of absoluteness and the lack of doubt. Knowledge turns into mere belief for the individual when doubt enters in. It is then that, although he can still say he *feels* sure and that he believes, he cannot say he knows. He cannot feel that his experience can be shown to be a true representation of the external world ("fact"). It is knowledge which the individual ultimately seeks and rests upon. This is to say, he works for a tally between what he experiences and what exists apart from him. If he knows, he can do the right thing. Knowledge is thus expressed in right action as well as in right experience. If he does not know, his behavior will be in conflict with his purposes and with external conditions. Various sense modalities, for example, may come into conflict with each other, in which case action does not serve the individual's purposes. An object may look to be in a certain position; but in reaching for it, the hand does not touch it so long as it is guided by vision. The person does not immediately "know" where the object is. The proof of knowing is in successful action. Whatever acts as a guide to successful action is a *means* of knowing. Perception is generally such a guide; therefore perceiving is a means of knowing.

Knowing has a more far-reaching implication than merely being able to move about in space successfully, or to find that one can use his perceptions successfully, one by one.

Perceptions themselves are more than the apprehension of things and their activities. Perceptions pertain to qualities of things, and to abstract relations between things. Perceptions integrate into concepts and judgments. The processes of integration and development go on and on until the individual himself consists in an endlessly complex fabrication of ideas, beliefs, and systems of knowledge. Inherent in them is their constant reference to a reality outside the believer or knower. This is where the essence of knowledge is crucially involved. The typical individual feels that he knows he knows certain things. With regard to these, it is difficult to shake him. To succeed in suddenly shaking him would be to dethrone him. The psychologist and the philosopher, however, are not necessarily greatly impressed by what a person declares that he knows he knows. That is, they are not led to believe in the declared correspondence between the person's *experience* and the features of external reality to which they refer.

Men through the ages have given themselves to metaphysics, a form of understanding of matters beyond physics. Epistemology is one form of metaphysics, and has to do with considering methods and grounds for obtaining knowledge, particularly with reference to its limits and validity. Epistomology asks how we can know anything. In every case, one's metaphysics, whether naïve or sophisticated, is manifested in what one says when he is dealing with such matters as perceiving, thinking, and knowing. Psychology has its own answer to the problem of knowledge and this is one of the things dealt with in studying perception.

Externality is divisible into that which actually impinges upon sense organs, and the remainder which does not. In the case of exteroception (vision, audition, and smell), the sources of the energy that reaches the sense organs are generally the factors controlled by the experimenter in a laboratory situation. We have already used the term target for the source of patterned photic radiation constituting the stimulus for vision. Acoustic source could well be the neutral term for the source of energy that impinges upon the ear. Some authors speak of these origins of energy as distal, or distant, stimuli, or stimulus objects, and of the actual energy that reaches the sense organs as proximal stimuli. These terms may well be conveniences and conventions, but they have limitations. We prefer to call only the energy reaching sense organs stimuli, and reserve the term object for that which is perceived. One does not perceive the stimulus. He is only made to perceive something by it. In some cases, it is the relation between the origin of the energy and the behavior of the organism that is of concern. The more direct question is, however, the relation between actual energy impingements and the perceptual end results. A number of "distal stimuli" may produce the same impingement upon the sense organs; hence, there is not the one-to-one relation that would be needed for us to ignore the intervening factor, the actual impinging energy.

Let us take the following example to illustrate the discrepancy between sources of energy ("stimulus" objects) and actual energy impingements. Let us suppose the experimenter uses as his presentation one or more wire rings. From the observer's standpoint, he is being presented items that are simply called targets. Their real natures are only what he can perceive them to be.

The objective of the experiment is to see what the observer's perceptions will be; that is, what the observer will perceive the targets to be. In such an experiment, there is no reality or criterion for reality beyond what the subject can gain through the sense modality involved.

The targets ("rings") may be presented to the observer in the usual sort of visual field, that is, one which is definitely structured. Perceptually, it is a field that contains objects in addition to the object in question. The target, in the present case, may be seen as a circle, or some sort of an ellipse. If the field is structured so as to be seen as a three-dimensional one—let us say, a table viewed obliquely—then the placing of one of the rings upon the table will be a process observed with such definiteness and assurance that the perceiver will say that he knows the target is a circular ring. The observer regards the table surface obliquely; and if the ring is laid upon the far end of the table, it is still a ring, but one seen obliquely. The ring that is seen is a "real" circle, both according to the common-sense definition and to Thouless (247), who first studied the matter. He called this "real" circle the real object, R.

According to geometry and trigonometry, it is known that the "real" circle is not copied by the eye as a circle, but is optically projected on the retina as an approximate ellipse. Thouless called this ellipse the stimulus object, S. He asked his observers to draw the actual shape which they saw, as they perceived the target to be an obliquely viewed circle. The drawing, too, was an ellipse, but not the same shape as the stimulus object, R. Thouless called this the phenomenal object, P. It turned out that in virtually every case the shape of the phenomenal object was a compromise between the circle (the real object) and the retinal image, S. This suggested to Thouless that the real object possessed properties influencing the observer toward seeing it as it "really is." This process of approaching the "real" object in shape was called "phenomenal regression to the real object."

Thouless' investigation is by no means representative of the whole gamut of conditions under which an observer may be called upon to perceive targets, and thus to perceive objects and their shapes. In not all situations does the observer have the opportunity to see objects in highly structured (thing-populated) fields. Under the most reduced circumstances, the observer may be called upon to react in a field that is totally unstructured, save for the portion provided by the target itself. Two kinds of such fields are possible. One is an illuminated but totally untextured field; the other, a totally unilluminated and thus visually untextured field.

Let us now consider rings in a totally unilluminated room. The rings may be made visible by having been coated with a substance that fluoresces when ultraviolet radiation hits them. In this case, with a blank field, there is no reference by which to perceive verticality and tilt. Here, perceptually, the rings will tend to lie in the frontal or vertical plane.

Experiment has shown that there is not much tendency for observers to see the various targets presented as lying in various other planes, that is, at various tilts from the vertical. This is despite the fact that various targets may actually be placed at various tilts. There is nothing at all that can be used by the observer to "ascertain," or "be sure," or by which to "know" that the targets are or are not in the fronal plane, or any other specified plane.

Even when the experimenter suggests to the observers that the targets may be in different planes, he does not always increase very greatly the tendency for the visual objects to be seen at various degrees of tilt. The perceptions are subject to alteration from trial to trial, due to the observer's own lack of assurance that he is "right."

In all of this, it should be very obvious to the reader that the real object is a concept that cannot be retained as a functional reference by the experimenter in all situations. He must give up regarding it as something that is bound to exist, and in existing influences the perceiver.

Thus it is that we can manipulate the knowing process in a number of ways, and can see that to know really means any one of a number of things. Knowing is not just one absolute process in which the knower is in tune with "reality" and "truth."

PERCEIVING AND LEARNING

The study of learning, or shall we say the development of learning theory, constitutes one of psychology's major activities nowadays. This study, as conducted by some, is the development of a set of equations connecting stimulation and response with the organism omitted. That which mechanism psychologists study as the organism itself is spoken of as the intervening variable or variables. Those theorists or investigators who pay no attention to the organism itself construct *hypothetical* intervening variables to account for the complexities in relation between stimulus and response.

It is our task here to indicate the connection and interrelation between perception and learning. The learning theorist or investigator has the same problems as the perception psychologist in stating what the stimulus consists in. It turns out that the two groups of men do not always coincide in what they consider the stimulus to be. The learning theorist insists on keeping the definition of the stimulus confined to physical variables, and insofar as he does this he is to be agreed with. The perception theorist often forgets and describes his stimuli in perceptual terms. When he does this he runs into difficulties which often he fails to see.

The student, whether of perception or of learning, must face the problem of what the organism does with the energies that impinge upon it.

Perception, as well as thinking, etc., consists in developing a signal value for every encounter. The organism builds a "language" out of its encounters with the external world. The significant thing is that at any and all moments the language which the organism possesses is as important for us to know as the physical description of the stimuli (the energies that are utilized as signals). The study of perception has been meant to be the study of the language of immediate response. To account for this language, the laws governing the building of the language must be discovered. This is the rightful study of learning for the psychologist. He must study the laws of change. The perceptionist's study is the determination of the laws governing the organism's immediate response.

To study learning is not to deny the existence of perception; at best it is to employ rightfully what is known about perception. To study perception is to utilize the facts and principles of learning.

All behavior of the organism as a whole depends upon lawfulness in the causal relations between the organism and its surrounds. The organism must be able to rely upon repetition of the same outside circumstances to provide for the same end results as the first time it encountered them. Repetition of the same responses must yield the same results time after time, so long as the response is to the same set of circumstances.

Exceptions to this, were they possible, would lead to chaos, and would forestall all orderly action, including the possibility of learning. Stating the matter the other way around, learning is based upon the orderliness of cause and effect found in nature. Certain circumstances elicit a given kind of action. The action may or may not satisfy certain internal conditions within the acting organism. If it does, the same reaction will be made upon repetitions of the same set of circumstances. If it does not, the failure is expressed in some sort of unresolved tensions (a pattern of organization) calling for a change in response to the repetition of the old set of circumstances. The very change, regardless of what it is to be, is posited upon the premise that externality is stable in the way implied in what was said above; that is, that a stable causal relation obtained between the organism's action and the results from it in repeated circumstances. This is the very stepping stone for behaving *differently* upon successive similar occasions to gradually reach a goal.

A very good example of a situation in which an animal, be it white rat or human person, could not learn would be one in which "gravitational pull" varied in its amount or direction with reference to the earth. One time, as one attempted to start down a pair of stairs, for example, he would step off into space and would not be pulled down to the next step, but would step off horizontally into thin air, or be wafted upward. There would be nothing which the individual could do that would run a very good chance of being "right," or successful. Each instant would be a pure adventure, with results that had no precedent.

To learn, the organism must be *sensitive* to the various conditions involved in the situation in question. The more factors in the situation which the individual is sensitive to, the greater the kinds of learning there can be. Encounters with situations help the organism to discover what it is in nature that goes together to make up constellations to which it can react. Repeated encounters with a given constellation or configuration of items leave their mark on the organism. They manipulate expectancies. Most of us have little expectancy of encountering a three-headed person. The main reason that most of us do not have such an expectancy is that, out of the millions of occasions in which we have seen other persons, nobody of that sort has ever appeared. Frequency of past encounter is in itself no logical or "scientific" basis for determining what the next encounter will be like, but it certainly is the kind of a basis used by the more basic learning processes, such as in conditioning.

What does the learning process, with the bases for it, have to do with perception? The same stability of causality described above underlies perception. Perception is but a cross section of the learning process, just as learning is a process made up of a sequence of occasions, each of which played a role in informing the organism about externality and the consequences of reacting to it.

Reaction to externality can be of two sorts: either that which is outward or that which is inward. That which is outward tends either to modify a portion of the environment or to relocate the organism within its environment. In either case a new perceptual section is made possible. This in turn becomes one link in the learning process, the step-by-step change toward a state that reduces tension, brings action to a standstill. Each perception is a guide for subsequent action toward the given goal.

While we have seemingly separated perception and overt action, such a distinction applies only in certain ways. Perception, whether overt or introspective, is an immediate reaction to a set of conditions that pertain now. If the reaction called a perceptual act changes something in the environment or relocates the organism in it, the next instant a new perception or apprehension of some sort is provided for. If the perceptual act is so restricted as not to involve skeletal musculature, or so much as an eye movement, then nothing is changed in the environment by perceiving, and the individual is put into no new spatial relation to elements in it. A new perceptual act the next instant would find the environment the same, barring advent of some other process change in the organism, such as underlying memories. It should be obvious, then, that perception is a factor in accounting for learning.

Whatever changes, either in or outside the organism, then provides for subsequent action's coming closer to satisfaction and aids learning.

Chapter 3

THE SYMBOLIC NATURE OF PERCEPTION

The relations between the stimulus situation and the response may be of various sorts. They may be easily predictable from knowledge of the stimulus, or they may be nearly impossible to predict. This failure may be due to overlooking the role that the organism itself plays in contributing to the perceptual end result. To see a color is supposed to be a direct result of a certain type of spectral radiation reaching the eye. In this case, the perception is said to be stimulus-bound. To perceive at a glance that a friend is disturbed, or is happy, is supposed to be a less directly and less simply determined end result of photic radiation. It would represent an abstract relation between stimulus and perceptual reaction.

The object of this chapter is to deal with the abstract nature of some reactions to stimulation. Abstractness very often, if not always, involves symbolism. We want to show how it is, therefore, that one can speak of perception being symbolic. At first glance, symbolism may not seem to be an appropriate matter to be dealt with on a solid scientific basis. Whereas this belief may have held sway some years ago, it is not nearly so common now. It can be shown that symbolism is involved in perceptual response, and ways are being found to deal with it instead of excluding it from laboratory consideration.

There are two ways, in general, in which behavior may be called abstract. According to the one, abstract behavior is perceptual behavior that depends for its differentiating characteristics upon some collateral contribution made by the higher brain centers that bring memory or conceptualization into play. Directly produced or "concrete" behavior, on the other hand, is behavior that is completely dominated by the stereotyped characteristics of the sensory pathways and peripheral mediating mechanisms.

According to the second view of abstract behavior, it is behavior, regardless of what it is like, that cannot be connected rigidly with some assignable characteristic of the stimulus.

In both cases, abstractness has to do with something unusual and lacking in stereotopy. In the first case, the irregularity or unpredictability is provided by the central nervous system through its bringing concepts and memories into play. In the second case, the irregularity is introduced by having nothing in the stimulus to which one can point as being the crucial origin of the outcome. Let us examine some examples of these two ways of regarding abstractness.

Let us take the case in which the observer perceives an apple to be *good*. That people can perceive good apples from bad apples is not to be doubted. What, then, can be said about the cases in which this sort of a perception occurs? Goodness is a quality that depends for its definition upon the perceiver's way of thinking. Goodness is a concept. Hence, when a person perceives an apple to be good, his perception is an application of his concept. Concepts of various perceivers differ. Therefore, according to our first view of abstractness, the behavior of perceiving the apple to be good is an example. It is an example because the perception is dependent upon a unique central-nervous-system contribution.

According to our second view of abstractness, the perception of goodness was not necessarily an example of behavioral abstractness. Abstractness is ruled out if every time goodness is perceived there is something about the stimulus that can be pointed to as the basis for goodness. If the good apple is one that has no soft spots in it, then the stimulus is something different than when soft spots are detected. Goodness of the apple is a result of a certain kind of stimulus. The use to which this stimulus is put can vary quite greatly from person to person, and can involve concepts and memories; but since there is a detectable stimulus basis, it is not abstract, according to the second way the term is used.

Before we come to describing perception in a way to show its symbolic nature, let us be sure we know what is meant by a symbol, and what symbolism is. Webster's dictionary says that "A symbol is that which stands for or suggests something else by reason of relationship, association, or accidental but not intentional resemblance, especially a visible sign of something invisible, as an idea or quality." Thus a symbol is a representative of something else. It stands for something which it in itself is not. The symbol substitutes by way of being or containing the essence of something while not copying the form. Sometimes a symbol is a part that stands for the whole. A symbol is something that carries vicarious meaning. The meaning is not inherent in the tangible item, but only arises through the assignment or development of a functional relation of that item to something else. A symbol, being a specific thing, is a carrier of the meaning inherent in a class.

SYMBOLS AND SIGNS

As far as the dictionary is concerned, the term symbol has a common synonym, *sign*. Thus we may tend to suppose that sign could be substituted for symbol. We find, however, that this is not the case. Several writers make a very definite distinction between the two words, and the distinction seems to be wholly justified. It is justified because there are two very different but related concepts to be labeled, and they thus require two words.

In the study of behavior, both animal and human, the word sign appropriately signifies the role that an impingement (the stimulus) plays. The stimulus is reacted to as a sign, or indication of something. This means that the impingement is something that evokes a response of a specified kind. For example, a stimulus reacted to as a traffic light is reacted to as something that is a sign to stop, or to proceed, as the case may be. To put it another way, such a stimulus is reacted to as an indicator. When we call an impingement a stimulus, we simply imply that it is a source of *activation*. It is as if the organism acts by being prodded. Energistically, this is a part of the picture. But another way of looking at the matter is that certain impingements serve not exclusively as prods but as indicators, or provisions for determining what activity to perform; that is, what response to make.

It can be said, then, that both lower animals and men respond to stimuli as signs. That is what the stimuli are to them. A word very similar to sign is the word signal. These two words may be synonymous. But on the other hand, it could be said that a sign is that which signals. The sign is the agency, and the signaling is the process carried on by the agency.

How do signs and symbols differ? We have just said that impingements are signs by reason of the way they are reacted to by the person. What is a sign to one may not be to another. Or what is one sign to one may be a different sign to another person or species, although the impingement is the same in all cases. A sign, however, does not stand for or substitute for something else, whereas a symbol does. We can say a target seen as a "traffic light" is a sign to go, or to stop, depending upon whether seen as a green light or a red light. If it is a symbol, it is only so in a remote way. The light may symbolize the unpleasantness, for example, of one's last traffic arrest.

Some very interesting and diverse conclusions have been expressed by writers in regard to the differences between signs and symbols. These views, of course, have been expressed more particularly with regard to the thinking process than strictly with regard to the nature of perception. To some, signals are stimuli that can be identified. This would mean impingements that evoke articulate responses as in contrast to those that evoke only incipient, diffuse, and ineffective ones. It might be said, however, that it is only a matter of degree rather than of kind that is involved. Some signals may be clearer than others, or the responder may be freer to respond as indicated in some situations than in others.

It has been asserted by some that no theorist would claim that subhuman animals can handle propositional symbols. Propositional symbols would be those abstractions that are in turn the ingredients of further abstractions. This would mean that these animals could not perceive given concrete situations abstractly and utilize the meaning derived as a premise for imagining something else. This would preclude the ability to imagine possible events that are yet to come. This denial is possibly the same as saying that subhuman species cannot reason. It is also the same as saying that what a subhuman species can derive from a concrete situation—that is, from an energy pattern impinging upon sense organs —is only what it can express immediately. The situation may have meaning (be a sign or have sign value), but this, if abstract, cannot be used as a step in a complex self-integrated procedure for the future. If this is actually what is meant by not being able to create or use propositional symbols, there certainly are animal observers who would disagree.

On the other hand, if we had to assert that language, a set of verbal or otherwise articulate units, had to be used in the procedure, all serious theorizers might agree that subhumans do not have the ability to form and deal with symbols of this sort. What subhumans do may be called reasoning, but it must be carried on by means less articulate than the use of words. Surely there is some part of what humans do that is not as articulate as using words. Some behavior is structured only in connection with feeling.

That identifiable and repeatedly usable units such as words are not always involved in thinking does not preclude the arrival at conclusions via an abstract route. Likewise, perceptions may involve high orders of abstraction that are more than expressions of simple conditioning. The qualities perceived in a given situation, while they may have novel characteristics and may represent integrations that have occurred within the organism, most certainly have been achieved by use of abstractions such as concepts and imagery, both of which are more than simple signs, but are vehicles of true symbolism.

One author who has concerned himself with the matter of symbolism points out that people could not do some of the very commonest things, such as make-believe, or lie, not to say plan for the future, if they were incapable of using symbols.

Make-believe is a form of behavior that involves symbolism. It is a form of "acting-as-if." This sometimes seems to be impossible in certain asphasic individuals. Such patients are able to respond to stimuli as signals, but not to them as symbols. For instance, one patient was able to respond to the command, "Drink it," when a glass of water was in front of him. He was unable to go through the make-believe (symbolic behavior) of drinking when the empty glass was presented to him.

SYMBOLISM AND ITS REFERENCE

There is more than one framework in which we can use the terms symbol and symbolism. It behooves us to keep these in mind as we use the terms, else confusion will result.

One framework involves the onlooker as a referent. Symbolism in this case pertains only to the description which he makes in depicting the relation between an act and some reference of the act to items not literally present. Symbolism of this sort is externally imputed.

The second kind of instance in which symbolism can be said to be involved is the one in which only the perceiver himself is aware of the stimulus substituting for something not present. This kind may never be observable on the surface. It is thus only knowable through the assertions of the perceiver himself.

In the first case, the legitimacy of the use of the idea of symbolism to describe behavior comes from being able to substantiate the claim as an onlooker. In the second case, it comes to light only through self-awareness of the perceiver. Since we have pointed out that all behavior is not described as being self-awareness, then some symbolic behavior may well go undetected, both by the perceiver himself and by the onlooker. It, as a class, will be spoken of, if at all, only by the theorist or system builder, as we are now doing.

SYMBOLIC RESPONSE IN ANIMAL BEHAVIOR

We have already been told, by certain animal experimenters, that sub-human beings do not manifest symbolic behavior; others state that they do. Surely the implied definitions of these two groups are not identical. Surely all agree on the descriptions of what animal subjects do. The difference must lie in the interpretation given.

Nissen (200), for example, points out that what he calls symbolic behavior does occur. He says that symbolic behavior is responding to stimuli that are not present at the time. This is said to be the case in the conditioned response. First, the animal responds to a given presentation. Along with this is juxtaposed another, which, by itself, may be ineffective. This second presentation (the to-be-conditioned impingement) is one that either is not responded to at all or is responded to very differently than the first. After a number of repetitions, this second presentation evokes a response somewhat like the first. It is then that the animal is said to be responding to the stimulus that is not present; that is, it is behaving as if to the originally effective stimulus.

It may be argued, however, that to state the matter in this form is highly figurative. What the animal is literally responding to is the stimulus that *is* present.

Reference to the earlier stimulus is made by the experimenter in his description of what the animal is doing now, as compared to what it did do on the original occasion. Thus the experimenter, if he chooses to look at it that way, can envisage the present response as having symbolic relation to the stimulation that first evoked it, but which is now absent.

Perhaps, as far as the animal is concerned, the conditioned response cannot be used as a general example of symbolic behavior. It is response, at least, to a very literal event at the moment. How the impingement (the present stimulus) became effective need not be at issue, and thus reference to the original stimulus need not be made.

On the other hand, one whole segment of the study of animal and human behavior, namely, the study of learning, is one given over to relating present behavior to past behaviors. Learning curves are drawn to show how behavior progressively changes from trial to trial. No single trial means anything by itself. If learning theory, then, can talk about present behavior in relation to past or future behavior, perhaps the theorist can rightfully talk about "responding to stimuli that are not present." We shall not be too decisive either one way or another about this point. Let it be something for us to think about further.

CONDITIONING IN HUMANS

Whereas some doubt exists as to whether conditioning experiments with subhuman subjects provide evidence for symbolic behavior, the case may be very different with human subjects, for we may ascertain certain kinds of facts about them that are impossible with the subhuman.

For an illustration of conditioning in the human subject, let us take the case of the development of the use of words. One of the ways to develop a language is to show someone an object, and then pronounce a word, and possibly write out the word as well. This is done repeatedly until the subject comes to the point of using the word in the way he would use the object. We know that he thinks about the object, and at times he thinks in terms of the word either audibly pronounced, "seen" in visual imagery, or "heard" in auditory imagery. We are able, in the case of the human subject, to say that the word is a substitute in many ways for the object itself. Since it is a substitute, it is a symbol for the object; and the use of words, then, can truly be said to be symbolic, if anything can be said to be symbolic. We can set up experiments in which immediate responses (perceptual responses) can be evoked either by the object or the name of the object. In that sense, perception can be said to be symbolic. It is not only symbolic for the performing subject but also for the experimenter or onlooker. Such symbolism is both an imputation on the part of the experimenter and an intrinsic quality involved in the perceptual behavior itself.

SYMBOLISM AND CLASSIFICATION

One feature of perception that was listed in the preceding chapter was its classificational aspect. Each environmental item, the instant it shows up, is dealt with as a specific case of a more general class of items. It is not dealt with as an isolate, but as a number of a class.

If the organism has the ability to classify, its performance must involve symbolism. Let us take the experiment performed many years ago by Fisher (75) on concept formation. She provided her subjects with nonsense material. The material was several sets of novel geometrical figures. Each member of a set corresponded to an individual object.

Each set corresponded to a whole species and was given a specific non-sense name. She exposed each figure in a given series, one at a time, and finally asked for a definition of the word she supplied as a name for the series. The definition represented, in some way, the concept which the subject built up through his encounters with the objects. For example, one of these series was a group of "derals," so she asked the subjects, finally, what a deral was. By means of the subjects' introspective reports, she followed the development of concepts from the early stages, in which remembrance of individual figures was carried in concrete visual, motor, and other images, to the point at which many of the images became largely verbal. Two examples of the series of forms called derals are given in Fig. 3.1, so that you can see the principles involved in the presentations. In all the separate derals, there were features that, in principle, were alike. On the other hand, wide literal variations were exemplified.

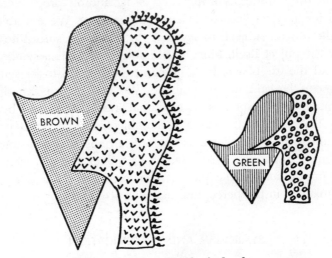

Fig. 3.1. Two specimens of Fisher's derals, or nonsense figures (S. C. Fisher, The process of generalizing abstraction, and its product, the general concept, *Psychol. Monog.* [1916], *21*:5–213).

After a certain point in this sequence of contacts, each new presentation could be reacted to either as a new member of this group or as something else. Each new presentation was not a wholly novel one calling for an entirely unique response. As evidence that classification had taken place, the subject could respond by either naming it a deral or naming it "not a deral," or, if so instructed, by naming it as a member of another class of objects. In everyday life, we not only have "derals," but we have myriads of additional classes of items, examples of which may loom up at anytime. Perception, or immediate reaction, will occur in a manner determined by the concepts already formed. We are not, for our purposes, mainly interested in how these forms of readiness to respond are developed, but rather *what they are like* and *how they influence* immediate response. We also want to know what relation the forms of response bear to the environmental items or situations that evoke them.

Granted that the perceptual response of recognizing objects is a kind of behavior that is classificational, we may wonder whether this response differs in any essential way from the recognition of a color in its basic relation to the stimulus. It will be recalled that the recognition of colors, that is, their discrimination one from the other, has been spoken of by some psychologists as a stimulus-bound reaction. It is as though there was a very definite and specific relation between parts of the spectrum and certain limited kinds of response, such as experiencing red or green. Such reactions have always been called simple, and at times called sensations in the attempt to show that they differed from naming objects or seeing the shapes of objects. The difference that is often overlooked lies in the usual nature of the task. In talking about a color, generally, we mean only the seeing of the color, not anything more definitive. In dealing with shape, size, and so on, some further discriminative process is implied or stated. It is possible that to see a color does not require symbolism, just as merely to see a deral does not; but to react to it, in the way specified in a set of instructions, that is, to name it, or to do any one of a number of things upon being presented with the visual target, does require symbolism.

Another illustration may be used. It may be asked how the "deralness" of a seen figure and straightness of a line can be in the same category. The common-sense answer would be that straightness is simply straightness. The form of the retinal image determines quite directly whether something will be called straight.

It must be remembered that a straight line, however produced, is either a concept or a perception, and thus we must not take the line as a reality, as a line, outside either of these two categories. All we know is that under certain conditions of impingement the perceiver runs a very high probability of having the experience of a straight line. The very fact that, for any reason whatever, he might not have that experience but a different one is demonstration that the relation is not absolute.

The main differences in the connection between stimulus and seeing a straight line and stimulus and seeing a deral are that one runs a higher probability of occurring than the other; the one was learned earlier in life than the other, and more people learn the one than the other.

There is still another form of perceptual behavior in which it may be argued that symbolism is absent. It is, for instance, the behavior that results when one is called upon to trace a star pattern. It is required that the tracing be congruent with the line that is seen. One could construct a photocell system that would guide a mechanical tracer so as to do a good job of line tracing. Having produced such an instrument, it could be said that symbolism is ruled out. This is true in the actual performance mechanism of the instrument. But in the case of the organism, symbolism is involved in hearing and understanding what task it is to be performed. The brain is functioning on the basis of symbols as it puts the task into operation, guiding the hand to do the tracing task rather than some other one. Symbolism is probably involved in the organism's setting up criteria of when the task is being performed according to instructions.

This is to say, that in order for a given task to be performed by a system capable of performing a number of kinds of tasks, acceptance of instructions or a choice has to be made, and this is accomplished by use of concepts, words, and so forth. The motor act is not all there is to such tasks as line tracing, for an "understanding" must underlie the selective features of activity the system performs. It is difficult for us to wriggle out of the belief that symbolism is involved in one way or another in virtually all, if not all, human acts by the time adulthood is reached.

CONCLUSION

In the foregoing, the idea and definition of symbolism have been introduced. Symbols have been distinguished from signs and the process of signaling. It has been shown that symbolic behavior occurs in humans, and that this includes perceptual response. The chapter was an attempt to preclude the separation of immediate discriminating response into stimulus-bound cases and cases obeying an entirely different set of laws. It seemed that once the various facets of the symbolism problem were examined, symbolism pervaded all of perception, as it is found in the human. Abstractness becomes a label with a different meaning than is often implied in its traditional usage.

Chapter 4

THE INTERRELATION OF THE VARIOUS SENSE MODALITIES

Whereas it is the usual thing to deal with one sense modality at a time, it is not to be inferred that the senses are isolated and do not influence each other. In fact, even in experimental situations it is difficult or impossible to eliminate the operation and participation of senses collateral to the one under study. Often, when the participation of senses other than the one studied is recognized, it is taken to be negligible in its influence upon the experimental results. At other times, if not negligible, it is looked upon as something having constant influence, so that it can be taken as a "constant error." Be that as it may, all too little has been done by psychologists and other biologists directly to study sensory interrelations. Their study is the exception rather than the rule.

The human organism possesses ten modalities of sensibility to the external world. They are vision, hearing, pressure and touch, temperature, kinesthesis (the muscle sense), pain, taste, smell, the vestibular sense, and the common chemical sense. This classification has involved four main criteria of long standing. The first of these is that in order to isolate a sense modality, a unique kind of experience must be demonstrated. The second is the demonstration of the existence of a special type of end organ as a mediator of the experience. The third is the existence of a separate pathway from the sense organ to the brain, and the fourth is the demonstration of a special type or range of energy as the adequate stimulus. The satisfying of all four criteria spells out a given sense modality. The use of these criteria has given us a number of modalities beyond the classical Greek number of five.

Our purpose in this chapter is to indicate the ways in which relations between sense modalities are manifested and studied. There are five different manifest aspects to the relations as we know them today, and these have led to their study according to the following classification:

(1) associative imagery and synesthesia, (2) intersensory facilitation and inhibition, (3) the manifestation of the same quality or property by two or more sense modalities, (4) common performances or functions in which a number of sense modalities participate, (5) performances that are called senses, but which are general functions not satisfying the criteria for a unique or separate sense modality.

The categories need some explanation from the very outset. Associative imagery is that imagery in one sense modality (let us say vision, for example) that is evoked by stimulation through another sensory channel (let us say, touch). Synesthesia is perhaps not an extreme form of associative imagery, but a performance lying clear outside the limits of associative imagery. In synesthesia, for example, the sense modality stimulated may be audition; but instead of hearing something, the person sees something. The seeing is not a collateral or secondary feature of the response, but rather the primary one.

Intersensory facilitation and inhibition are the end results evidenced by the fact that stimulating a second sense modality, while stimulating the first, changes the responses stemming from the first modality. It may reduce thresholds, or it may raise them.

The third category, in which two or more kinds of sense experience are describable by a single word, is illustrated by the case in which both visual and auditory experiences can be called bright or dull. That is, a surface of a visual object may be bright, and a sound may also be said to be bright.

Certain bodily functions, such as the maintenance of posture and coping with gravity, are accomplished by means of several sense modalities. To maintain posture in a gravitational field, or to determine what is the experiential vertical, involves the vestibular sense, the muscle sense, vision, touch or pressure, and, in other cases, hearing.

In many cases, it is said that organisms have a time sense. The use of the word sense in this way is certainly different from the way we are using it for the most part. Perceiving time is not based upon a specific set of sense organs, a peculiar kind of stimulus, a specified and separate afferent pathway, although it does consist in a unique kind of experience, or a unique overt relation to externality. It is an accomplishment of the organism that may be expressed in immediate behavior (perceptual response), or it may be manifested in extended performance.

There are still other cases in which what is given a label all its own does not tally with the criteria that have been set up to define a sense modality. What is called taste, for example, is not the direct end result of the activation of taste buds alone. Taste, for most people, is the result obtained when something is placed in the mouth. A number of modalities are usually stimulated under such circumstances. Not only the taste buds in the tongue, but pressure endings, temperature endings, pain endings, and smell receptors in the nose, are activated when some things are put into the mouth. For the typical observer to be able to analyze just which of these modalities is contributing to the "taste" experience as a whole is possibly too difficult to expect of him. To say the least, in this instance, we have one of the very best and most convincing demonstrations of the interaction of the sense modalities.

VIEWS REGARDING SENSORY INTERRELATIONS

There are two opposing views in regard to the interrelations between the senses. The classical or conventional and much more prevalent view, held either by implication or by explicit statement, presumes the initial independence of the various sense modalities. It assumes that the modalities were initially separate, and that learning of certain sorts has played a role in interrelating them. It does not overlook the fact that there are certain pathways in the central nervous system that may function to interconnect the modalities to some degree or other. This view does not seem to give any weight to the fact that the organism has been, from its very beginnings, a unitary system. It takes as its starting point the structural separateness of the afferent pathways and end organs from each other in the adult. The theory operates as though a variety of kinds of input is fed in over the various channels from sense organ to brain, rather than a single kind made up only of nerve impulses, all indistinguishable from each other. This view gives little weight to the fact that the experiencing organism is frequently unable to distinguish which modality is the recepient of stimulation.

The second view, as was said, is quite opposite to the one just described. It differs from it both in its deductions regarding underlying perceptual processes and in the expectations it makes regarding outcomes that have as yet been untested.

Instead of beginning with body structures in the adult, which we know are separate, and proceeding as if sensory experience was dependent wholly upon the mechanisms confined to the modality in question, it begins with the early organism. It adopts the view of the embryologists; namely, that tissues at any stage in the development of the organism evolve out of the simple and less differentiated tissues of the preceding stage. Thus, although we find different kinds of sense organs distributed independently about the body, the forerunners of this condition represent points at which such separations were not the case. To put the matter in other words, the second view begins and proceeds by regarding the organism and its sensory mechanisms as a unity. Considerable emphasis is given to the role played by the central nervous system rather than to the diversity of sense organs.

This view not only regards the adult diversification of tissue into body organs, including the several kinds of sense organs, as having occurred through a developmental process, but regards the development of sensory response in the same manner. The experiences which the adult calls vision, hearing, touch, pain, taste, smell, etc., did not originate as totally different sorts of response and then gradually fuse, but, instead, developed from something less separate into the variety of modalities and separate sensory experiences that characterizes the adult.

There are certain facts that are difficult to account for by the first view. One of these, for example, is synesthesia. The most common form of this is "colored hearing," the experience of visual phenomena when the stimuli are acoustic rather than photic. Colored hearing is not a case of the subject transforming or translating auditory experiences into visual ones, or having auditory experiences accompanied by secondary visual experiences, but rather of having the primary end result occur in a sense modality whose sense organs are not directly impinged upon.

According to the second view, this end result might come about by the failure of the underlying mechanism common to both modalities to differentiate properly in the course of development, or, after having differentiated well enough for the subject to be able to have experiences in both modalities, to suffer some distortion and anomaly of further development. Sometimes a blind person will develop synesthesia of the colored-hearing form. Possibly overall shock, along with the deprivation in one modality, may lie at the basis of the development of the synesthesia.

To say the least, the two opposing ways of viewing the sensory system possess different expectational possibilities and can well guide the further investigations in the interrelations of the senses.

ASSOCIATIVE IMAGERY

Each sense modality provides for two functions: a direct experiential result ensuing from stimulation of sense organs, and an associated result we call imagery. Imagery is the experiencing of objects and all that pertains to them, either by way of memory or by way of association with some modality that is being activated through its own sense organs. We may call this latter form of imagery *associative* imagery. We seldom hear a sound, for example, but what we imagine to some degree or other in visual terms—what the sound source is. It is a natural part of the hearing of sounds to identify their sources, and this identification includes visual imagery. When the visual experience so aroused has to do with literal visual identification of the sound source, as has just been described, we call it a normal process. There are times when the visual components of the overall experience evoked by acoustic stimuli do not have to do with imagined sound source, but rather with other meanings. This is particularly true in the case of music, in which case color, and visual and kinesthetic movement, may enter in very predominantly.

All normal incidents elicit imagery from sense modalities not directly stimulated at the time. A person in the dark feels his way about his room and manually contacts objects, each of which tends to arouse visual imagery. In fact visual imagery of the room and its objects as an overall space manifold is constantly in operation in such cases. Were there not a close neural connection between sense modalities, this elicitation of imagery would not be expected to occur. It is to be remembered that in all cases of imagery, the imagery involves modalities that are *not* stimulated directly. The directly aroused component and the indirectly aroused component of the overall experience (response) are quite intimately entwined. It is difficult to say at times whether the fact that experiences in one sense modality are, in some respects, so closely like those in another is because of associative imagery or because of an actual commonality.

Photistic Visualizers

There seems to be a fraction of our population that is able to use visual imagery to carry the major meaning of acoustic stimulation. There is some temptation to call such persons synesthetics (or synesthetes), but we should prefer to reserve this term for those whose whole perceptual and cognitive behavior is compellingly photistic, even when the original stimuli are acoustic rather than visual.

Karwoski and Odbert (135), and Karwoski, Odbert, and Osgood (136), studied photistic visualizers among student populations. Of the 276 subjects studied, over half fall into the class of photistic visualizers. They find that exciting music may be pictured by the photistic visualizers as etched bright-red forms. While many other people verbalize auditory impressions in visual terms, there is the tendency on their part to say that these visual phrases are metaphors. When such terms as bright, fiery, luminous, filmy-thin are given to what they hear, they feel the words certainly are appropriate, but at the same time they disavow them as being anything more than verbalisms. The very fact that they have the appropriateness they do is some testimony in favor of the substitutive ability of one modality for another, particularly the use of the visual modality for the auditory and the tactual. It also testifies to the fact that a considerable degree of this ability to substitute is subject to intentional learning, once the individual becomes sympathetic to the idea. Karwoski and Odbert found that many of the photistic visualizers could point to their first marked synesthetic-type experience. In many cases, it turned out to be a traumatic occasion in early life.

Some of the persons in question characteristically imagined the entire visual field as uniformly colored, the various hues succeeding each other as the music progressed from one tempo to another. Others described multibanded fields in which the bands were in motion in time to the music. Qualitative features of the music as related to what is ordinarily experienced as timbre are expressed by various horizontal layers of the bands. It was also found that the geometry of visualized figures reflected the music's tempo. Fast music was reflected in sharp and angular figures, and slow music gave rise to large rounded forms. That the associations just described are not uncommon suggests that perhaps those who make them do not deserve a special label.

Synesthesia

There is actually, in some persons, what is called *synesthesia*. The most frequently mentioned example of synesthesia is that of *colored hearing*. In some persons, stimulation through the auditory mechanism produces very definite visual effects, the outstanding feature of which is some sort of a color experience. The color experience carries meaning in and of itself. Voices and other sound stimuli are often seen in visual imagery by the blind. As was said earlier, the process is not primarily that of hearing and then translating the sound into a learned color. The color itself emerges immediately and with meaning for the synesthetic individual. Blind persons may identify people around them via voice, but when they do so in terms of the colors evoked by the voice rather than in terms of auditory quality, they are synesthetic.

Whereas chromesthesia, or colored hearing, is the most common sort of synesthesia, there are other forms such as colored tasting and colored smelling. So far it has been impossible to demonstrate that synesthetes possess any set of unique or peculiar neural connections that would account for the behavior. Hence, so far, we must suppose that the achievement comes about through the mechanisms potential in everyone.

No one has adequately studied the origin and development of synesthesia. A suggested explanation offered by Stagner and Karwoski (232) runs something like the following: The synesthete begins as a youngster with exceptionally vivid imagery. Circumstances surrounding his development start the condition of seeing colors in connection with tones and other sounds he experiences. The phenomenon is likely to be fairly obtrusive and thus somewhat disturbing to the youngster, creating tensions within him. The tensions are reduced if and when the colors are developed into patterns, that is, if the colors come to take on forms that have relevant meaning. A natural consequence is the relating of the colors to tonal scales. In this way, the child may tend to feel he has some control of the situation. The authors point out that this initial disturbance may be something like that evoked by a child's moving to a country in which a new language is spoken. The insecurity and dissatisfaction felt are relieved by learning the language. To say the least, it is likely that special circumstances must intervene in the life of anyone who becomes a synesthete.

The major reason why we do not possess the kind of information which we desire about synesthesia is possibly because the phenomenon cannot easily, if at all, be produced experimentally. Were it to be producible in a short laboratory experiment, or by means of a learning sequence, it would be evidence in favor of the first of the two views mentioned earlier. In fact, if the second view is right in its main implications, synesthesia would be expected to be producible mainly in relatively young individuals.

A few attempts have been made to condition a color response to the acoustic stimulus that initially and naturally produces a tone. Several authors failed to be able to do so. One investigator, on the other hand, reports finding that tones and colors can be associated by long training.

INTERSENSORY FACILITATION

The idea of intersensory facilitation is based upon findings and interpretations in physiology. Certain pathways connecting the various areas of the brain, such as the auditory and visual areas, provide cause for supposing that facilitating and inhibiting reactions between the two mechanisms are to be expected.

We now turn to some examples of interaction found in the laboratory. The reaction time to an acoustic stimulus has been found to be shorter in colored light than in darkness. The reaction time to acoustic stimuli is nearly at a minimum when such stimuli are used alone. The use of electric shock with an acoustic stimulus reduces it about 9 msec. on the average, and an additional 4 msec. by adding photic stimulation. It must be recognized, of course, that results depend upon whether the subject is set to hear sound or to see light.

It has also been shown that reaction time to light is facilitated by the presence of a continuous noise. Whereas to account for the effects of transient forms of secondary stimulation "attention" has been used, at least in part, to explain the shortening of reaction time, with a continuous background of secondary stimulation the attention explanation loses a great deal, if not all, of its force.

Various workers before and around the turn of the century found that acoustic stimuli enhanced the subjects' sensitivity to photic stimuli. That is, the threshold for photic stimulation was reduced. In one case, half of a group of subjects showed increased auditory acuity when the tests were made under extremely bright light. Likewise, when light and tones were experienced together, the sensitivity to the acoustic stimulation was enhanced. In a lighted room, tones also seemed higher in pitch. It was found that low tones could be manipulated in "brightness" by varying the intensity of the accompanying photic stimulation. It may be argued here that the subjects were really responding to the photic stimulus and calling the tones bright. Even if such an oversimplified view be granted just for the sake of argument, it would still be a case of the interaction of two sense modalities. It would be a demonstration of a case in which the subjects were not able to tell which property belonged to which experience.

Some workers brought the experimentation of intersensory effects to a further step in definiteness. Child and Wendt (59) reported that a brief photic pulse would lower auditory threshold most when it preceded the acoustic stimulus by a half second. This was corroborated by another worker. This result could be attributed largely to attention. But even though it is admitted attention plays a considerable role, it does not necessarily destroy the argument that the senses are greatly interrelated. Attention is the name given to an overall organizational pattern in the behaving organism that focuses its activity in some certain direction. If the use of a photic stimulus can succeed in realigning the behaving individual so as to react more sensitively to a second stimulus, it demonstrates a kind of interaction (though indirect) between the stimuli pertinent to two modalities.

Further experimentation in this area could well take the form of attempting to determine the threshold-lowering value of a first stimulus in a given modality on a second stimulus presented a half-second later. This effect should be compared to the effect brought about by the first stimulus when involving a *different* modality.

Kravkov (*148*), a worker much interested in the interrelation of the senses, believed that an acoustic stimulus would raise the excitation level of the central nervous system, and thereby facilitate the "irradiation" of white surfaces, through this process in the visual cortex. According to the classical expectations of visual irradiation, acoustic stimuli, in increasing irradiation, should make a white area between two black ones more visible than otherwise, and a black area between two white areas less visible. Kravkov found that a 2100-c.p. acoustic source did increase the acuity of black on white and reduce that of white on black as expected. Hartmann (*104*), who studied the same problem, states that improvement occurred in both situations, not only in one. In contrast to these two workers, Serrat and Karwoski (*225*) failed to find any facilitation. At present it is impossible to state what is back of the conflict.

Brogden (*35*) reported that a photic pulse and an acoustic stimulus, presented together a number of times without reinforcement, will each elicit a response later if only one of them is reinforced in the meantime. Sensory preconditioning of this sort operates possibly by way of slight intermediary responses made initially to both the stimuli, even without reinforcement, according to a view expressed by Harris.

Synesthetic imagery is very common among the blind. Cutsforth states that most of the conscious mental structure of the synesthetic consists in visual photisms of color, form, and movement, each of which has its own definite meaning. These photisms are the tools of thinking, just as are words in the case of the nonsynesthetic. Thinking thus takes place by either actually or passively viewing the visual field (field of visual imagery). This is in contrast to the more usual case in which individuals think in words that tend to be imagined auditorily. That is, to most people, words are generally patterns of sound. Only for special purposes does the person try to see what words look like.

In the visual type of thinking of the synesthetic, words are said to be formed visually by the synesthetic and thus the formation of acoustic words for him is a hindrance to thinking. When words become necessary for communication, their formation takes considerable time, hence leading to halting speech, without full coherence, and with little verification of the thought behind the words.

This description of the synesthetic is injected here, not as a description of a peculiar kind of perception, but in the attempt to show how one modality may become substituted for another in the economy of some individuals. It is significant for our purposes, because acoustic stimuli may not evoke auditory experiences but visual ones. These are not aroused by a secondary or intervening process but quite directly, and this testifies toward some commonability between modalities, else they could not be exchanged in this way, one for the other.

INTERRELATION IN THE LOWER SENSES

Probably the best evidence for intersensory relations is to be found in the lower sense modalities, such as those of taste, smell, etc., which are modalities that are more poorly differentiated in the first place. That we specify them as poorly differentiated modalities implies, among other things, that the experiences they involve are more poorly distinguished from each other. In many cases, the experiences elicited can scarcely be designated as those of smell rather than taste, or vice versa. The main criteria lie in whether a substance has been placed in the mouth or, for example, something is experienced as a result of sniffing.

Common observation indicates that various beverages taste differently at different temperatures. This could be accounted for in either of two ways. Either the effectiveness of a substance is dependent upon the molecular activity that is called thermal or else the activation of the temperature receptors puts an additional ingredient into the taste experience by way of the central nervous system. It is probably the latter, if not both, for the qualitative effects of thermal stimulation on taste is probably more subtle than those induced solely by manipulation of thresholds for the four taste components: sweet, salt, bitter, and sour.

Not only are strict taste and smell qualities confused, but the experiencer is not clear as to what roles other sense modalities are playing in the overall experience that is generally called taste or smell. Not only the thermal sense but also pain and the sense of pressure are involved. One of the very most satisfying features of foodstuffs is their mechanical characteristic. We generally like crunchy materials. Some substances seem too pasty; others have too much elasticity, and are thus not chewable. It is difficult to say how these factors relate to those that are more technically called taste proper, but it would be unthinkable to conclude that they are not involved at all.

In the sense of smell, pain and temperature factors are also effective. There is, likewise, a possible astringent (mechanical) effect, one that is even more pronounced during oral stimulation.

Hahn and Günther (*101*) carried out an important line of experimentation on the role of thermal stimulation on taste. They brought the tongue to the temperature of the taste solution which they would subsequently use, and maintained it constant as long as needed. The results for four substances are shown in Fig. 4.1. Such complex temperature effects, as shown in the figure, suggest that stimulation is not a simple chemical reaction between stimulus substance and taste cell. Most purely chemical reactions are enhanced as temperature rises. But in taste, en-

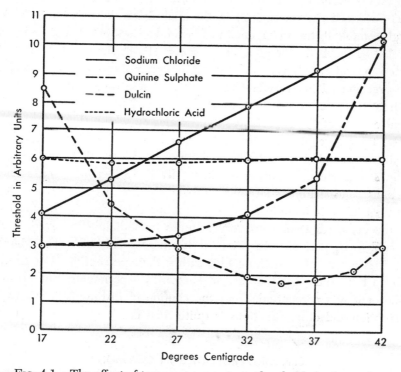

Fig. 4.1. The effect of temperature on taste thresholds for four substances (II. Hahn, Über Ursache der Geschmacksempfindung, *Klinische Wochenschrift* [1936], *15*:933–935, Fig. 1).

hancement holds only for the sweet substance used, and it even reverses above 37° C. Different subjects as well as different sweet substances show unlike curves in relation to temperatures. We must fall back on something other than solely chemical reactions at the taste cell to account for temperature effects. When we do so, we are admitting that the neural results of thermal stimulation and the neural results of taste stimulation interact to give us the complex end result. This is another example of the intimate organic basis for interaction.

In the modality of taste, the four qualities just mentioned are generally considered the primary elements out of which all tastes are compounded. Certain authors, such as Hahn, Kuckulies, and Taeger (102), believe that a fifth elemental taste, alkaline, is to be included. Most other workers believe that alkaline is a combination that may even include nongustatory ingredients, such as touch, smell, or pain. Thus we see how difficult it is to isolate the components that are supposed to stand independently as features of separate modalities. This very thing tends to call into question the absolute discreteness of the sense modalities.

The work of Hazzard (106) in the analysis of olfactory qualities is a good example of the involvement of several senses in what is ordinarily labeled as the behavior of a single sense. His findings had to do with dimensions of smells that do not often become verbalized or perhaps even recognized in everyday descriptions. These dimensions had to do with texture, volume, brightness, other spatial features, and the temporal courses of the experiences. The scales on which the observers ordered their perceptions were as follows: heaviness-lightness, looseness-tightness, smoothness-roughness, softness-hardness, thinness-thickness, dullness-sharpness, brightness-dullness, liveliness-inertness, surfaceness-deepness, and smallness-largeness. Obviously, the observers were allowing themselves to include considerable aroused imagery in their reports. To the extent that such imagery is quite immediately involved, it can be said to be part of perception. If it emerges only after considerable lag, it is a part of something else rather than perception. We are not able to tell which was the case in Hazzard's experiments, but presume some of it was perceptual. Here the caution of distinguishing between perception and other functions is quite relevant.

SENSORY PROPERTIES IN COMMON

In Hazzard's study, we are reminded that various senses may have properties in common. The question may resolve itself into whether two senses do share a single property, or whether, when a word from vision is used in describing touch, smell, or hearing, it is only descriptive of collateral imagery evoked in these senses. Criteria for calling something imagery, and for envisaging it in some other way, have not yet been worked out.

Let us examine the dimensions reported upon in Hazzard's olfactory study. Some of the dimensions seemed to refer to the tactual sense. The following seemed to be in this group: looseness-tightness, smoothness-roughness, softness-hardness, and possibly dullness-sharpness. Dullness-sharpness also seems to refer to the pain sense. Heaviness-lightness refers to kinesthesis. If so, here is where it is possible that modalities that are not directly stimulated come into play through imagery. Liveliness-inertness might also refer to kinesthesis. Four of the dimensions refer to vision, namely, thinness-thickness, brightness-dullness, surfaceness-deepness, and smallness-largeness.

It must be noted that certain words may not need to refer exclusively to a single modality. Take for instance the term *brightness*. Sounds are experienced as bright, as well as are the objects we see. We are faced with the problem, of course, as to whether brightness is a visual effect evoked by acoustic stimulation. If it is a visual-imagery component of sound, then perhaps the term bright, in its most strict meaning, is only a visual term. If it could be shown that brightness is a true auditory property, then the term would apply to two categories of sense experience.

THE PERCEPTION OF TIME

We indicated earlier that certain perceptual functions seem to be related to no single set of sense organs in accord with the criteria for isolating senses already set forth. In the case of the "time sense," we have a very good example. Despite there being no specific time-sense mechanism, we often hear the term time sense used. By the time sense it is meant only that time is something experienced, or that the human can relate himself to clock time in a fairly successful way.

While we cannot make time perception the function of a specific body mechanism, as in the case of the true senses, it cannot be denied that the organism is active in a clock-time continuum. It may be that the very nature of certain body processes, including the activities of several sensory mechanisms, is responsible for the experience of time and the ability of the organism to relate itself to the clock. Just what these mechanisms and processes are is not yet known. It is difficult to conceive how any specific process which we might isolate would participate in the overall process of time perceiving.

Most of the work on time perception has related more directly to determining the human subjects' ability to judge durations rather than to determining what the responsible processes might be. What we ordinarily call attention is possibly one of the variables in the overall picture. Whether to try to manipulate it directly or to vary certain forms of sensory stimulation is a question. We need to know, however, a little about what has been done in this field, and what the results have been.

PERCEPTION OF INTERVALS

Three types of temporal arrangements have been used as stimuli for obtaining reports on the experience of duration: (1) empty intervals marked off by acoustic stimuli yielding clicks, (2) sources providing the hearing of a continuous tone, and (3) periods of continuous photic stimulation. This is to say, reports have been made on the basis of three kinds of experiences: empty intervals, continuous tones, and continuous lights. In general, the thresholds, when pairs of these are compared, are lowest for certain short durations, and increase both above and below this short range.

Empty intervals, for example, were studied by Blakely (27). He found the experiences of duration to be most accurate at intervals of 0.6 and 0.8 second. The limen here was about 8 percent of the standard. While the limen for perceived differences varied both above and below the standards just mentioned, the values stayed less than 10 percent for an overall range from 0.2 to 1.5 second. The limen rose to 16 percent for the range of from 2 to 4 seconds. For the range from 6 to 30 seconds, the limen rose to 20–30 percent.

For continuous tones and lights, the accuracy was quite similar to values just quoted for empty intervals. For example, for the range from 0.4 to 2 seconds the limens were from 10 to 12.5 percent. For continuous light, the accuracy of discrimination was 7 to 14 percent for duration ranges from 2 to 8 seconds.

Woodrow (273) points out that there are two classes of factors affecting the perception of time. The first is, of course, the "objective" or environmental set of factors, and the second is the attitudinal. As he says, "temporal perceptions are reactions to stimuli." Woodrow manipulated not only the interval between bounding stimuli but also the duration of the bounding stimuli themselves, and found that the stimulus duration was a factor. He cautions that the whole series of pairs of stimuli used in a given sitting or even during a whole experiment, although conducted over many days, affects single trials within the series. There seems to be a tendency for the subject to become "adapted" to an interval frequently repeated. Whatever adaptation is, it seems not only to pertain to given intervals but also to be expressed in reactions to other intervals as well. This would seem to be a manifestation of Helson's (112) adaptation-level principle.

Information at hand regarding attitudinal facts seems to have come only from introspective reports. Woodrow says that it is amazing the variety of internal activities that go on when a subject is simply required to tell which of the short intervals is the greater.

A fraction of the subjects form a single pattern out of the two compared intervals. Others introduce differences in emphasis or accent into the interval. This has been called rhythm or phrasing. In the case of two intervals being marked off by three acoustic stimuli, this phrasing becomes pronounced in its effect. Some subjects note the first interval, and then start "reproducing" it as the second interval begins. One of the most significant kinds of reports is that which involves production of a kinesthetic experience. Woodrow (270, 271, 272) says this kinesthetic experience may be sensory or imaginal. In some cases, the subject turns away from the experiences produced by the stimuli used and concentrates upon the experience of duration itself. Interestingly, this experience is of two kinds. It is either one of passive waiting or else one of awareness of strain. The strain that has detectable kinesthetic origins may arise from muscles in almost any part of the body. Sometimes experience of strain involves the arm and legs, but in other cases it involves the muscles in breathing and the muscles of the vocal organs. When the latter occurs, auditory imagery may be a part of the total experience pattern.

The various reports indicate the involvement of musculature and kinesthesis, so it may be said that certain sensory activities occurring at the time are part of the background for time experience. This conclusion is reinforced by experiments in which it was shown that if the subject gave "maximal attention" to the second of two tones, the interval being bounded was "overestimated." When subjects did just the opposite, that is, listened passively, the interval was made shorter than otherwise.

When Woodrow instructed subjects to listen to the sounds bounding an interval, the reproductions of these intervals were much shorter than when the subjects were instructed to attend to the interval between the sounds.

Theories of Time Perception

The durational aspect of the experience elicited by a stimulus is some-times called its *protensity*, as a term paralleling intensity. Protensity has sometimes been called a fundamental aspect or quality of all sensory experience. The term used in this way is not always applicable to the experience of duration of an interval between two experimental bound-ing stimuli. One may find, however, that the experience is based upon body processes going on during the interval and providing a sensory background. Obviously, there is an intellectual and/or an affective com-ponent in the situation, just as in many other forms of perceptual be-havior. One of the things that is important to us is that Woodrow finds that what he calls the perception of time or the experience of duration is an immediate response, or an immediately given property of experience.

Some workers believe that the attribute of *progression* applies to all consciousness. Some believe that the appreciation of duration or time is based upon change, the change being in the stimulus realm. It might be supposed that this factor of change could apply to appreciation of body processes as well as to events external to the body. The facts suggest to some that time is always appreciated indirectly by means of some process that serves as a "cue."

None of the suggestions we have reviewed help us to understand the relatively accurate appreciation of long periods of time, such as several hours, during sleep. Something is utilizable, and it does not have to be a conscious experience that spans the interval to be reported upon.

When we deal with still longer periods of time, we must surely come to the level in which conceptual and memory processes predominate, or are exclusively involved. Hence we pass beyond the realm in which we can deal with time predominantly perceptually. Prior to this, various sense modalities are intertwined in the provision for the single form of reaction we call the perception of time.

Perception of Movement and Position

Overall reactions not based upon the operation of a single sense modality are the perceptions of position and movement. Something about this will be given in Chapter 11. It is not so common to hear of there being a movement sense as there being a time sense, hence the appre-ciation of movement lies in a different category in our original classifi-cation. It is an example of item 4.

Chapter 5

THE DEVELOPMENT OF PERCEPTION

It is important to note that most of our perceptual behavior is modifiable, even in adulthood, and that it did not emerge full blown at the very beginning of infancy. Perception runs a course of development, and a number of features of this development are well worth discussing in this text.

The development of perception may be studied in several ways, since more than one kind of phenomenon is evidence of it. Accordingly, we shall examine perception in the following ways: (1) Through the study of its comparative aspects. The perceptual behavior of some animal forms is more poorly differentiated and represents a cruder set of sensitivities and a simpler set of relations to externality (the environment) than does behavior in other forms. (2) Through the study of changes in perception in the human being as a function of age. This is the ontogenetic study of perception. It is, on the one hand, the study of maturation, and on the other, the effects of incidental influences that impinge upon the individual as he progresses through life. (3) Through the study of the changes brought about in specific perceptual reactions as an expression of the learning process without regard to age. (4) Through the study of the subject's set or stance. (5) Through the study of the forms and degrees of completeness, etc., of perception as a function of presentation time, or stimulus intensity. And, finally (6), the cultural influences upon perception, which, of course, determine what perception develops to be as a function of the perceiver being part of a group. This topic will be more adequately covered in Chapter 18.

These six approaches deal with the following problems respectively. How do human perceptions compare with and extend beyond those of lower animal forms? What are the characteristics of the shifts in or the developments of perception that are common to humans as a class?

What are the particular steps in the perceptual learning of a single individual? Is the analytical response a development of perception beyond the nonanalytical? How does perception become fuller and more complete (more adequate) as duration of intensity of stimulation is increased?

THE COMPARATIVE PICTURE—PERCEPTION UP AND DOWN THE ANIMAL SCALE

The lower animal forms begin life as more or less completed products, possessing, at birth or soon thereafter, all behavioral manifestations they will ever exhibit. On the contrary, the higher animal forms pass through an extended period during which their anatomical mechanisms develop. With this develop certain subtle capacities aside from the directly observable changes in anatomy. Both aspects of this growth taken together are called maturation.

In studying perception in lower animal forms, it is often necessary, or at least convenient, to use learning experiments. The learning situation consists in the attempt to get the animal to discriminate one stimulus from another. This is done by using repeated presentations and by reward. Aside from the information that is generally obtained regarding learning, the behavior may indicate the nature of stimulus manipulations that are necessary for perceptual discrimination. That is, they may be arranged so as to demonstrate the minimal differences between stimuli that can be discriminated. Hence, if we cite certain animal experiments here that seem like learning experiments, this need not be surprising, for some of these have, as was said, demonstrated something about the animal's perceptions.

Earthworms have been trained to make consistent right and left turns in Y- and T-shaped mazes. This is an example of the animal's ability to perceive the difference between the two. These habits can be reversed, and reversed more easily than the habit can be learned in the first place. This seems likely to be due to having set up conditions in which the kinds of stimuli used by the experimenter have become prepotent.

Mollusks have been conditioned to make T-maze discriminations. The experiment ran as follows. The unconditioned stimulus was lettuce touching the mouth region. Pressure on the foot was the conditioned stimulus, a kind of stimulus that when given alone inhibited mouth opening. Initially, the foot stimulus was prepotent over the mouth-opening stimulus. After approximately 250 trials the conditioning was accomplished. Mechanical pressure by this time, when given alone, had come to elicit the opening of the mouth. It took only 12 trials to extinguish the response, but it was quickly relearned. In the experiment, one sees the same principles at work as are demonstrated in the much higher animal forms. Perceptions, that is, discriminatory responses, do take place, and they are subject to learning. The mollusk is able to learn to do something opposite to the behavior that appears to be a more or less simple and stereotyped form of inherited behavior.

Ants, a representative of the arthropods, or particularly the insects, are capable of learning their way through long intricate mazes. In many respects their performance is not inferior to that of mammals, and is even better than many of the lower vertebrates. Among the vertebrates, the reptiles seem to be better than fishes and amphibians (frogs, etc.) in maze performance. Fishes, such as the goldfish, have been taught to discriminate between various levels of illumination in a series of compartments to which they were free to swim. This behavior was truly configurational and thus was in every respect discriminational. The fish could choose between the greater, the medium, and the lesser intensities used, regardless of the general level of illumination.

Primates (apes and man) seem to have difficulty in developing normal perceptual facilities if their development has been precluded during earlier life. This is attested to by the difficulties in visual performance following experimental darkness during infancy, and the difficulties encountered by humans when they have been victims of cataracts obstructing vision during the first few years of life. Both the apes and the humans are unable to perceive the meaning of the visual targets for a long time after they have been first rendered able to receive images on their retinas. While those difficulties may be described as features of the learning process, they are nevertheless descriptive of the state of perception under the conditions mentioned.

Certain experiments regarding space perception in domestic fowl were made by Katz and Révész (138), and by Révész (220), which are both interesting and instructive. Fowl feeding upon grain and other small objects plentifully strewn about them will cease pecking if the illumination drops below a certain level of intensity. This is taken to indicate that the pecking response is dependent in some way upon vision. In darkness, the rattle of falling grain, which tends to excite the fowl when under illumination (induce definite overt reactions), leaves them outwardly inert.

Révész (220) points out that although a hen may be in the state of running about to examine its surrounds, to scratch and otherwise search for food, it does not stay and search at a spot where it has seen food hidden. In this respect, too, it seems to be entirely a visual animal. The behavior of fowl toward hidden food objects shows that they either do not possess visual imagery (visual representations) at all or, if they do, they are not such as to be usable as "motives" or means toward definite action. The hen never seems to profit by single experiences; rather, it requires an accumulation of them before it can make anything out of experience. This seems also to be evidence that visual imagery, or any other sort, for that matter, is not very serviceable if it exists. Révész tried various conditions under which he hoped to get his experimental hens to go after hidden grain, first by covering it with transparent material, and later with opaque, otherwise having the same visual characteristics. With the transparent, the hens pecked at the material but could not reach the grain. With the opaque, the hens were inert. He tried covering part of the grain. Here, again, the hens would not do anything more than peck and eat the visible grain. This is, of course, in contrast to behavior with mammals, such as monkey or dog, which would have tried to get the hidden food first. Repetition, and some happy accidents, in which the animal did push the paper slightly aside and get some previously covered grain, led to some learning. Finally, the animal in question did come to exert some effort to uncover the grain. In the end (that is, in a relatively few trials), the hen came to the point of pushing anything aside that was used to cover the grain. Hence it could be said that hens are capable of learning to uncover hidden food in specific situations in which a series of practice trials is assured. But, as Révész puts it, the animal must be actively and continuously engaged in reacting to optical stimuli in order for the achievement to develop.

In a very different situation, in which the experimenter covered the grain with a pane of glass, the hen could not be induced to try to push the glass away. The sight of the grain through the glass was so compelling that the only reaction inducible was that of attempting to reach the grain through the glass.

Révész analyzed the pecking behavior of the hen into *aiming, quick movement* of head, and the *picking up* of the grain. Pecking does not occur without aiming, and aiming cannot occur except toward visible objects. This explanation seems to account for the hen's failure to peck in the dark. Not only is aiming necessary, but a certain distance or positional relation of food and head must exist for pecking. Révész has called this distance the *pecking elevation.* When the experimenter places the beak of a hen in a basin of grain, the animal does not eat. It seems unable to do so. Apparently it can only do so when the head can assume a position at the necessary distance from the grain. This interesting analysis of animal behavior is carried on further, but we are forced to pass on to still other features of and conditions for the hen's visual perception.

Another set of experiments by Révész showed that hens left for several days in the dark did not consume a single grain of the food left with them. There was some evidence to indicate that methods could be devised to train them to consume part or all of their usual supply of food in the dark. One author has reported special conditions under which pecking and the obtaining of food did occur in the dark, but it is not clear just what these conditions were.

Révész trained hens to discriminate between the smaller of two plane geometrical figures, such as circles, rectangles, triangles, and squares. After certain behavioral criteria had been reached in doing this, the investigation passed on to the use of a certain geometrical "illusion," namely, the Jastrow illusion. This is shown in Fig. 5.1 The two portions

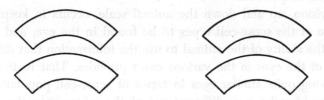

FIG. 5.1. *The Jastrow illusion.* In which of the two pairs of sectors are the sectors equal? In the left, they are metrically but perceptually unequal; in the right, they are perceptually equal but metrically unequal.

of the target were placed in various positional relations to each other. For the hens, however, the two portions were made metrically unequal. The choosing of the smaller of the two was the performance learned. After this preliminary training series, in which the animal procured the grain from the proper one of the two target elements, the two target elements were made equal in size. The elements were now such as to be perceived unequal by the human observer. The problem was to determine whether the hen would choose the perceptually smaller target element. If so, it would indicate that it was, in effect, subject to the Jastrow illusion. The test turned out positive, and it was concluded that perceptions of the hen certainly did not tally with metrical size of the targets, but were something like those of the human in such situations.

Animal reaction to intermittent photic stimulation, such as is produced

by a rotating disc with "black and white" alternate sectors, or by a revolving drum with alternate "black" and "white" sectors, within which
drum the subject is placed, indicates sensitivity somewhat like that of
human subjects. Animal forms all the way from insects to various vertebrates, including reptiles, fishes, birds, and man, all react to rapid rates
of intermittency as to uniform steady stimulation. All animal forms that
do this act quite consistently, and curves relating the c.f.f. (critical
flicker frequency), the rate at which uniformity is just perceived, to the
intensity of the photic stimulus, have characteristics in common. The behavior in all cases, regardless of the position in the animal scale, seems
to be largely determined by two things: the presence or absence of certain types of *sense-cell populations* in the eye, and the mechanism
whereby the inputs from these large populations are *integrated in time*
and *in amount*. These two mechanisms are supposed to follow common
principles in all the animal forms to which we have alluded, regardless
of how differently the integration is used in the ultimate economy of the
animal form in question.

Color vision, up and down the animal scale, occurs in keeping with
the nature of the sense-cell types to be found in the eye, and in keeping with the ability of the animal to use the information that differential
behavior of the eyes in the various cases provides. That is, two animal
forms having quite similar eyes in terms of sense-cell populations, etc.,
may certainly make very different use of the information the eyes can
provide. Actually, one animal form might even manifest no behavior that
could be called color perception, while understandably the other form
might. Thus it is that the term color vision has more than one way of
being defined. Were we to use the term color perception, then we could
say that any animal form that showed no overt signs of differential response to the various portions of the spectrum was devoid of color perception. Or perhaps we should be more precise than this and say that
the animal forms that can react differentially to various portions of the
photic spectrum have *spectral perception*. This term would not imply
color experience as we know it. But if differential experience is evoked
by various parts of the spectrum, then these animals would possess *color
perception*. If we went no further than to examine retinal anatomy, we
might make guesses as to anatomical equipment for either color perception or spectral perception. If we recorded the electrical activity of the
retina and found differential response to various parts of the spectrum,
we might say that the animal's peripheral sensory equipment was adequate for either spectral perception or color perceptions. Which it would

actually be would be dependent upon whether the animal's central nervous system could make appropriate use of the peripheral information. To be sure, we would have to have the kind of evidence we require and get from human subjects, and this is impossible. In examining the eye only, all that can be said is whether or not there is sense-organ detection on a spectral basis, which we may call *peripheral adequacy* for spectral or color vision.

ONTOGENETIC DEVELOPMENT

The very earliest response to tactile stimulation is manifested in fetal life (prebirth stage) of the individual, where such factors as temporal and spatial summation are evidenced. Repeated contacts of the fetus with a light hair are effective when a single contact is not. Contact with a brush containing a number of hairs is effective, whereas a single hair is not. Different responses are elicited in premature infants by grading impingements (contacts) from weak to strong. Response is quite consistent from trial to trial and depends upon the zone contacted.

The fetus responds to warm and cold, according to Preyer (213) and Blanton (28). Pratt, Nelson, and Sun (212) found that the responses of newborn infants to stimuli that are colder than the body are more intense than to those that are warmer than the body.

Cutaneous pain does not seem to be evokable in the fetus, as is attested by the relative weakness of overt reaction to impingements that cause destruction to skin and underlying tissue. Sometimes no overt response is elicited in premature infants during the first day, even when the impingements draw blood. Carmichael (53, 55), in this connection, remarks that less response is evoked in fetal guinea pigs by such impingements than by contact with a fine hair at the same point.

Taste receptors have been reported to be more widely distributed in the early fetus than in the adult. It has been found that the human infant at birth can distinguish between salt, sour, and bitter as against sweet.

There is some evidence that the auditory receptors of the human fetus can be stimulated under some conditions. For example, it has been reported that a distinct response of a child in the womb was elicited again and again by striking the bathtub in which the mother was seated. A wide range of tones was used to stimulate the child *in utero* by certain other investigators.

Response indicating distinction between light and dark can be elicited in a 7-month (premature) infant. This is, of course, despite the fact that the optic nerve and other visual structures are not fully mature, even at 9 months, the normal time of birth.

So much for some of the very beginnings of immediate discriminatory response of the human individual to his surrounds. We now turn to some of the individual's developments during later stages. The development of perception as a function of age in the human subject has best been exemplified by the work of Gesell and his colleagues over the past several decades. They particularly studied visual perception in the growing child from birth through his early years.

In dealing with the topics of sensory development in the child, we shall follow quite closely *Vision, Its Development in Infant and Child* by Gesell, Ilg, and Bullis (83). These workers gave attention to the perceptual growth of the child by studying five aspects of his behavior. The first of these was *eye-hand coördination.* [The neonate was observed to begin at once to deploy his eyes, to move and stop them, which signifies a beginning active endeavor to adapt to the circumstances around him. This beginning behavior, however, is very crude, incomplete, and ineffective. Pursuit movements of a sort and the ability to fixate come in the first four weeks. By 12 weeks he can follow an object 180° with blinking, jerky movements. By 16 weeks he can retain a toy in hand, with occasional observation of it. By 24 weeks he discriminates between strangers. By 36 weeks he feeds himself a cracker. By 48 weeks he plays alternately with several toys. By 52 weeks he offers toys to another person, and enjoys a give-and-take performance. All of this is, although ordinarily thought of in terms other than perception, a sense-guided type of behavior.

By 2 years the child has freed his eyes from his hands and may inspect objects with eyes alone. At 2½ years "an object in another child's hand may be seen without regard for the child" himself. At 3½ years the child moves his head close to a magazine page to identify something, or may move away and withdraw the head to a greater distance. By 4 years a free and fluid eye-hand relationship is achieved.]

These and many more things may be said about the typical child, indicating the development of a relation between him and his environment which has involved several achievements: the control of his ocular manipulative mechanisms, the manipulation of his geometrical relations to his surrounds, and the utilization of his surrounds to achieve purpose. During this time, the early limitations in behavior that were very evident can be seen to slip away, stage by stage, freeing him for a freer and more fluid relationship with his surrounds. Perception plays a predominant role at all stages.

2   The second general aspect of behavior studied by Gesell and coworkers was *postural orientation*. During the first 4 weeks, the head is rotated toward a preferred side. By 8 weeks, the head is held erect, but bobs considerably. By 20 weeks, the head can be held erect while sitting. By 24 weeks, direction of sound source is localized. By 32 weeks, there is strong bilateral employment of hands. He can then hold simultaneously two objects. By 40 weeks, he pulls himself to a standing position through grasp of a supporting object. By 44 weeks, there is definite use of the preferred hand. By 48 weeks, he pivots freely in a sitting position. By 18 months, he can push a toy, and may walk backward in pulling it. He observes an object at distance of four or five feet, and approaches it directly. By 4 years, he makes simultaneous spontaneous gestures. By 5 years, he likes to act out a story. He runs and climbs. At 6 years, he wrestles, tumbles, paws at other children, and plays tag. In all of this, we are dealing with proprioceptive, visual, and other forms of feedback from active muscles and the exteroceptors.

3   The third general aspect studied was that of *fixation* of visual regard. In this performance, Gesell follows an illustrative case. At 30 weeks, the child's eyes converge. He is able to fixate a dangled bell. He then shifts his regard to the examiner's hand, and his regard shifts up and down the string dangling the bell. This is, of course, an ocular pursuit movement.

At 1 year, the child spontaneously releases his regard for the bell and turns it to the examiner. This is done quickly, and with no gross deviation in the behavior of the two eyes in working together. At 2 years, the child is able to pick up the target with a rapid glance. In following the target, one eye is jerky. At 2 years, as the target is moved closer to the eyes, the child may withdraw his head. At 3 years, fixation occurs readily and the hand is brought to the bell held in the examiner's hand. When the child's hand accompanies the eyes as the bell is brought closer to the eyes, their convergence is smoother than without the hands.

By 3½ years, great individual differences from child to child are usual. By that time, some can obey the command to "just look" or to "just point," while others cannot. Even at 4 years of age, eyes may still be a bit wobbly in performing movements when changing fixation. It is still observed that when the hand is used to grasp or touch the moving object, the eyes are steadier.

The fourth aspect of performance studied was what is called the *ret-*

inal reflex. This is a term used in retinoscopy to signify the accommodative (focusing) action of the eye. In conventional office practice among those who examine vision and prescribe glasses, the retinoscope, or the ophthalmoscope, is used to determine the refractive condition (or behavior) of the eyes. In this procedure, the measurement is a more or less static one, for no intended manipulation of target positions, etc., is carried out by moving the target while the patient makes his observations. Likewise, no manipulation of target in its degree of "familiarity" is employed. No test is conducted whereby the "rejection" or "acceptance" of the material by the patient is observed by the examiner.

Gesell and coworkers adapted retinoscopy to the study of perception, and thus took it out of the category of mere determination of refractive state for their purposes. That is, they interpreted the shifting accommodation (focusing) of the eye to be an indication of whether or not the patient was grasping the meaning of what he looked at. Assuming this, they virtually had an intelligence test according to the way they used the retinoscope. This form of retinoscopy has been called *book retinoscopy*.

To understand the results, the reader must understand the focusing of the eye for near and far targets, and the relation this bears to what is observed through the retinoscope. The observed phenomenon is a form of movement of a light or shadow within the eye, and a change in brightness. The motion called "against" indicates a minus refractive value, and a myopic or near-sighted condition. This need be simply a condition of the instant, for the eye may change. A "with" motion indicates just the opposite refractive state: a far-sighted condition at the instant. With shifts to the "against" motion, a brightening of what is seen through the retinoscope (the retinal reflex) occurs.

It should be expected, then, that the child (or adult) would show a "with" motion in the reflex when he is looking at distant targets, and an "against" motion when viewing close-up material. This much is the conventional expectation. The discovery was, of course, that the "with" and "against" motions may occur under conditions not predicted by conventional expectations. With this in mind, we are ready to note what the examiners found in some illustrative cases of children at various ages.

At 30 weeks, a distant object evoked a slow "with" motion, then an "against," and then oscillation back and forth between the two. When a near target was presented, there was a definite "against" movement. When the child regarded a toy, there was an increased "against" and a brightening of the reflex. As his hand reached out to approach it, there was a "with" motion. As he grasped it, the reflex changed to "against" and brightened. As the toy was manipulated, there was an oscillation between the two reflexes.

At 1 year, for an intermediate target, there was a change from "with" to "against." For a near target, the change from "with" to a rapid "against" occurred. When the targets were a pellet and a bottle, the movements were "against, against, with." As the child reached, an "against" movement occurred. With the object in the mouth and the child regarding the examiner, the movement was "with."

At 21 months, for targets toward which the child was indifferent, the reflex was very dull and difficult to observe. A transient brightening occurred as apparent recognition of a target occurred.

When near measurements were taken, the child looked at the lens and grasped it. In this, the reflex was "against." With some difficulty, the child's attention was directed toward the examiner's face. This evoked a "with" motion; but as the child's regard settled down a bit, the "with" motion reduced, but did not change to "against." Again, while regarding the lens, an item of interest, strong "against" motion occurred; but when he touched the lens, a "with" motion developed.

At 4 years, the lively fluidity of the retinal reflex assumes a more positive and understandable pattern. The variability appears to be much more adaptive to change of circumstance within and without the child. At 5 years, the child seems to be more tightly bound by book tasks than at 4 years, although his visual system moves with greater ease between near, intermediate, and far distances.

The fifth aspect of visual behavior that was studied was that of *projection*. This is what Gesell and coworkers admit is a vague concept, but one that is suggested by a variety of visual and motor behavior patterns. It is the concept that the eye, just as the hand, is a manipulative organ, and both are governed by the cerebral cortex. This being the case, it is the cortex that deals with the outer world—using eye, hand, and mouth as media or instruments for its purpose. The means whereby this is accomplished is termed a projective process, although it is truly a reciprocal or two-way process between brain and the media just mentioned. The outcome is both an externalization and an internalization. These two processes have their correspondents in the "with-against" and the "against-with" adjustments manifested in the eye-hand prehensile (grasping) mechanism. Thus, if we comprehend the eye and vision as a prehensile tool, the "with" and "against" movements of the retinal reflex make sense and are good indicators of perception in the most meaningful connotation of the word.

By the time the child is 3½ years old, he is able, for example, to identify the picture shown in a stereoscope. If he is asked where it is, he says that it is "out there," for example. If asked to touch the picture, he declares he cannot because of its distance. He may try, however, and begins to reach out into space. Finally, his hand may get down to the stereogram (picture), but without being about to put his fingers on the actual objects pictured in the stereogram.

At 4 years, the child elaborates the items in the stereogram picture more in detail. He locates the scene by pointing to a position somewhere between the two stereogram pictures.

From 4 to 8 years, various progressive steps in the use and interpretation of the stereoscope are observed. It is only at 8 years that the child gives definite evidence that he realizes another person can view a scene differently than he does. He likes to consider it from the other viewpoint as well. During examination, he asks many questions which indicate he is interested in the relation of cause and effect; that is, what the examiner does in relation to what can be seen in the stereoscope. He begins to ask questions about himself, such as whether his eyes are good. It is at this time that children impute fatigue to their eyes rather than to themselves. The 8-year-old child's consciousness of rate is manifested also. He will tell the examiner that he went too fast, or did not go fast enough. When he does not see something continue to change, he declares the instrument is not working.

By the time the subject is 9 years old, he approaches the examination in a businesslike way. He comprehends that his eyes are being examined. He may remark about the differences in his two eyes, and may voluntarily report ocular symptoms, telling about his habit of rubbing his eyes and stating he does not know why. He is still more inquisitive about the instruments used in his examination than was the 8-year-old child.

The 10-year-old child shows more improvement and can be distinguished from the 8-year-old. While Gesell did not progress beyond the 11-year-old child, he does not doubt but that certain further developments in the individual's perception of space and causal relations in it would emerge.

CHANGES IN PERCEPTION OF SPECIFIC TARGETS

The third category in the study of the development of perception has primarily to do with the development of the perception of specific targets. This development may be studied as the reaction to a given stimulus as a function of repetition.

There are those who are concerned with the problem of whether or not the perception of simple geometrical figures is learned; and if learned, what there is about such perceptions that is learned, and how this learning takes place. In this category, there are such workers as Hebb (*107*), who deals with this general problem in his book *The Organization of Behavior.*

There are others who have much to say about perception and the factors making for its development, and who relate perception to other aspects of the functioning individual, such as need. Thus, in the thinking of these workers, perception and motivation and perception and personality theory are linked together. Such workers have been classified as functionalists in regard to perception, in contrast to those who deal with the more rigid or invariant stimulus factors and resulting perception. The latter individuals have been called *formalists*.

There are those, too, who are concerned with the relation between perception and learning. In this section of the present chapter, we wish to give some attention to each of these groups of workers.

One of the more recent authors to deal with the problem of the perception of simple geometrical forms is Hebb. To quote him, his attempt has been "to show that 'simple' perceptions are in fact complex: that they are additive, that they depend partly upon motor activity, and that their apparent simplicity is only the end result of a long learning process."[1] To assert that perception is a product of previous encounters, and responses to them is not to indicate any new belief. To assert that perception depends upon motor activity is to state pretty much what is generally believed by those who believe perception is a product of learning. Hebb's contribution is a formulation of how learning is accomplished, and that it applies even to very simple forms and not only to the geometrically complex. Before stating his views on this, Hebb brings up the dilemma of whether perception is dependent upon the activation of specific cells in the nervous system or upon a pattern of cells whose location in the aggregate is not fixed. He points out that Lashley, on the one hand, and Gestalt theorists, on the other, have held the second view. He opposes the Gestalt view in this matter. Hebb proposes that a specific perception does depend upon the activity of a specified group of cells somewhere in the central nervous system. The Gestalt theorists assert that the perception, such as of a square or circle, is given directly as a unique whole, not needing a learning process to have achieved it, and not through any previous recognition of the component parts of the figure.

[1] D. O. Hebb, *The Organization of Behavior,* John Wiley & Sons, 1949, p. 17.

Hebb sets out to show that simple figures are not perceived as unique wholes, but that perception of a square as a square depends upon a sequence of previous excitants from the components of the geometrical target. He finds that he must make a start somewhere, and thus he begins with a form of innate reaction, which he calls reaction to *primitive unity*. This really is the experience of figure-ground relations as first pictured by Rubin.

This achievement, the figure-ground perception, is a segregation of the visual field into two portions, and is thought to be a direct and inherent result of the pattern of sensory impingement and the inherited features of the nervous system upon which the impingement occurs. Thus this two-part structure is what is seen by any normal person, and even by the congenitally blind, who finally view their surrounds for the first time after years of inability to see, due to cataracts. This figure-ground perception is also given some credence in the behavior of rats raised in darkness and now put into an illuminated environment for the first time. This much Hebb credits with being independent of prior experience, and thus not dependent upon integration of even more simple perceptions. Hebb would allow the possibility that certain groupings or an ill-defined patch of "color" can be perceived as a unit and distinguished from its surroundings. Here we seem to be talking about sensorially determined relations that are responded to as such. But Hebb calls attention to non-sensory figure-ground organizations. These are ones that involve boundaries of figures not determined by gradients of luminosity of the visual field. Such segregations are determined by experience and other non-sensory factors. Hebb points out that the nonsensory figure emerges whenever the observer responds to a limited portion of a homogeneous field, as when one looks at the "corner of the room," "the middle part" of a suspended rope. In each one, the part in question is perceived to have an identity distinct from the rest. This identity is not sensorially determined by geometrical boundaries or other such stimulus features.

Hebb interprets the findings relative to the congenitally blind's early visual perceptions as indicating that they are almost completely lacking in what he calls identity.[2] Cases are reported in which such individuals were not always able to distinguish between spheres and cubes. Color, on the other hand, seemed to dominate the perceptions of such persons, and thus would seem to be quite primitive. One of the outstanding cases

[2] Identity is defined by Hebb as the property of association as pertaining to perception, whereby the object perceived is taken to be a member of a class of objects, or different from certain others and similar to still others.

was the case in which an egg, a cube of sugar, and a potato were repeatedly shown to the subject until he could name them correctly. The mere placing of these in colored light negated their recognition. Likewise, the context had a great deal to do with recognition, as in the case of the subject recognizing the cube of sugar in the examiner's hand, but not when suspended by a thread against a different background.

As an example of a case of learning to perceive a simple figure as such, Hebb uses the case of perceiving a triangle as different from some other figure. He pictures the case of perceptual acquisition as following a course from dominance of color, through an interim of separate attentions to the various portions of the target, to a final though gradually achieved identification of the whole target as a whole. Thus there is a progress from a serial apprehension of portions of it to the final simultaneous apprehension of the whole. The example is given of a patient taught to discriminate between a square and a triangle. At the end of 13 days, he had accomplished little, and to make the discrimination at all he had to count the corners, one by one. According to our definition of perception, he could make no immediate reactional distinction between square and triangle. He only arrived at a *judgment*, after several sequential operations, each of which involved a perception of a corner. The perception of corner, whatever it was, was probably related to his previous tactual explorations while still blind. It was said that by this time the examiner had a feeling that recognition was in the process of becoming automatic, and that someday the patient would be able, at a mere glance, to distinguish between triangle and square. The suggestion was made that anyone seeing the patient then, for the first time, would simply take it for granted that the form of a simple target was something inherently given in the target (stimulus) itself.

This example leads to Hebb's conclusion that eye movements are an inherent part of learning to see simple forms, for it is they that provide for shifts in inspecting the various parts of the targets. To put it in other words, multiple fixations on various parts of simple targets are necessary for the achievement of the perception of form, as we know it in the adult.

Hebb is basically interested in the neurophysiological foundation for perception, and to accomplish the explanation of learning (learning to perceive), he makes certain postulates regarding nervous activity. The first of these is the process of *association;* that is, when any two cells or systems of cells are active again and again concurrently, they will tend to become linked in such a way that activity in one facilitates or induces activity in the other. A solid three-dimensional mass of brain tissue, for example, would become assembled in a functional way. This, he thinks, is in part dependent upon a principle announced some time ago by a noted physiologist, according to which adjacent cells are so interrelated anatomically with each other that nerve impulses feed back into the pathways along which they travel, by reason of branches that bend back upon themselves. This forms, within the system, a reverberating activity that does not cease the instant the assembly is acted upon from tissue adjacent to it. Various assemblies may gain temporal overlaps in activity this way and tend to become associated. The interrelational effects of various assemblies are such that after many influences upon each other they evolve into a superordinate assembly that may underlie the perception of the target as a whole. The sequence of interactions of the various component assemblies is called a *phase sequence*. A train of thought, as well as the sequence that has to do with the acquistion of a perception, is also taken to depend upon a phase sequence in the underlying nervous system. Actually, what Hebb describes as a phase sequence includes not only the neural activities just outlined but also the motor accompaniments that are involved as the subject looks from corner to corner of the triangle during his encounters with it.

As was stated earlier in this section, the relation of perception and learning has been studied by a number of workers. Some learning theorists treat perception as response. That is what we have been doing, of course, in the way we have defined it. The main difference that exists between the learning theorists and your author is that he does not identify perception with all response. The response must be an immediate discriminative one. Response, taken generally, on the other hand, includes reactions that are called judgments. While judgments accrue from perceptions and may be fairly good indicators of what perception is like, they cannot be taken indiscriminately as interchangeable with perception.

Ellson (71), some time ago, studied the way in which repeated pairing of a photic and an acoustic stimulus influenced the formation of an auditory hallucination. He concluded, however, that the well-known principles of conditioning and extinction did not govern the hallucinations. Ellson's experiment consisted in pairing an acoustic stimulus, having gradual onset and decay, with a photic stimulus. It was the conditioned stimulus, and finally came to evoke the experience of hearing a tone, when it alone was presented. This was called the hallucination. In a second set of experiments, Ellson failed to obtain extinction in the

16 subjects who developed hallucinatory responses. Instructing the subjects that the acoustic stimulus would be omitted reliably reduced frequency and duration, and increased the latency of response in the ten test trials that followed.

In a still later investigation, Ellson compared the effects of using acoustic stimuli with gradual onset and those with sudden onset. The former was found to be much more effective. He also compared the effect of telling his subjects the purpose of the experiment and that the acoustic stimulation would not be presented in a later test period, with the effect of withholding this information. The two groups did not manifest a significant difference in their behavior. The same proportion of the subjects falsely reported hearing the tone when the stimulation was not given.

The work of Lambert, Solomon, and Watson (152) indicated that apparent object size varies as a function of the amount of reinforcement involved.

Various students of learning, each in his own way, have involved the idea of perception as inherent in learning, but what they have done has not been a direct study of perception itself.

The influence of past experience on perception has been studied by means of certain geometrical targets in an "impression series" presented tachistoscopically to determine the effect upon the perception of a subsequent set of different targets. This series also contained the targets of the impression series. It was found that the presentation of certain types of target in a short impression series plays a role in changing the perception of other figures given later. The effects produced by the impression targets were specific to the types of target used. Even simple targets vary considerably in the ease with which they are perceived. The influence of the impression series is related to the inherent difficulty in perceiving the test targets.

THE INFLUENCE OF SET, STANCE, AND OTHER FACTORS ON PERCEPTION

Obviously, the influence of factors represented in the observer himself is important in the determination of perception. We wish to select only a few examples in which the growth or change of perception is manipulated by the contribution of the observer rather than by outward circumstance.

One of the best kinds of perceptual experiment to show up the large contribution of set is that having to do with the perception of heaviness or weight. This is spoken of as a weight-lifting experiment, and in it two cubes may be compared with each other. One is the standard, S, and the other is the comparison, C. Various C's are compared with S. This is often done by having the observer lift S, and then C, with the same hand, and in as closely the same manner as possible.

As any observer lifts a weight, he does so in an anticipatory way. He does not know fully what to expect. So, consciously or not, he possesses some stance with regard to the task. If he lifts the weight as though it is heavier than it is, it may appear one way. If he does the opposite, it may appear another way.

Müller and Schumann (188), many years ago, proposed that the observer was prepared to lift C with a muscular force just previously found sufficient to lift S. If C comes up quickly and easily, it is perceived as light, that is, even lighter than S. If the opposite occurs, it is perceived as heavier than S. Weight lifting is usually performed under blindfold; but if not, and S and C are greatly different in metrical size, the larger of the two will be perceived as the less heavy. This is the so-called size-weight illusion.

Payne and Davis (207) put the Müller-Schumann theory to test by recording action potentials from the observer's arm while he lifted the various weights. It was found that "heavier" reports were associated with records indicating stronger muscle action. The strength of lifting varied and was not in accord with the actual metrical value of lifted weights. The strength of lift for the standard, S, varied from trial to trial. This had its effect on the perception of C. The authors concluded that their results were in line with the theory's prediction, but preferred to use a peripheral rather than a central nervous explanation. In either case, the factor is organismic rather than environmental.

Time-order errors occur in lifting weights. That is, since the second is lifted at a time after the first, the effect (trace) of the first has already faded somewhat, thereby emphasizing the second. Such errors have been found in dealing with successive photic presentations also.

One of the very well-known effects upon the perception of a given presentation is the series effect. If a number of items, varying in some property, are presented in a random series, the property in question of each item will come to be perceived in reference to the series. In fact, the ability of any subject to perceive anything in terms of smallness, heaviness, and so on, so as to be able to answer that it is small, medium-sized, or large, or whether it is light, medium-heavy, or very heavy, implies a frame of reference of some kind or other. We do not know the processes providing this reference. All we do know is that as far as outward behavior is concerned, it is as though there is a frame, and that it may be displaced, extended, or compressed by subsequent experience.

All of the findings that have just been described or mentioned are examples of the factors influencing the character of perception, apart from purely stimulus conditions of the moment, and thus can be taken to be those that influence the development of perception.

DEGREES OF RESTRICTEDNESS IN PERCEIVING

It may seem at times as though the total impingement in a given sense modality is responded to, and at other times that only a segregated or restricted portion is actively involved. Various questions could be asked about these two opposite cases. One of these is quite relevant to the understanding of the development of perception. It is, What are the factors governing the segregation of the portion of the impingement total to be responded to? All species and all members of the same species do not seem to be equally capable of performing a given segregational response. For example, Witkin (269) concealed a visual form within a field by using various colors. He used certain colors for the concealed figure in such a way as to favor seeing some of its parts connected with other portions of the field. He found that men were quicker than women at picking out the concealed figure. In other cases, the perceptual ability seems to be a matter of learning.

The study by Leeper (156) on the perception of ambiguous figures is a case in point. Ambiguous composite figures were projected on a screen, one at a time, and subjects were asked to write down what they saw. Another group of subjects was first presented with a drawing of one of the components of the composite picture. Then the composite picture was shown. To a third group, instead of one of the components, a verbal description was first given, and then the composite was shown.

The showing of the component had a marked effect in determining what was seen, whereas the verbal preparation had little, if any, effect. The results were different for another picture. For it, verbal instructions were effective. It would seem, then, that if the preëxperience is perceptual, it has a positive effect. If it is only ideational (verbal, etc.), a positive effect might or might not be demonstrable.

Stimulus Strength, Duration, and Perception

Various studies upon the relation between perception and the quantification of stimulation lead us to another aspect of perceptual development. For example, if a subject is presented with a very weak photic stimulus—a target in very weak illumination—he will not see a well-contoured object. But as luminance becomes more intense, the target becomes more and more effective. A more detailed, highly differentiated perception is made possible.

Helson and Fehrer (*114*) studied the "role of form[3] in perception." The investigation consisted in the determination of the thresholds for seeing light itself, for perceiving just noticeable form, and for definite form for six different targets, all equal in area. The targets were an isosceles triangle, a rectangle, a circle, a semicircle, an inverted-V figure, and also a square. These targets were cut from low-reflectance cardboard and placed on the screen of a Nagel adaptometer, which is essentially a lamphouse with a large opal-glass screen, the intensity of which can be precisely adjusted over a very wide range. A fixation spot was used. With three observers, the three thresholds mentioned earlier were obtained. With another observer, the procedure was simply that of increasing the intensity until light was seen, and to report on shape if discernible. If the target was undiscernible, or if the observer was incorrect, she was instructed to continue increasing the intensity until shape could be seen, and to indicate it and the certainty involved.

The three thresholds found in all cases were called the Light Limen (threshold), Form 1, and Form 2. The authors found that in every case the thresholds for light were lower than for just barely perceived shape. The thresholds for light in the study were influenced somewhat by the geometry of the targets. It required about 25 times as much photic flux to recognize form correctly as just to perceive light, and twice as much flux to perceive shape in a vague way as just to detect light. The authors showed that shape perception is not primary, and this is a corroboration of incidental observations in many routine experiences in precise laboratory work. Some target forms require less light than others to recognize correctly. The rectangle seemed to require the least among the six targets investigated. Among some of the targets aside from the rectangle, the thresholds and the judgment of goodness of form also differed.

Some O's respond rather easily to the form of a stimulus complex and all that it entails, other O's do not respond at all, and still others (if the "trait" is nor-

---

[3] Although we are describing an investigation in which form is a word applied by its authors to the perception as well as to the stimulus, we prefer to use *shape* for the perception and *form* for the visual target. This is part of our effort throughout the text to find separate terms for the two domains.

mally distributed) fall in between the first two groups. How, then, is it possible to assert that form is a primary datum for all O's, that it is first in the history of the individual and the race, that it is constitutive in perception and behavior? Even under the conditions most favorable to form as such, *i.e.* when the O's were required to report the form seen, some O's fail to discriminate between forms or to be affected by the shape of the stimuli. Having found that it is impossible to set up criteria governing the effectiveness of form *qua* form, since various criteria give contradictory results, we now find that it is impossible to legislate for all O's regarding any influence of form whatsoever since some O's are apparently unaffected by differences in forms, even when set to observe them. We are therefore forced by our experiments to deny that the factor of form is always or even, as Köhler has tried to ameliorate the generalization, "the most important property which a whole may have." It may be a determining factor for some individuals in some types of experiment, but this is different from the assertion that it is the primary or most important condition in perceptual behavior. The broad generalizations respecting the role of form in perception made by the configurationists constitute another example of the fallacy of generalizing from "some to all."[4]

This quotation would make it appear that the matter of shape in perception is a developmental achievement. First, shape is not primary. Then the very first something that is detectable is too vague and diffuse to describe in terms of shape. Second, all persons do not achieve the same ability to perceive shape under a given set of threshold or slightly suprathreshold conditions.

If three-dimensional targets, under moderate illumination, are presented for increasing lengths of time, beginning with about .01 second, the objects seen are quite vaguely defined and are two- rather than three-dimensional. As more and more time is put into the presentation, more and more details are recognizable, and the two-dimensionality shifts into three at some given point. The identity of the object also changes. Even though throughout a given range the identity may be fairly certain, the ultimate identity, when longer stimulation is given, will differ and provide the observer with the maximum certainty—the kind usually experienced from day to day in seeing familiar objects.

CULTURAL DETERMINANTS OF PERCEPTION

Anthropologists have noted many forms of behavior that differ from group to group. Some of these would seem to involve differences in perception. An example of one of the interesting cultural effects upon per-

---

[4] Harry Helson and Elizabeth V. Fehrer, The role of form in perception, *Am. J. Psychol.* (1932), 44:37–102.

ception is embodied in the fact that Trobriand Islanders refuse to see or declare they cannot see resemblances among maternal kinsmen, while noting in an exaggerated way those in the paternal line.

What is heard in one part of our country as normal speech stands out vividly as dialect or accent in another. Some people will declare that a given person has a marked Southern accent, whereas the accent cannot be perceived by others, depending possibly upon the previous regions in which the judges have lived.

Bartlett (8) studied a group of phenomena that would seem to lie part way between the purely cultural or anthropological and the specifically experimental. His study had to do with the reproduction of stories and pictures alien to the culture in which they were a part. He found that the reproductions were typically modified toward what was familiar to the subjects. Unfortunately for us, Bartlett did not distinguish how much or in what ways these modifications had to do with perception and/or with subsequent interpretation. We have no concrete evidence from his study to put forth here to demonstrate the differential involvements of perception from the one culture to the other, but it is very probable that this occurred and could be done.

No matter which way we turn, we find kinds of situations which laymen and psychologists alike believe illustrate cultural influences on perception, but, notwithstanding, the psychological literature is almost empty of good empirical studies of the matter.

We may cite one very good example of an experimental approach to the matter of cultural influences on perception. Sherman (227) took moving pictures of the behavior of young infants to stimuli which Watson, the father of behaviorism, had said elicited fear and anger responses. These movies were shown to graduate students in psychology, to medical students, and to nurses. These individuals, of course, were indoctrinated with the behavioristic teaching regarding what was elicited by the stimuli in question. The observations (perceptions) of these subjects or judges coincided quite well with those of Watson. It will be recalled that Watson's behaviorism was a protest against the ambiguity, the lack of concreteness, in psychology. It was supposed to be solidly scientific and objective.

In other showings, Sherman removed the frames of the movie that showed what the stimuli were, whereupon the judgments of the observers bore little agreement to the Watsonian observations. In other words, Watson and the student observers had been seeing what they expected to see. This is not to disparage their sincerity and "objectiveness," but rather to indicate that being "objective" is one thing under one set of conditions and something else under another set. The experiment was a most excellent test of the cultural or social influence upon perception.

CONCLUSIONS

It can be said that the material in this chapter has demonstrated the changeableness of sensory response. It shows that what we consider as perception in the adult has come to be what it is through a long and many-sided development. This is one of the most significant things that can be said about this basic, immediate, discriminatory behavior that relates the individual to his surrounds. To discard the idea that sensory response can be cryptically disposed of by calling it stimulus-bound is to recognize a new possibility in its study. To recognize that perception is a true and useful expression of personality and, like its other expressions, follows discoverable laws is to invite its study for the solution of many problems in psychology approached heretofore only in other ways.

The study of discriminative behavior of subhuman species may well be seen as a demonstration not simply of the abstract thing called learning, but rather the educability of the most basic forms of response. Much of what has been classified as sensory has been simply attributed to the peculiar differentiating ability of the sense organs. Change, when it has occurred, has been abstracted into a category by itself. It has been studied as *learning*, not as the development of perception. Seeing it as the latter might be quite helpful in gaining a better understanding of the whole animal kingdom.

The comparisons between human and subhuman reactions to given target material have led to information which helps bridge the gap between what we may deal with in terms of experience (consciousness) and what we can deal with in other ways. The reactions of chickens to geometrical forms ("illusions") is a good case in point. These animals, for instance, without showing any evidence whatsoever of being able to verbalize, react as do humans. They see the "illusion"—the same discrepancy from the metrical size of the presented geometrical forms. In this connection, the educability of the hen, although its original ability manifests certain marked limitations, has been brought out, and this, too, shows how perception may develop.

The work of Gesell and his colleagues (83) with book retinoscopy has demonstrated that in the nonverbal expressions of perception, in the very reflexes of the eye, the ebb and flow of understanding are manifested. This comes out in a way hitherto undreamed of. This discovery has shown that intelligence is concretely expressed and measurable in a nonverbal body mechanism—a perceptual response itself—rather than by formal paper and pencil tests. Furthermore, the oculomotor expression can be dealt with without using formal instructions that none but an older child or an adult could comprehend. The same tests can be used, furthermore, to measure the growth of intelligence—or the growth of perception. This is a long step in advance of having to deal with the organism through one or more intermediate mechanisms to tap the understanding of complex stimulus material.

Chapter 6

ADAPTATION AND BRIGHTNESS DISCRIMINATION

Thus far we have been busy mainly with the task of orientation. We have been describing perception and showing the difference between how we must look at it and how the man on the street deals with such matters. Extended descriptions of laboratory experiments so far have been avoided. We are now ready for a new phase in the study of perception, namely, the presentation of what has been done in the laboratory regarding certain problems. In the first few succeeding chapters, vision is to be broken down into its basic aspects according to the way it has been studied in the laboratory. Other chapters will deal with other sense modalities in the same specific ways.

The material in this chapter has to do with two very common processes that those who study vision generally pay attention to. They are the processes of adaptation and of brightness discrimination. Adaptation is the adjustment of the visual mechanism, mainly the eye itself, to various intensity levels of impingement (stimulation) so as to perform at its best. It is obvious that, on this account, adaptation that is confined to the eye is not actually a perceptual process. But it is so intimately bound up with what the organism as a whole (organism as a person) does that we shall indicate its general nature.

Brightness discrimination is simply the process of perceiving differences in intensity between various portions of the target, whether the target is an experimental presentation or whether it constitutes the whole visual field. Brightness discrimination is based on the same ocular processes that are studied as adaptation, but it is certainly much more than that. It involves the central nervous system and the individual as a whole.

One of the very first tasks is to get an idea of the enormous range of intensities to which the individual can respond. Human experience elicited by photic radiation varies all the way from the tiny amount of light perceived in a dark room or on a moonless night to the dazzling light at noonday on a desert. Of course, when the individual looks directly at a source of radiation, such as a bright lamp, or the sun itself, even much greater intensities than just suggested are involved. If we put the stimulus range into quantitative terms, the range covered is one to about ten billion. This is a most amazing range, and no single recording instrument is able to cover it without accessory stepwise adjustment devices to take care of the matter. For example, when we use voltmeters for very tiny voltages, they must be constructed for that purpose. Such meters would actually be destroyed by large voltages. Other meters, of course, are built for higher ranges. So to cover the total number of ranges man deals with, several different voltmeters would be necessary. The human visual mechanism as a single "measuring instrument" is able to cover the enormous range we mentioned, and just how it does this has long been a rather puzzling matter. Whatever the process of doing this is, it is to be understood as adaptation.

Most of the adjustment called adaptation occurs in the eye. Part of the adjustment is photochemical, and part is neural. Aside from the adjustments involved in the eye, possibly there are still other less prominent forms located in the central nervous system. Ocular adaptation provides not only for adjusting the eye as a receptor mechanism for the general levels of illumination that are met with, but it is also the process involved in the ability to see light and shade in juxtaposition in the visual field at any given time. The very essence of seeing is that of being able to apprehend differences in the amounts of radiation reaching the eye from different parts of the visual field. The ability to perceive one part of a target as darker or lighter than another is generally spoken of as brightness discrimination. Hence, the discussion of adaptation and brightness discrimination goes hand in hand.

TERMINOLOGY

Before we proceed to describe how adaptation and brightness discrimination work, it is necessary that we understand each other regarding some of the terms which we shall frequently use from this point onward. It must be kept in mind that, in general, we have two different sets of phenomena about which to talk. One of these is spoken of, in general, as the stimulus and the other is the perceptual response. Some terms which we shall use will always refer to the stimulus, and others will always refer to the response. It is necessary to be aware of this caution, for, as was indicated in an earlier chapter, conventional terminology has not always been kept as clear about such matters as it should be. Many times, the same word is used both for response and for stimulus. In such cases, only the context of what is said enables the reader to understand what is meant. In science, technical words should not get their meaning from context, but rather from explicit definition.

As was mentioned earlier, there are two words that come up when the environment is referred to. One of these, the most common, is the term stimulus. We wish to use two words, stimulus and impingement. Of the two, impingement is the broader and more general. It is the term labeling the energy that strikes sense organs. When any detectable organic or organismic result is elicited, the impingement is a stimulus. Some impingements, then, are effective, and some are not. Those that are we may legitimately speak of as stimuli. Thus, all stimuli are impingements, but not all impingements are stimuli. This obviates the inconsistency of speaking of stimuli which do not stimulate.

There are certain adjectives which apply to the stimulus and should not be used with reference to the corresponding characteristic of the response. One of these is *intensity*. We shall never use intensity in describing response. Intensity of the stimulus is the factor which is correlated with certain experiential qualities which we speak of in various ways, such as brightness, lightness, brilliance, and so on. Hence, stimuli are not bright, or light, or brilliant. Stimuli may only vary in intensity and thus are weak or strong.

Sometimes photic stimuli are very brief in duration. We shall call such brief presentations *pulses*. These photic pulses generally give rise to definite kinds of experience which we call *flashes*. In most of the literature that you will read, you will find that the word flash is used both for the stimulus and the response. We feel that this is unfortunate, and not a logically consistent way of doing.

PHOTOMETRY AND RADIOMETRY

There are two ways of measuring the energy in the photic impingement. One is by the use of *photometry,* and the other by the use of *radiometry*. In general, photometry is a procedure in which a human observer makes instrumental comparisons between an established standard quantity and the stimulus whose intensity is to be determined. There are other procedures for measuring intensity, in which an instrument not involving the human being is acted upon by photic radiation and gives us a quantitative reading. You, no doubt, are acquainted with what is called an electric eye or a photocell. An application of the principle involved in the photocell can be used to measure photic radiation quantitatively. Photocells are somewhat selective in their sensitivity to the different wave lengths involved in ordinary photic radiation. Some of them are very much like the eye in this respect, and for some purposes this is an advantage. For some other purposes, however, it is a disadvantage, as when we wish to know the total energy in the impingement or stimulus without regard to wave length. Measuring photic impingements without the intervention of a human observer is known as radiometry.

The Photometer

You will have a much better idea of how photic radiation is usually measured if you understand the principle of the photometer. One of the most commonly used photometers is the Macbeth illuminometer. It is pictured in Fig. 6.1. It consists essentially in a photic source whose effectiveness upon the eye can be varied by varying its distance from the eye. The next essential element is a prism whereby the radiation from

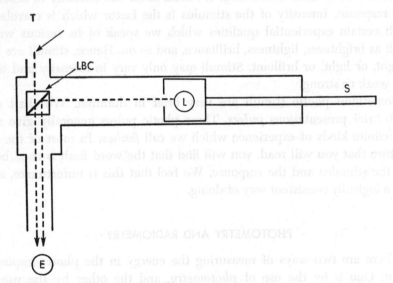

Fig. 6.1. Diagram of a Macbeth illuminometer, a very common photometer. S is a stick that moves L, the standard source of radiation with respect to the Lummer-Brodhun cube, LBC. T is the test source; E is the eye. It receives radiation both from test source and standard source.

both the source and the target is directed into the eye. The prism is so constructed that the radiation from the instrument is visible as a ring and the radiation from the test target forms a disk within the ring. The task of the observer or user of the photometer is to adjust the intensity of radiation in the instrument so as to have the ring and disk match each other in brightness. The instrument is calibrated so that when the adjustment is made and the two fields match, a reading is obtained which can be transformed into any of the standard units for photic measurement, such as candles per square foot, or millilamberts.

When we want to know the value of the illumination supplied a working surface, such as a desk, we place on that desk a disk of matte-white magnesium carbonate whose percentage of reflection is known. Such a disk usually reflects back to the photometer about 70 percent of the radiation falling on it. Thus, when a reading is taken with the photometer pointed toward this disk, we know then that the reading represents 70 percent of the radiation falling on the disk, and is thus the same percentage that falls on the desk or table. If we pointed the photometer directly at the desk, we would not get the same reading, for the desk's percentage of reflectance is different than that of the disk. Since we do not know what this percentage is, we would be unable to say what the level of illumination at the desk surface was. (See Fig. 6.2.)

On the other hand, when we want to know the quantitative value of a target as viewed directly, we can point the photometer toward it and translate this reading into units which have to do with the effectiveness of the radiation as it directly strikes the eye. Sometimes these units are spoken of as *apparent brightness units*, or luminance units. They are candles per square foot, candles per square meter, candles per square centimeter, candles per square inch, and also millilamberts. Very often, the targets we look at directly are original photic sources such as opalglass plates behind which there is some form of lamp (electric bulbs, for example).

THE MEASUREMENT OF THRESHOLDS

Over the years there have been many systematic descriptions of the relationship between target intensity and the response of the observer. In this procedure, the quantities measured have often been thresholds. There are, in general, two forms of thresholds. The one is obtained when a target of restricted visual angle is presented in a totally dark background. When we speak of targets having restricted visual angles,

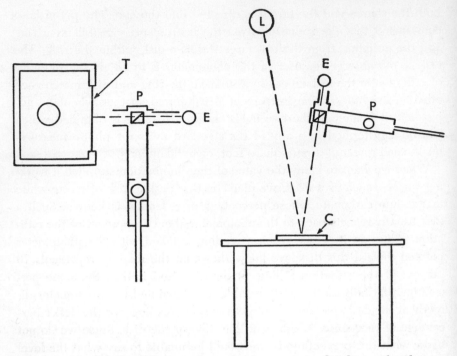

Fig. 6.2.   The left-hand diagram shows that in measuring *brightness* the photometer (P) is pointed directly at the target surface (T). The right-hand diagram shows that in measuring illumination the photometer is pointed toward a calibrated reflectance surface (C) at the working surface, such as a table. E indicates eye position.

we mean targets which occupy only small portions of the visual field. The visual angle is the solid angle subtended by the target at the eye. To understand this better, look at Fig. 6.3. In the process of determining this first form of threshold, the intensity of the target is raised from zero to a point which will just enable the observer to see something. Whatever the observer first detects, it will not be a uniform area with a sharp boundary. It will rather be a very, very faint, indistinct, blurred patch of light. It will be so dim that he will not be sure that it exists. In other words, he will see it only a part of the time. To systematize the procedure, it is customary for the experimenter to present a number of exposures of such a target, each exposure extending only for a brief time, generally a second or less. If the target is low enough in intensity it will never be seen, but if it is made progressively more intense it will be seen part of the time; that is to say, it will be seen in some of the exposures and not in others. A good percentage might be thought of as

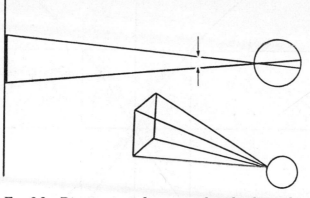

Fig. 6.3. Diagrams to indicate visual angle, the angle included between arrows. This angle is the best way of designating the effective extent of an image on the retina.

50 percent; but this will not be fully satisfactory, for one can even guess about the existence or nonexistence of the presentations and be right in a certain percentage of the trials. The number of times a correct response can be made by purely guessing is taken into account in determining the value we wish to speak of as the threshold. If the conditions of the experiment are such that two answers and two only can be given, the subject can say he sees the target or he does not see it; or if there are two positions in which he may see it, then he could be right 50 percent of the time. If there are three possibilities, he could be right one-third of the time by guessing. When the intensity of the target is much greater, of course, the target can be seen and seen correctly on every presentation. The threshold value, then, has been selected as the intensity of the stimulus needed for correctness half of the time above the chance values we have just spoken of. Thus the threshold value, when two alternatives are possible, is 75 percent; when three alternatives are possible, 66⅔ percent. See Fig. 6.4.

When we deal with the emergence of some visible feature of a visual field on a totally dark background, we are dealing with *absolute thresholds*. It is as if we were occupied with something emerging out of nothing. Often this emergence is spoken of as emergence of a *figure* upon a *ground*. From this point on, we shall often use the terms figure and ground, or figure field and ground field. This is a very useful concept to

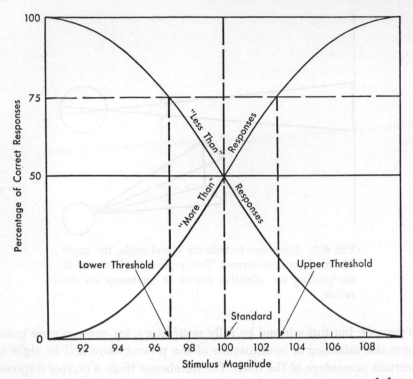

FIG. 6.4. The relation between percentage of correct responses and the difference between standard and comparison stimulus magnitudes. With two possible kinds of response, threshold is at 75 percent; with three kinds of response, three curves are involved and threshold is at 66.7 percent.

employ in describing many phenomena and in characterizing the operation of perception.

The second sort of threshold that is often dealt with is the *differential threshold.* A differential threshold is measured by the value of the stimulus required for a figure to emerge upon a ground having an intensity value *greater* than zero. In describing the absolute threshold, we were talking about a ground of zero intensity and a figure of something greater than zero. In the present case, we are talking about the difference between two values both of which are above zero. An examination of Fig. 6.5 will be of help.

Sometimes the ascertaining of a differential threshold has to do with a small target on a homogeneous field. In that case we are dealing with the threshold required for the target to stand out above the broad visual field as a whole. At other times we are dealing with a target that has two parts, one of which is more intense than the other, and our task in this case is to determine how different in intensity these parts must be in order to be just perceptibly different. It will be seen that when we are dealing with the situations just described, we are also dealing with intensity differences between the two parts. So long as we are dealing with actual obtained values in terms of target intensity, we are dealing with thresholds. When we are concerned with differences in intensity *between* various portions of the target, we are dealing with *limens*. Figure 6.6 will indicate this distinction for you.

From this point on, when we describe experiments and their results, it will be understood that in most cases the data obtained represent threshold values. The char-

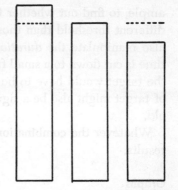

Fig. 6.5. *Thresholds.* The middle bar indicates the standard stimulus value; the left bar, a comparison stimulus just perceptibly greater; the right bar, a stimulus just perceptibly less than the standard.

acteristic thing, then, in performing an experiment in adaptation or in brightness discrimination is to manipulate target conditions and obtain threshold values for each of the manipulations made. Sometimes it is intensity alone that is varied, though at other times other properties are varied in a stepwise fashion. One can manipulate target *area*, for ex-

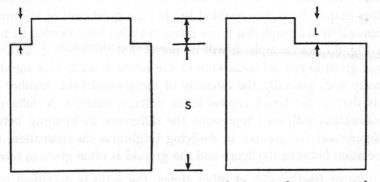

Fig. 6.6. *Limens.* Value S is the standard; L is the incremental value, making the comparison stimulus just perceptibly different than S. This is the difference limen. The two diagrams illustrate the case in which a central target surface is more intense than the peripheral, and in which one-half of the target is more intense than the other.

ample, to find out whether targets subtending large visual angles have a different threshold than those subtending smaller visual angles. One can also manipulate the *duration* of target presentation. If the presentation time is cut down to a small fraction of a second, it might be expected that the target would have to be more intense to be readily perceived. *Shape* of target might also be a significant factor in the determination of threshold.

Whatever the combination of factors manipulated, one can graph the results.

Graphs

A typical graph plots the values of two factors against each other. The one dimension of the graph represents various values of one factor; the other represents values of the second factor. These factors are often called variables, and in an experiment there are two kinds of variables. One is spoken of as the *independent variable* and the other as the *dependent variable*. It is customary in plotting these two variables against each other in a graph to picture the independent variable on the horizontal axis and the dependent variable on the vertical axis. The points represent the value of one of the variables used to produce the result in question when the given value of the other variable is used. Shifting the value of one variable would generally, though not always, be expected to shift the required value for the other variable. Every point along a curve, then, represents a combination of the two variables that will give the end result that is being measured. When one develops some skill in reading graphs, he is then enabled to obtain a great deal of information for himself from a graph that is not given in verbal form in what he reads.

In Fig. 6.7, for example, it will be noted that the labeling of the two axes is given in symbol form. One of the labels is an I. This stands for intensity and, generally, the intensity of the ground field. Another symbol is that of the Greek capital letter delta, a triangle. A delta given in connection with an I represents the difference in intensity between the figure and the ground. In studying brightness discrimination, then, the relation between the figure and the ground is often given in terms of the ratio or fraction $\frac{\Delta I}{I}$; at other times, the ratio is described in the reciprocal of this.

In the use of graphs to picture relations between variables, it is important to use the best units and the best scales of representation. The simplest scale is the arithmetic scale, in which equal spaces on the axis

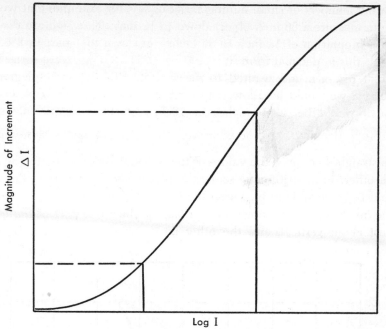

Log I

Magnitude of Standard Stimulus

FIG. 6.7.   The S-shaped curve shows relation between intensities I
and Δ I. The dashed horizontals and the solid vertical lines indicate
two sample relations.

of the graph represent equal quantities. This means that a two-inch
distance on a graph would represent twice the value of the property
mentioned that one inch on the graph would represent. Even though
the arithmetic scale is the simplest, it is not necessarily the most appropriate. Other times, equal distances on the graph are made to represent
unequal values, that is, certain kinds of systematically increasing values.
The most common such scale is the *logarithmic scale.* You may not be
familiar with logarithms, but you can be told enough at this point to
understand how they apply here. In graphic representation of a logarithmic scale, a certain unit distance is selected on the axis to represent
values from 1 to 10. The next unit distance will represent values from
10 to 100. The next will represent values from 100 to 1000. Thus it is
that each successive unit of distance upon the graph represents ten
times as great a value or range as the one preceding it.

Obviously, this is a proportional scale; that is, one capable of measuring
the same proportional values in ranges, whether these ranges have to do

with big numbers or small numbers. Let us say, for example, that we are able to measure a 36-inch object down to ⅛ inch. Thus, we are dealing with a proportion of ⅛ inch to 36 inches, or down to 1 part in 288. (If we put this in decimal form, it would be .00347.) If we were measuring a great distance and wanted to measure it with the same degree of accuracy, we would be allowed to err 1 part in 288. In the case of one mile, it would be 224+ inches or 18.68 feet. In a logarithmic scale the proportionality, $\frac{1}{288}$, or whatever else it might be, is represented by a straight line, since the values of the two variables are plotted against each other. In an arithmetic scale, the plot would be a curved line that would be impossible to plot usefully if a wide range of values happened to be involved. This is shown in Fig. 6.8, in which one part of the curve is just about vertical, and the other part virtually horizontal. In such

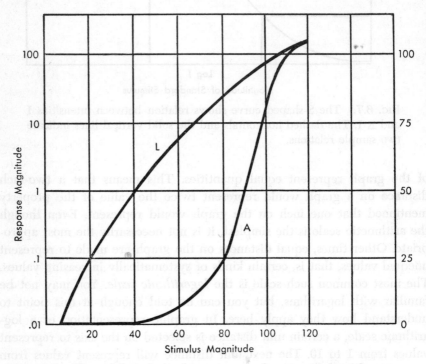

FIG. 6.8. Plots of the relation between stimulus magnitude and response magnitude. When the stimulus values are plotted on a logarithmic scale, curve L results. The same data plotted on a simple arithmetic scale produce curve A. Note that portions of curve A are unusable for accurate representation.

portions of the curve the values of one or the other variable are not represented in space units of proper size to be detectable.

If you keep in mind the two types of scales and what can be done with each, the graphs in the remaining portion of the text ought to be useful to you.

The first fact that made the use of a proportional scale most appropriate for graphing human response was that great ranges of stimulus value are often involved. The second fact is that perceptual response is, itself, proportional to the magnitude of the stimulus level used.

ADAPTATION AS A COMMON EXPERIENCE

Everyone knows that when he enters an unilluminated or weakly illuminated room, such as a movie theater from the street on a bright sunny day, he cannot see very well. In a few minutes, this inability diminishes and objects begin to be seen fairly well. This is the experiential aspect of *dark adaptation*. The same initial inability is a well-known occurrence when one passes from an unilluminated room to one that is illuminated. The process in this case, however, is called *light adaptation*. The photochemical processes that go on in the eye are largely responsible for both forms of adaptation. That these processes can be located in the eye does not rule them out as being something that is irrelevant to us in dealing with perception. In speaking of adaptation, we are, among other things, describing the fact that ability to perceive *varies* under various conditions. To comprehend perception, we must become acquainted with the condition that manipulates adaptation.

Adaptation is one of those features of biological response that is not modifiable by learning. Thus the ever-changing behavior of the individual is at the mercy of the fixed processes in the eye, and is based upon them. Since the amount of adaptation is determined by the photic level and the length of time exposed to it, it is important to take this into account when describing and attempting to understand visual response, visual perception. The individual's perceptions and judgments of the degree of grayness or lightness, for example, are dependent, first of all, on adaptation level.

Some Laboratory Findings in Adaptation

There are several ways of manipulating conditions to study adaptation, but the most common procedure is to use an unilluminated eye.

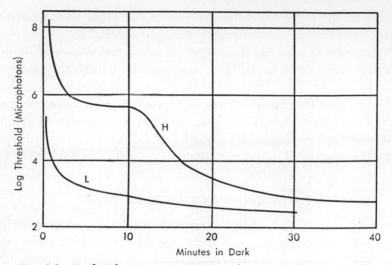

FIG. 6.9   *Dark-Adaptation curves.* H is the course of dark adaptation starting from a preadapting intensity of 400,000 trolands. L starts from 263 trolands (S. Hecht, C. Haig, and A. M. Chase, The influence of light adaptation on subsequent dark adaptation of the eye, *J. Gen. Physiol.* [1937], *20*:831–850, Fig. 2).

This generally means putting the subject in a darkroom for stated lengths of time. Dark adaptation takes place under such conditions, and it would be expected that, up to a certain limit, the longer the eye is unilluminated, the greater the adaptation. This has been found to be true. One of the methods for determining this involves the brief presentation of very weak targets from time to time without light-adapting the eye any more than can be helped. The intensities of the just visible targets are ascertained for known instants following the placing of the subject in darkness—let us say, every five minutes. According to our expectations from common everyday experience, we should expect that from trial to trial threshold targets would become weaker and weaker. This has been found to be the case, and is shown in Fig. 6.9.

THE RODS AND CONES

The sense cells or receptor cells in the human eye are of two sorts. One, called the cones, is sensitive to high, medium, and low-medium levels of radiation. The other, called rods, is sensitive to high-medium, medium, and down to very faint intensities of radiation. By this it is meant that the two ranges of sensitivities overlap. Each of these groups of cells has other distinguishing characteristics. The two kinds of cells are not equal in speed of reaction. The cones respond differently to various parts of the spectrum and form the basis of our ability to see various hues and saturations. Rods do not possess this property.

The retinal distribution of these two kinds of cells differs. Figure 6.10 indicates the general nature of this distribution. From the diagram you

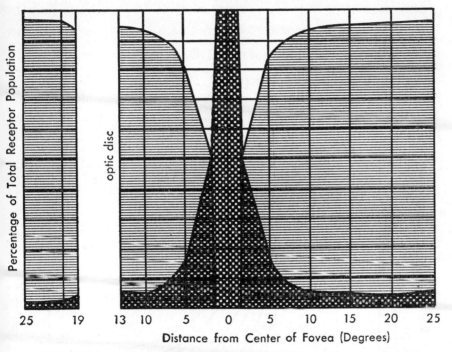

FIG. 6.10.   Diagram to show the percentage of rods and cones in the different portions of the retina along a horizontal axis. Checkered area represents cones; the barred area, rods; overlapping area, both (data of Østerberg used).

can see that the center of the eye, called the *fovea*, is rod-free. Beyond this, in all directions, the cone population diminishes in density and the rod population increases up to a point, and then it, too, diminishes progressively and markedly.

An examination of the dark-adaptation curves given in Fig. 6.9 shows that one of the curves is not smooth, but manifests an abruption or inflection. This is interpreted as indicating the diversity of behavior of the rods and cones. The early upper left-hand portion of the curve in question is called the cone portion, and the other part of the curve is the rod portion. Dark adaptation of the cones is completed in ten to twelve minutes or thereabouts, whereas the adaptation of the rods continues at an ever-decreasing rate for many minutes longer.

If various portions of the retina are tested for adaptation rate, the curves differ, owing, at least in part, to the differences in the rod-cone population in the various parts.

EXAMPLES OF LABORATORY FINDINGS IN BRIGHTNESS DISCRIMINATION

Figure 6.11 shows a number of curves, each of which represents the relation between $\dfrac{\Delta I}{I}$ and level of retinal illumination (both in logarithmic terms) for a given-sized target (disk). The diameters of the disks vary from 23.5 minutes of arc to 24 degrees. That would be roughly a range of 1 to 60. The largest target would have sixty times as great a diameter as the smaller one. All of the disks were looked at directly, hence their

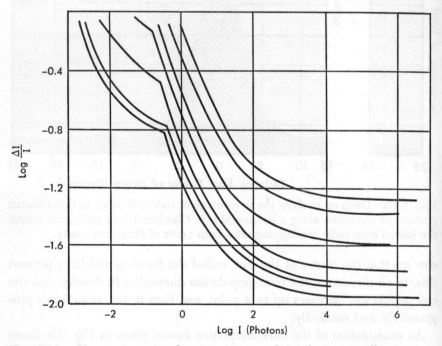

FIG. 6.11. Human intensity discrimination as dependent upon illumination and size of target. Each curve is for a separate target; the visual angles subtended are as follows, reading from the upper to the lower curves in order: 23.5′, 31′, 56′, 2° 14′, 5° 36′, and 24° (J. Steinhardt, Intensity discrimination in the human eye. I. The relation of $\Delta I/I$ to intensity, *J. Gen. Physiol.* [1936], *20*:185–209, Fig. 2).

images were centered on the fovea. When the smallest three targets were used, their images fell fully within the fovea. When the succeeding targets were used, they included retinal areas farther and farther from the fovea, and thus activated many rods.

This family of curves is intended to show how such factors as target size and general intensity of target background determine the threshold value for perceiving a target. That is, the curves show the conditions under which the typical observer can just distinguish a target from its background.

You may wonder whether every observer sees the disk at the same threshold intensity. The answer is, he does not, but the general shape of the curves depicting the factors that we plotted is the same. Hence these sample curves picture the principles involved.

Brightness Discrimination in Everyday Situations

It is well known that there are two ways that radiation may reach the eye. It may come directly from a source, or it may reach the eye by reflection from a surface. Radiation, being reflected from a surface, must reach that surface before coming to the eye, and there are two general ways in which this may happen. The radiation cast on the surface may be the same as that falling on other objects around, or it may be different. When we speak of scenes, there are three general ways in which radiation may reach the eye from portions of the visual field. It may come directly from a source, it may be reflected by a target receiving radiation from a general illuminant, or it may be reflected from localized illumination not cast on all the targets in the field. As far as the observer is concerned, it will be found necessary to include one more possibility. This is the presence or absence of conditions giving rise to perceived texture. This condition arises at the reflecting surface in question. Texture can be defined as lack of uniformity in the reflectance of a surface, and this is perceived as a physical property of the surface itself. The fine-grained roughness that a surface possesses may produce simply what is visually a matte surface. On the other hand, texture may possess considerable coarseness. Whatever the texture may be, it plays a role in making the existence and position of the surface visible to the observer. Complete absence of conditions for texture would make it impossible to see surfaces.

There are important differences between the lightness of a surface and the quality of light seen as illumination. One difference comes from the fact that the surface is localized in space perceptually, but the change in appearance of illumination is not so simply described. Radiation reaching the eye as perceived to be reflected from a surface appears more intense than it does when seen as apparent luminance (i.e., an original source). If one takes a white square of cardboard and places a small gray square upon it, one cannot find any sort of room conditions under which the large square will appear gray in any sense of the word. This is true even though under some conditions the light reflected from the white cardboard is much less (than under certain other conditions) than the light that was reflected from the small gray square. If one uses two such white cardboards with gray squares pasted on them, one of these cards can be placed in bright light and the other in dim light somewhere in the room, both visible at the same time. Although it can be said that the card in dim illumination is still white, the flux reaching the eye from it is not so intense as that from the gray in the other card in full illumination. This perception of comparison, however, is distinct from the perception of the border of the card as white. This is an example, in the one case, of seeing the light and, in the other, of seeing the card. The two modes of seeing, one the luminant mode and the other the object mode, are very commonly alternated in visual perception in everyday life. Since there are these two modes involved, it pays for the reader to recognize that there are two; and that to get the two results just mentioned, there must be a shift from one mode to the other.

Brightness

Brightness in general increases with the intensity of the stimulus producing it. If a single source of restricted visual angle is the only one in the field of view, the light increases or decreases in its brightness as intensity increases or decreases in amount without changing its spectral energy distribution. The visual system is much more sensitive to the rate of change than it is to absolute intensity as such. A subject's judgment of the physical intensity of radiation may be in error by factors as high as several hundred times. The amount of error depends upon the recent conditions to which the eye and the subject have been exposed. If change in stimulus intensity is rapid enough, a change of a very few percent or even much less will be easily detected. When the subject observes brightness produced by a constant source, the perception or judgment of brightness may be greatly in error, since the subject has nothing to go by except his concept or memory of brightness. In such cases, there is no way of stating the exact amount of error, because there is nothing on hand to use as a reference. It is possible only when the subject returns very quickly to a known situation.

Thus an absolute brightness does not exist, except as a conceptual phenomenon. Such a concept is vague and indefinite as compared to the physical intensity scale to which it may refer. This conceptual scale should be kept in mind when we later discuss the phenomenon of brightness adaptation, since it will be discovered that the eye has a strong tendency to hold brightness constant under different intensities of flux. If this tendency was a perfect achievement, all fields containing illumination of a single quantity would appear equal; but this is not actually what happens.

In sharp contrast to this vague way in which absolute brightness is dealt with in simple everyday situations is the exceedingly precise perception of relative brightnesses of two lights of the same quality when seen side by side. The visual system can distinguish equality with great precision. It can also detect equal small differences with reasonable accuracy. This is a property that is also illustrated in the other senses in about the same way. For example, lighter or heavier is an easy perception, but the determination of absolute weight is difficult. It is easy to perceive something as being warmer or colder, or louder or softer, but, here again, absolute perceptions or absolute judgments are not reliable. This sort of thing is an outcome of the general adaptability of the organism to its surroundings, and is one of the fundamental characteristics of its behavior.

Whiteness, Grayness, Blackness

Of major concern in understanding brightness discrimination is a delineation of the conditions for the perception of whiteness, grayness, and blackness. As we have already begun to realize, the amount of radiation reaching the eye is not the principal factor in determining which of those three qualities is experienced. The salient factor seems to be the relations between the various portions of the field in intensity. These can be manipulated in such ways as to produce a distinction between what is perceptually attributed to illumination (that is, to the illuminant, or "light" source) and what is attributed to object surfaces. In our descriptions, we are, of course, dealing both with radiation *sources* and radiation *reflectors*. The scenes we view in everyday life, however, are largely produced by reflected radiation. Thus the lightnesses we observe are those experienced as properties of surfaces. When a visual target is visually evaluated (perceived as being a certain lightness), this evaluation is only a part of a more pervasive process that is dealing with all portions of the visual field simultaneously. The lightness of an area not seen as a photic source will tend to appear white, except where it is a surface having very low reflectance. It will then be seen as a gray. Surfaces that have reflectances above 50 percent will be perceived as white under most conditions, just so long as they are the portions of the field seen as the lightest.

Direct light sources may be seen as brighter than surfaces in the immediate surrounds that look white. We may well call them a superwhite. This is, of course, where the distinction between brightness and lightness comes in. Brightness is the adjective pertaining to radiant sources, and lightness is the adjective pertaining to targets seen as surfaces. Surfaces that appear as light as the lightest perceived surfaces are all seen as white. On the other hand, some surfaces may appear less light than others, and they may appear gray. Certain configurations of light and less-light areas may be seen as objects and the shadows they cast. That which perceptually lies in a shadow may appear white, even though it is not reflecting as much radiation to the eyes per unit area as the surfaces outside the shadow. Whether it is light would depend largely upon its reflectance. If the reflectance of the target giving rise to a surface in shadow is equal to the target responsible for the white surface, then the two will be white. Relative reflectance of portions of the target can be manipulated so that the one providing the less radiation to the eye will be seen as white, and the one providing the more will appear gray, or even will be identified as black.

Let us use, as the two portions of an overall target, a piece of coal and a sheet of typewriter paper. The typewriter paper may reflect 70 percent of the radiation falling on it, and the coal may reflect 8 percent. If we put these items in two adjacent open-ended boxes and illuminate the coal 100 times as intensely as the sheet of paper, despite this the coal will still appear black and the paper white. The coal is receiving 100 units, and reflecting 8 units. The paper is receiving 1 unit, and reflecting .70 unit. Thus, the reflectance produced by the coal is over 11.4 times as great as the radiation reflected from the paper, but nevertheless the coal is black and the paper is seen as white. An organism-contributed feature of perception is identification. The individual in the case described is looking at coal and typewriter paper. The target situation as a whole has contributed what is required by the individual for him to perceive coal and typewriter paper. The factors we have been discussing were limited to restricted portions of the visual field.

They were such as to work against seeing one portion of the field as coal and another as white paper. On the other hand, the field as a whole in conjunction with the organism's bias toward identification has succeeded in the perception of the two items just mentioned.

We may show to some extent, by eliminating them, the role of factors other than the mere amount of radiation reaching the eye from two restricted portions of the field. To do this, we may eliminate the differences of form and area in the "coal" and "paper" portions of the field and homogenize the remaining field by placing a screen in front of the whole field, leaving radiation to reach the eye from portions of the "coal" and "paper" areas through equal-sized circular holes in the screen. (See Fig. 6.12.) Now the observer sees in the new field only two disks

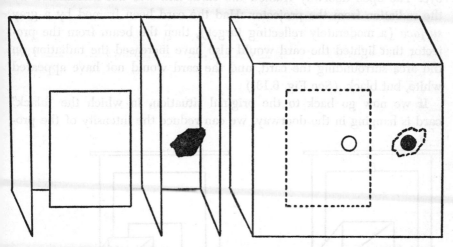

FIG. 6.12. Comparison of typewriter paper and coal: two targets with different reflectances. In the left-hand situation, the illumination of the two may be very different, the paper reflecting less radiation per unit area, and yet the coal looks black and the paper white. If a cover is interposed so that only portions of the two targets are seen, and thus not identified, the "coal" may look lighter than the "paper."

of different lightness. These, although they are portions of the old coal and paper targets, no longer are seen as surfaces of coal and paper respectively. They are now comparable only on the basis of the *amount* of radiation they send to the eye. They no longer are effective in terms of their *reflection factors,* shapes, textures, and so on. It must be recognized, of course, that if textural differences do show up to a great extent, they will still have their influence; but we have assumed that the experimenter has eliminated them by his choice of the portions of the coal and paper targets used for exposure.

The following illustrations of the principal features of lightness perception are effective. Take a sheet of black cardboard (a target whose surface is a poor reflector) and hang it in an open doorway of a dimly illuminated room to be viewed from an unilluminated room. The cardboard, of course, *looks* black. Now cast a beam of a projector on the cardboard and it can thus be made to appear white. If a piece of white paper (a target with a highly reflecting surface) is interposed between the cardboard and the projector, the part of the cardboard that can still be seen will look black. To begin with, the cardboard appeared white because it was receiving and reflecting considerable radiation to the eye. The open doorway framed the card, and was not illuminated by the radiation from the projector. Had the card been framed by a gray *surface* (a moderately reflecting target), then the beam from the projector that lighted the card would also have increased the radiation on the area surrounding the card, and the card would not have appeared white, but black. (See Fig. 6.13.)

If we now go back to the original situation, in which the "black" card is hanging in the doorway, we can reduce the intensity of the pro-

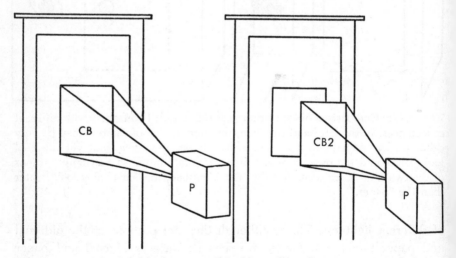

Fig. 6.13.   In the left-hand case, a "black" cardboard, CB, is suspended in a doorway to a dimly illuminated room. The cardboard looks black. It appears white when illuminated from a projector, P. In the right-hand case, a highly reflecting ("white") card, CB2, is placed so as partly to overlap the first card. The two can be seen side by side. Now no manipulations of illumination intensity will alter either card from its original appearance.

jector beam; and as less and less radiation falls upon the card, it discontinues appearing white and becomes a series of grays until finally the card appears black. Keep in mind all the time that as these and other adjustments in the intensity of radiation are being made, the level of illumination of the adjoining room, which frames the card, remains physically constant and thus provides a constant level surround.

As a final step, hang a highly reflecting card ("white" card) alongside the poorly reflecting card ("black" card), and then none of the intensity manipulations that have already been described alter the identified lightness (that is, blackness and whiteness respectively) of the two cards.

The same principles can be illustrated by a two-projector arrangement. In the first projector, place an opaque slide, except for a half-inch circular hole. This card will project a beam giving a perceived disk of light on a dark background. The second projector contains a slide that is also opaque, except for a transparent ring whose inner diameter is one-half inch. When the two projectors are properly pointed, the second one will provide a light ring around the disk. If the projectors are provided with means for manipulating intensity, the operator may vary the relative and absolute intensities of ring and disk as the occasion requires.

If the intensity of the disk is held constant, and the intensity of the ring is manipulated over a wide range, the lightness of the disk may vary all the way from white to dark gray. If, on the other hand, the intensity of the disk is varied, while the ring's intensity is held constant, lightness of the ring varies from white to gray.

With manipulation of the intensity of the projector beam, when one or the other target is shown alone, the target (ring or disk) changes from that of a surface color to that of a luminous source depending upon intensity. The radiation reflected to the eye from the target varies while the radiation from the surrounds remains constant, at a very low level. A target seen as a luminous source is one that is sending a great deal more radiation per unit area to the eye than its surrounds. This remains the case whether the surrounds are intense or weak reflectors to the eye.

SPECIAL STIMULUS CONDITIONS

We have just been dealing with the more usual everyday conditions of visual stimulation and the brightness and lightness perceptions they evoke. In addition to these common conditions, there are some special conditions of whose perceptual end results we should be aware. We shall therefore briefly review them.

Intermittent Stimulation

Whereas the eye is more usually supplied with uniform radiation that continues for some time, it is sometimes presented a series of short pulses. When the pulse rate is low enough, the observer sees a succession of alternations between light and dark. When the rate is increased, the end result is spoken of as flicker. Experiments with intermittent stimulation are therefore often called flicker experiments. The first end result of significance to us is that when the photic pulse rate is made sufficiently high, the human observer ceases to see flicker or any sort of fluctuations whatsoever. The point at which the light seen becomes perfectly steady is called the *fusion point*. The pulse rate at the point is called the *critical flicker frequency*, or the c.f.f. Most of the study of intermittent stimulation over the past century has had to do with the stimulus conditions that have to do with c.f.f. In addition to pulse rate itself, several other factors, such as stimulus *intensity*, the *part of the spectrum* used, the retinal *area* covered, and the *position* of the image on the retina, have been studied. Fig. 6.14 indicates, in general, the relations between stimulus intensity, stimulus area, and the c.f.f. The horizontal axis represents stimulus intensity in logarithmic units. Each curve is for a separate stimulus area, and the values are given in degrees of visual angle (angles of arc on the retina). It will be seen that as area is increased, the result is a raising of the c.f.f. for most intensities. When intensities are extremely low, only the rods are activated, and the results are different than when cones are also involved. The curves flatten out and a different set of c.f.f.'s result as intensity is varied. That is, c.f.f. is not always changed as much, or in the same direction, as when the cone portion of the intensity range is involved. Thus we find that the events in the eye itself are crucial in determining the perceptual outcome. Critical flicker frequency is also manipulated by using different parts of the spectrum.

Over 100 years ago, the father of modern photography, Talbot, found that there was a simple fixed and thoroughly dependable relation between brightness which an observer would see and the fraction of the cycle of intermittency occupied by the pulse. Let us say, for example, the photic pulse itself occupies as much time as the interval between pulses. This gives a one-to-one ratio (50 percent to 50 percent). Talbot found that the light looked half as bright as it would look if the stimulation was the same intensity and continued throughout the cycle; that is, i

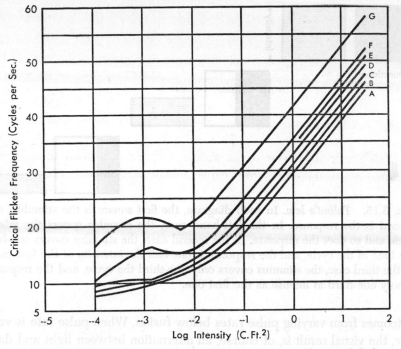

FIG. 6.14. Relations between target area, intensity, and critical flicker frequency. Each curve is for a target of different angular subtense. A is 51'; B, 1° 18'; C, 1° 50'; D, 2° 44'; E, 3° 42'; F, 5° 6'; and G, 31° 51'. The stimulus and no-stimulus phases of the cycle are equal (S. H. Bartley and J. L. Seibel, A further study of entoptic stray light, *J. Psychol.* [1954], 38:313–319, Fig. 1).

it was produced by steady stimulation. He states that with intermittent stimulation the perception of steady light produced is as bright as it would be were the same total stimulation distributed evenly throughout the cycle. This is known as *Talbot's law.* (See Fig. 6.15.) Accordingly, if the stimulus part is one-third of the cycle, the brightness will be one-third as great as if the same stimulus was to be continued throughout the whole cycle. If an experimenter wants to reduce the effective intensity of a target by any amount, he can do so by interrupting the light source with a rotating open-sectored disk whose ratio of blade to open sector is proper.

Brightness Enhancement

The study of the perceptual outcomes from the use of intermittent stimulation has not been wholly confined to pulse rates at and above the fusion point. Bartley (12), for example, made a survey of the visual

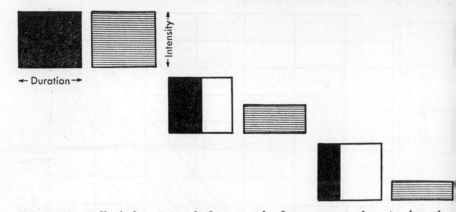

Fig. 6.15. *Talbot's law.* In each diagram, the first square is the stimulus; the second is the response. In the left-hand case, the stimulus covers the whole cycle and so does the response. In the second case, the stimulus covers one-half the *time* of the cycle, and the response is one-half the *intensity* of the first case. In the third case, the stimulus covers only one-third the cycle, and the response is only one-third as intense as the first one.

outcomes from varying pulse rates below fusion. When pulse rate is very low, the visual result is, of course, an alternation between light and dark periods. As pulse rate is increased, the dark period disappears and becomes merely a period less light than the original light period. As pulse rate is further increased, the visual result may be described as a light field composed of two components: a steady light one and a superimposed fluctuating one. As pulse rate is still further increased, the fluctuating component becomes less amplitudinous and less conspicuous until finally it disappears, leaving only a steady field. Inspection of Fig. 6.16 will show the results just mentioned.

In discussing intermittent stimulation, our purpose here is to indicate its relative effectiveness as compared to steady stimulation. The Talbot effect has already been pointed out. It represents an effectiveness of intermittent stimulation that is less than that of steady stimulation.

With pulse rates failing to produce steady light—that is, with subfusional pulse rates—the effectiveness of intermittent stimulation varies from the approximate Talbot level to levels even greater than steady stimulation. Figure 6.17 shows this. In it, the curve representing the effectiveness of intermittent stimulation rises as pulse frequency is reduced. Finally, the curve reaches the point at which steady and intermittent stimulation are the same. This is the case when the ascending curve reaches the horizontal line in the graph. The increased effective-

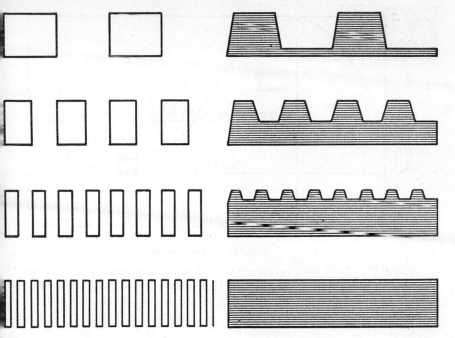

Fig. 6.16. Schema to indicate that with slowly repeated photic pulses the response is an alternation of light and dark. With increasingly frequent pulses, the alternation is replaced by an undulation of light and dark, with progressively decreasing amplitude (flicker). Finally, the result is a field of steady lightness or brightness. The open figures are the pulses; the diagrams on the right are the visual end results.

ness of intermittent stimulation over that of steady stimulation is called brightness enhancement, or the Bartley effect.

Brightness enhancement of a different sort is produced by single short pulses of radiation. If one compares the effect of a short pulse to that of continuous radiation of the same intensity, it will be found that the pulse is the brighter. According to one way of regarding this result, it is the end effect of reducing pulse frequency to its lower limits. In another sense, the result does not always approximate what would be expected from reducing pulse rate, since, under some conditions, a brightness enhancement maximum is reached when pulse rate is reduced to approximately ten pulses per second. From there downward, at least for some distance, brightness enhancement diminishes considerably. This, too, is shown in Fig. 6.17.

This perceptual end result has been attributed to one or the other of two origins. Authors who have accounted for a number of other quan-

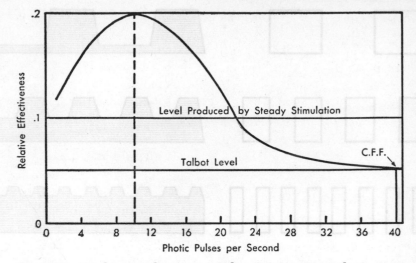

FIG. 6.17. *Brightness enhancement.* Whereas intermittent photic stimulation produces a lesser brightness than steady stimulation of the same
intensity when pulses are near, at, and above critical flicker frequency,
it produces a greater effect when definitely lower than c.f.f. This is
called brightness enhancement (S. H. Bartley, *Vision: A Study of Its
Basis,* Van Nostrand, 1941)

titative features of brightness discrimination (perception) by the photo-
chemistry of the rods and cones have felt that the same photochemical
mechanisms would account for brightness enhancement. No definite work
has been done to ascertain whether this is actually the case. On the
other hand, considerable work that has been done by Bartley and
Bishop in delineating the nature of the neurophysiological mechanisms
at work in the optic pathway seems to provide a basis for brightness enhancement. The theory which Bartley described to account for enhancement has been called the *alternation of response theory.* It is possibly
not appropriate to take up space here to describe the theory in detail,
but it may be said that it is a form of response theory in which it is
shown that a greater effect per unit time is produced by temporally
bunching stimulation than by evenly distributing it. (See Fig. 6.18.)

Stray Retinal Illumination

In the section on intermittent stimulation it was indicated that the
sense organ itself had a considerable hand in the determination of the
perceptual outcome. This is of considerable significance in understanding
perception, and in knowing what to expect of human behavior. In the

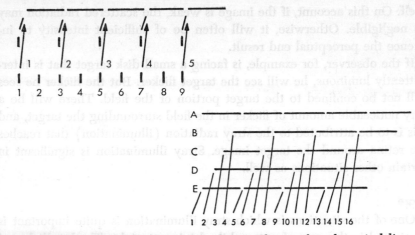

FIG. 6.18. *Alternation of response theory.* The numbered vertical lines indicate photic stimuli (pulses). In the left-hand diagram, each pulse produces activity in a given channel, when not too frequent. When twice as frequent, only alternate pulses may produce activity owing to the fact that the channel does not recover quickly enough. In the right-hand diagram, the first four pulses activated different channels, since the available channels were not all activated by the first pulse. By the time the fifth pulse is presented, the first channel has recovered and can be reactivated. This is called alternation of response.

present section, another factor that exerts considerable influence upon the perceptual outcome is to be introduced. It is the factor of the stray illumination of the eye. Those who know about visual matters only superficially suppose that the eye acts like a good camera, and that the retina is supplied with a precise image just as is the film or plate in a camera. There is, of course, a retinal image determined by the focusing mechanism of the eye, but there is also some unfocused radiation in the eye. Some of it enters the interior of the eye and reaches the retina through the coats of the eye. Some is scattered by the fluids and lens of the eye; for these optical media not only refract the photic radiation, but at the junctures between them they scatter it.

The scattering of radiation in the eye provides the retina not only with an image but also with radiation that is nonfocused. This scattered radiation, of course, covers the whole eye. For example, if the image of a target of restricted visual angle—let us say, a small luminous disk in a "dark" field—is focused on the retina, the retina is not only illuminated in the disk image but receives radiation of some intensity or other on every portion. The scattered illumination is less intense than the image itself. On this account, if the image is weak, the scattered radiation may be negligible. Otherwise, it will often be of sufficient intensity to influence the perceptual end result.

If the observer, for example, is facing a small disk target that is intermittently luminous, he will see the target flicker. But the flicker he secs will not be confined to the target portion of the field. There will be a very noticeable amount of flicker in the field surrounding the target, and this is to be attributed to the stray radiation (illumination) that reaches the retina around the target image. Stray illumination is significant in certain other situations as well.

Glare

One of the situations is which stray illumination is quite important is illustrated in the case of automobile driving at night. The headlights of oncoming cars, of course, appear quite bright. Not only is this so, but they tend to obscure whatever else might be seen in other portions of the visual field. That is, the driver cannot see pedestrians, for example, on the road, or to the side of the road. Why is this? It is primarily because the radiation from the headlights not only produces intense retinal images of them but also covers the rest of the retina with stray illumination. This is much more intense than the weak radiation reaching the eye from other visual targets in the field. The weak retinal images produced by pedestrians as visual targets are definitely masked, and therefore are as if nonexistent. Whatever becomes nonexistent as a retinal image is certainly nonexistent as a visual reality to the perceiver.

Figure 6.19 is a diagram indicating the general principle of scattered or stray retinal illumination. The details are given in the legend. It is sufficient to say here that the vertical axis of the diagram represents stimulus intensity, hence a target with sharp contours is represented by a rectangle. A tapered intensity distribution is represented by a curve that slopes off from a peak of some sort.

The Two-Flash Phenomenon

One of the best illustrations of a discrepancy between energy input and response output is what we may call the two-flash phenomenon. Under the very simplest outlook upon the relation between stimulation and perceptual response, one would expect that a single brief photic pulse would elicit a single brief light experience called a flash. It turns out, however, that under certain conditions this is not the case. The single pulse produces a pair of flashes instead of only one. This phenom-

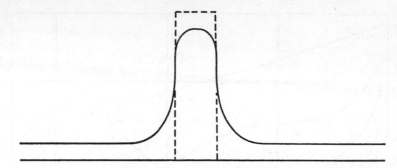

FIG. 6.19. *Stray illumination.* Instead of all of the radiation being contained in an image whose distribution corresponds with that of the target, the radiation is scattered so as to form a tapered distribution covering the whole retina. The dotted line represents the target distribution, the solid line the retinal distribution.

enon might seem to have little significance other than its curiousness. It is, on the contrary, a manifestation which anyone interested in the mechanisms of perception might well wish to study. In fact the matter has been studied, and we shall describe the findings briefly.

When the experimenter begins his study with a brief weak pulse of "light" as a stimulus, he elicits a single flash of light. If he makes the pulse stronger, step by step, he finally reaches an intensity value that will elicit the two-flash experience. If he further raises stimulus intensity, he finally obtains a value that again elicits only a single flash. This means that throughout a midrange of pulse intensities, two flashes instead of one are elicited; whereas, with very weak and very strong intensities, a single flash is elicited. If the experimenter, on the other hand, manipulates pulse duration, he is again able to elicit paired flashes throughout a midrange of duration.

If, instead of manipulating pulse intensity or pulse duration, the *area* of the target is manipulated, it is found that the two-flash phenomenon is not obtainable with a target subtending only a small visual angle.

Bartley has deduced from his findings that the two flashes are obtained when both the rod and cone populations are activated, and that the one population reacts more quickly than the other population. This difference gives rise to two separate inputs into the central nervous system from the eye, well enough separated to give rise to two flashes instead of only one. For a diagram showing the findings in graphic terms, turn to Fig. 6.20. In it, there are several pairs of curves. Throughout the region, to the left of one curve in each pair, a single flash is obtained

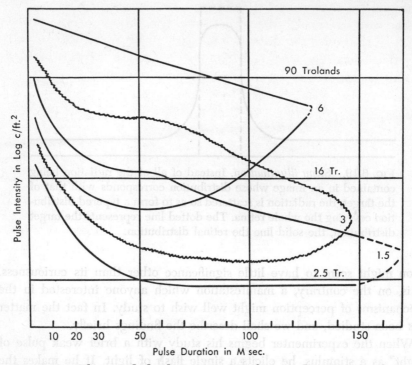

Pulse Intensity in Log c/ft.²

90 Trolands

6

16 Tr.

3

1.5

2.5 Tr.

10   20   30   50   100   150

Pulse Duration in M sec.

FIG. 6.20.   *The two-flash phenomenon.* Each pair of curves joined at their right-hand ends encloses an area representing the conditions for a double flash. Each pair is for a different target size. The target subtenses are 6, 3, and 1.5 degrees. (S. H. Bartley and F. R. Wilkinson, Certain factors in producing complexity of response to a single pulse of light, *J. Psychol.* [1953], 35:299–306, Fig. 3).

for the conditions signified on the two axes of the graph. To the right of the second one, a single flash is also obtained; but in the region between the two, a two-flash experience is the perceptual end result. Bartley also found, in the optic-nerve discharge of the rabbit, a double response under the midranges of similar conditions already described. He interpreted this to indicate that the double flash was peripherally originated.

The distribution of the energy on the retina is a factor in the determination of perceived brightness. Let us say, we use a certain area of image on the retina. This area can be in the form of a square, or it can be in the form of a rectangle. In the latter case, the rectangle can be very long and thin. This will necessitate the image extending over considerable of the retina in one direction, but relatively little in the other direction (at right angles to the first). Were the perceptual brightness of the seen light to be determined solely by the total energy impingement on the retina, the shape of the target would not matter. All shapes would produce the same end result. This does not happen to be the case. The shape of the target does determine threshold.

Factors for and Against the Perception of Edges

When the photic radiation (luminous flux) reaching the eye from certain portions of the visual field differs from others in amount, the observer usually perceives areas of different levels of lightness. Many of these areas will be perceived as *objects* with abrupt edges. This need not always be the case. At other times, when the *spatial* features of the stimulus involve marked intensity contrasts, but the timing of the successive components of the target's presentation is altered, that which was seen as a sharply bounded area loses its edges and entirely disappears. In other instances, perceived areas lose their sharp edges and shift to areas of tapered brightness, or grayness, with indistinct or practically nonexistent edges. Here, again, it is sometimes a matter of timing that is responsible. Thus we may say that timing of stimulation is a crucial factor in the perception of surfaces and edges. As examples of this, we may turn to some experiments of Werner and of Bartley.

Werner (256) presented pairs of targets of many forms, varying from circles and disks to irregular and "incomplete" forms. In one case, for example, a target perceived as a solid black disk (when presented alone) was briefly presented on a light background. (See Fig. 6.21.) In about

FIG. 6.21. *Werner's figures.* The disk and ring are presented in succession and their centers are at the same point (H. Werner, Studies in contour. I. Qualitative analyses, *Am. J. Psychol.* [1935], 47:44, 46, Figs. 5, 9).

150 msec., another target centered on the same point in the visual field was presented. When this target was presented alone, it appeared as a black ring. With the interval, as just specified, elapsing between the presentation of the first and second targets, the disk was never seen.

This is to say, the area within the ring was not black. When the temporal sequences of the targets was reversed, the black disk *was* seen. The timing of the disk-ring succession that eliminated the seeing of the disk is more or less critical. If the rate of succession is slow, the disk will be seen to precede the ring. If more rapid, the ring is seen with a darkened inner field. If still more rapid, the inner field, which might have been expected to be a dark disk, lightens, and may become lighter in some cases than the light field outside the ring.

It is possible to interchange the intensity relation between disk or ring and the ground on which they are made to appear, so that the figures are now light and the ground is black. In this case, the original phenomenon will still occur. That is, the object that ought to have emerged in contrast to the ground will not do so.

It will be noted that the second figure, a ring, had both an inner and an outer edge;[1] whereas the disk, when it exists, of course has only an outer edge. Since the results differed in keeping with which of the two targets was presented first, they indicate that the outer border of the second target played a part in the outcome. The same results, it may be added, occurred whether both targets were presented in one eye or to separate eyes.

This may be what actually underlay the outcome. When the disk target is presented first, but is followed very soon by the ring target, the border contour for the disk does not have time to form. Since the contour process has not formed in the only time given it to do so, the ring simply develops as a ring without the disk ever being seen. At a critical stage in the decay of what was formed of the contour process for the disk, the contour process of the ring target may be able to utilize it to accentuate its own inner edge, for the directions of the two developing gradients would be the same. This account is based upon the principle originally recognized elsewhere in threshold studies—that contour processes must develop and complete themselves before differences in brightness of two areas can be distinguished. Whatever depresses or precludes edge formation precludes the appreciation of the brightness a surface would have.

We may continue with the account by detailing the possible process events when the order of target presentation is reversed. In this case, the

---

[1] For the sake of clarity, we shall call the bounds of the target its *borders*, and the bounds of the visual object its *edges*. In doing this, it will be clear whether it is target or perception that is being referred to. Since there is an intervening process in the nervous system responsible for the seeing of objects and their edges, we shall refer to it as a *contour process*.

temporal interval between the presentation of the two targets is not critical. Regardless of how soon the disk target is presented after the ring target, the disk appears as a black surface. This is to say that if the disk target is presented *before* the contour process for the inner edge of the ring is developed, it is simply forestalled and never completed, and the whole figure is seen as a large disk whose outer edge is the outer edge of the ring. If the inner contour process of the ring has time to develop, however, before the presentation of the disk target, this event, by changing the illumination within the ring, obliterates the condition for its continuance. That various contour processes in adjacent portions of the eye or nervous system interact with each other will be discussed in the section that follows.

Bartley's (12) experiment had certain features in common with those of Werner. Bartley used a target arrangement that provided for seeing a figure of two parts: a disk that was surrounded by a ring whose inner edge was the outer edge of the disk. The stimulus flux for the disk could be alternated so that a light disk would alternate with a dark one, while being surrounded with a gray or only medium-bright ring. If the intensity level of the ring target was raised above the mean value of the two disks, it caused the light phase of the disk alternation to become less predominant than the dark phase. If the level of the intensity of the ring target was reduced below the mean, the light phase became predominant. Along with this shift in predominance, a difference in edge properties of the two phases of the disk developed. The predominant phase possessed a sharp edge; the "diminished" phase lacked an edge and became a mere "shadow." The predominant phase seemed to occupy more time, thus taking up most of the cycle.

In order to subordinate the light phase of the disk and make the dark phase predominant, the intensity of the ring target (when alternation frequencies are low) must exceed not only the Talbot level but the photic intensity for the light phase of the disk. Increasing the alternation rate reduces the level of the ring target needed until it reaches Talbot level. The light phases of the disk grow less bright as c.f.f. is reached. To have the light phase predominate, the target conditions just described must be reversed.

Additional Conditions Manipulating the Emergence of Edges

It has been found that the distance between two target border processes has a great deal to do with the emergence of object edges in perception. This was measured by the intensity values in the different parts of the field required for edges to emerge; that is, it was measured in threshold experiments. For example, the target intensity differences between the two parts of the target producing a small disk figure on a large disk ground are diminished as the size of the ground is increased, and thus its border is shifted farther and farther away from the border of the inner-lying disk already mentioned. This is indicated in Fig. 6.22.

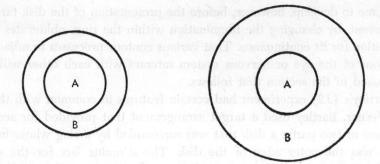

FIG. 6.22. Targets made up of a central disk area, A, and a surrounding ring area, B, the latter being manipulated in size.

In it, it will be seen that the distance between the two borders is greater in B than in A. It is a question, then, whether it is area or distance between borders that makes the above-mentioned difference in threshold. It was long customary to attribute it to area. Fry and Bartley (80) showed that contour processes were responsible. The first step in this demonstration was the employment of the target given in Fig. 6.23. In this target, there were three stimulus areas: A, B, and C. Areas B and C were separated by a thin ring whose size could be varied from being close to A to being close to C. Varying the ring size left constant the

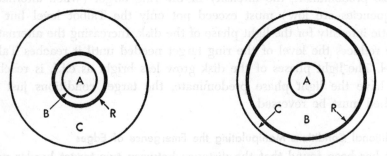

FIG. 6.23. Targets made up of a central area, A, and an outer area, B plus C, which is constant. The distance of border of ring R from the border of A is varied.

total area, B-C, lying outside of A, but it did manipulate a border in the vicinity of A. Since total area outside of A was held a constant, no shift in the threshold for the emergence of A as brighter than B should occur, *if* the customary area explanations were to apply. On the other hand, since a border was being varied in distance from the outer border of A, a threshold manipulation should occur, if the contour-process explanation was to be correct. Experimentation tallied with the contour-process expectation. Further manipulations of target conditions were added to the one just described, and all of them gave results in line with the idea that two parallel contour processes inhibit each other; that is, require greater intensity differences on their two sides for the emergence of perceived edges. The same investigators found that nonparallel borders, that is, those at right angles to each other, actually resulted in facilitation rather than inhibition.

Chapter 7

VISUAL ACUITY AND THE RETINAL IMAGE

Visual acuity is the ability of the individual to distinguish (i.e., discriminate) closely adjacent components of a visual target. The closeness of these components is measured in terms of the size of the visual angle they subtend at the eye. The ability to distinguish the target's adjacent spatial features is somehow dependent upon optical resolution, the property of separating details. Thus, optical resolution is a prime factor to take into consideration in studying visual acuity.

Visual acuity involves the eye as an optical device, the retina as a mosaic of receptors, the neural part of the eye as an organizer of the activity set up in the mosaic, the lateral geniculate body and the projection area of the brain as further organizers of the visual input, and, finally, the rest of the central nervous system to utilize the input. The visual system also guides the posturing of the eyes for the purpose of receiving the radiation in the first place.

If the optical media of the eye are clouded or transmit certain wave lengths more readily than others, visual acuity is lowered. If the mosaic is so coarse as to preclude fine spatial resolution, it, too, may become a factor in reducing visual acuity. Many other factors operating along the pathway and in the rest of the organism also may, in their own ways, impoverish visual function.

VISUAL-ACUITY TARGETS

Visual-acuity targets are used in two different kinds of situation. They are used by clinicians in testing visual functions, and they are used also in the laboratory to further the understanding visual mechanisms.

Many years ago, Snellen tested a large group of young men, and his findings were used to establish what was to be considered normal visual acuity. The standard test distance was 20 feet. It turned out that the bulk of the subjects could see a separation between two portions of a target that subtended a visual angle of one minute of arc. Since such subjects could see at 20 feet what one would expect them to see at 20 feet, their visual acuity was called 20/20. Such subjects should be able to resolve a space interval twice as great, twice as far away; or three times as great, three times as far away. The minority of all the subjects required greater or lesser target-element separations for resolution. The subjects who required separations of two minutes at 20 feet were called 20/40, for the normal subjects at 40 feet could pass the same test. To put it in other words, the subjects with subnormal vision were designated in terms of how far away the normal could be and still see the target-element separations. Hence, we find that there are people who have 20/30, 20/40, 20/100, 20/200, and many other designated visual acuities, depending upon the minimum visual angle between target elements which they can resolve.

The targets used in the clinic are generally rows of letters with elements separated by known visual angles. It is easy for the subjects to indicate whether they are seeing properly simply by calling out the names of the letters. Such material has its limitations, for not all letters are of equal difficulty because of their intrinsic shapes as well as the separations of their components. Since letters are familiar material, the subject is aided in guessing, and this also is a biasing factor.

Level of illumination of the target chart is also a factor in the recognition of the targets, particularly if other portions of the visual field are illuminated at different levels than the chart. Intensity contrast between the target and its ground is a further factor in visual acuity. Intensity contrast is often spoken of in a confusing way, for it is a term used not only to designate difference in the photic flux reaching the eye from two adjacent portions of the target field, but also to refer to the observed difference in brightness of the two portions of the field. Thus in one case contrast is a property of the stimulus, and in the other it is a property of the sensory experience (the perception). Where we say intensity contrast, we shall be referring to the stimulus. When we say brightness contrast, we shall be referring to the sensory experience.

Laboratory Targets

For testing visual acuity in the laboratory, several different kinds of targets are used, such as (1) a pair of parallel bars; (2) a broken circle or Landolt C; (3) a grating, that is, a field with contrasting stripes of equal width; (4) a single fine line on a homogeneous background; (5) a single area, such as a disk on a homogeneous field; and (6) an interrupted contour by which vernier visual acuity is studied.

The separations involved, when single disks or single fine lines are used, are the separations between the opposite borders of the disks and lines themselves. In the case of the single disks, visual acuity and threshold target size become identical.

In the laboratory, visual acuity is stated not in the terms described for the clinic but in terms of the minimal visual angle that the relevant elements in the target must subtend in order to be seen (resolved). Thus visual acuity is the reciprocal of the visual angle measured in minutes of arc. The ability to resolve target components of 1 minute is a visual acuity of 1.00; the ability to resolve those of 0.5 minute is a visual acuity of 2.

Fig. 7.1 shows the relation between threshold target size and contrast in which the target has a diffuse reflectivity of 3 percent, and the backgrounds range in diffuse reflectivity from 3.4 to 80 percent. Each of the curves is for a different level of illumination. It will be seen that the

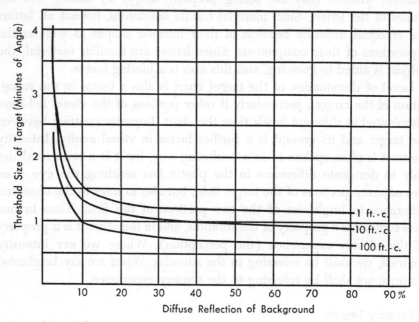

FIG. 7.1. Relation between target size and reflection factor of the background for each of three levels of illumination: 1 foot-candle, 10 foot-candles, and 100 foot-candles. Diffuse reflection factor of target = 3 percent (data from Luckiesh).

threshold size varies considerably for the different reflection values of background; that is, for the different contrasts between target and background.

Fig. 7.2 turns the same information into visual-acuity values. It will be seen that visual acuity varies considerably over the contrast range

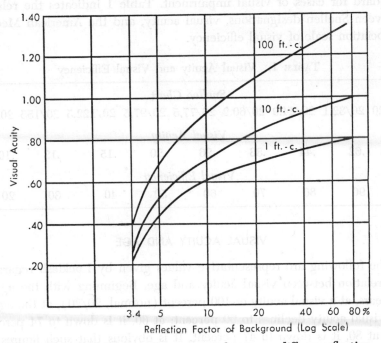

FIG. 7.2.   Visual acuity for a target having a diffuse reflection factor of 3 percent for various background reflectances and at each of three different illuminations: 1, 10, and 100 foot-candles (data from Luckiesh).

used. Both of these graphs were constructed from data presented by Luckiesh (167). He has given a good summary of the relationship between target contrast, illumination, exposure time, and the behavioral results of visual acuity and size threshold. Its substance is as follows: as target illumination varies from 1 to 100 foot-candles, threshold size varies from 15 to 5 minutes of arc for low contrasts in the target, and from 1.1 to 0.6 minute for high contrasts. Under the same two sets of conditions, visual acuity varies from .067 to .200 and .90 to 1.67, respectively. For targets with low contrasts and varying exposure time, from 7 msec. to 300 msec., threshold size varies from 20 to 13 minutes, and visual acuity from .050 to .077. With the same ranges of exposure time, but with high contrasts, threshold size varies from 1.3 to 1.1 minutes, and visual acuity from .77 to .90.

The American Medical Association, some time ago, developed a scale of visual efficiency relating to the Snellen chart ratings of visual acuity. While this visual-efficiency scale is quite arbitrary, it does function as a standard for cases of visual impairment. Table 1 indicates the relation between Snellen designations, visual acuity, and the American Medical Association scale of visual efficiency.

TABLE 1. Visual Acuity and Visual Efficiency

Snellen Chart								
20/20	20/32.1	20/44.9	20/60.2	20/77.5	20/97.5	20/122.5	20/155	20/200
Visual Acuity								
1.00	.62	.44	.33	.26	.20	.15	.13	.10
Visual Efficiency								
100	90	80	70	60	50	40	30	20

VISUAL ACUITY AND AGE

The following are representative values given by Luckiesh regarding the relation between visual acuity and age. Beginning with the age of 20 years, at a visual acuity of 100 percent (normal, 20/20), at the age of 40, visual acuity declines to 90 percent; at 60, it is down to 74 percent; and at 80, it is down to 47 percent. It is obvious that such figures are only statistical and may not apply to any given individual, but on the other hand they indicate that, in general, considerable decline is to be expected.

VISUAL ACUITY AND PUPIL SIZE

Pupil size is a factor that influences three features of visual functions: sharpness (definition) of retinal image, resolution of detail, and the experience of brightness. Definition of a lens increases as aperture decreases; thus, as the pupil constricts, sharpness of image is increased. Resolution increases as lens size increases, and thus resolution improves as the pupil dilates. It turns out, however, that in the eye these factors just about offset each other over a considerable range of pupil size. Visual acuity, with constant brightness of seen object and constant intensity of retinal image, does not change greatly with pupil diameters ranging from two to six millimeters. This is actually most of the range over which the pupil varies in the usual day-to-day situations.

On the other hand, a person may improve his ability to see certain targets in low illumination by supplying himself with an artificial pupil. For example, if one is viewing a projection screen in a very weakly illuminated room, the material, such as tables of numbers, may not be legible. If one punches a small hole in a card and views the screen, through the hole, with one eye (the other one being closed), he will likely be able to read the tabular material.

In the literature, we find various statements indicating that for older subjects drop in illumination affects visual acuity, whereas for younger subjects no great effect is brought about in this way. Is it that the pupils of young and old behave differently to manipulations in level of illumination, or is some other factor responsible?

GRATINGS AND BROKEN CIRCLES

Shlaer (228) determined the relation between visual acuity over a background illumination range of about eight log units for a grating, and also for an open circle (Landolt C) with a background subtending a

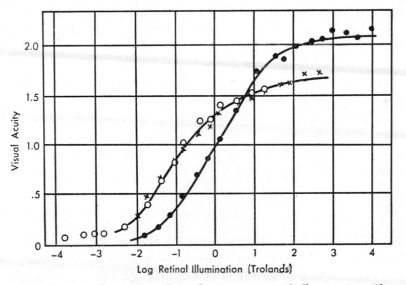

FIG. 7.3. Visual acuity as dependent upon retinal illumination. The filled circles represent the outcome with the C target. The open circles and crosses represent the outcome with the grating target (S. Shlaer, The relation between visual acuity and illumination, *J. Gen. Physiol.* [1937], *21*:185–209, Fig. 2).

visual angle of 30 degrees. Thus he was measuring the effect of a virtually nonluminous ("black") test figure on a luminous field. Fig. 7.3 shows the results. The grating provided for higher visual acuities under about 7 trolands,[1] and lower visual acuities above this illumination.

The greatest acuity possible with the grating was 30 percent lower than with the open circle. Shlaer showed that with an aperture of less than 2.33 mm., the pupil is the limiting factor in the resolution of grating; whereas, when the aperture is larger than that, the size of the central cones governs it. Various other workers studied this matter, but did not use artificial pupils and failed to use a single viewing distance. These factors lead us to use Shlaer's work as the standard for visual acuity for "dark" targets on "light" backgrounds.

BACKGROUND SIZE

Fisher (74) measured visual acuity for a grating in a two-degree foveal area when the intensities of the area were 0.193, 10.97, and 318 trolands. Monocular fixation, with a 2-mm. artificial pupil, was used, while the other eye was confronted with a uniform field of low intensity. Annular surrounds varying both in subtended visual angle and intensity were also employed for the measurements. The radial widths of the annuli were 2.5, 5, 7.5, 12.5, and 20 degrees, while their intensities varied from 0.0566, 0.193, 10.07, 318, and 8560 trolands.

Under these conditions the results were as follows. When the annulus was more intense than the test area, visual acuity became poorer with increase in size of the annulus. When the annulus was less intense than the test area, visual acuity became better with increase in size of the annulus. When the two were equally intense, changing the size of the annulus had no consistent effect upon visual acuity. This last effect was similar in principle to one of Shlaer's experiments.

PARALLEL BARS

Wilcox (263) used conditions quite different from Shlaer's. He used "light" targets on "dark" backgrounds as well as the opposite, and parallel bars instead of broken circles or gratings. His results are shown in Fig. 7.4. The left curve shows the results with "dark" bars; the other

---

[1] A troland is a unit of retinal illumination that takes into account pupil size as well as target intensity. Were the pupil aperture to be 1 sq. mm. and the target intensity to be 1 candle per sq. m., the retinal illumination would be 1 troland.

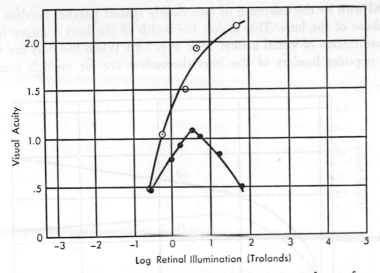

FIG. 7.4. Visual acuity for parallel bars. The open circles are for dark bars on a light background. The filled circles are for the opposite (modified from Wilcox, in S. H. Bartley, *Vision: A Study of Its Basis*, Van Nostrand, 1941).

curve shows the effects when the luminosity (intensity) relations between bars and ground were reversed. It will be noted that, up to a certain point, increase in illumination favored visual acuity, and beyond this a reversal set in.

VISUAL ACUITY AND BAR WIDTH

Fry and Cobb (*81*) found that broad and narrow bars do not act alike when used to test visual acuity. They used two pairs of bars. The bars in the one pair were 1000 seconds in width, and in the second pair were 168 seconds in width. Their lengths in both cases were 2000 seconds. The results are plotted in Fig. 7.5, in which it is shown that as the intensity of the bars is increased from a very low level up to 3 footcandles, visual acuity first rapidly rises, but for the narrow bars falls again very slowly. For the wide bars, it continues to ascend slowly after the first rapid rise.

To explain this, they used the Fry-Bartley (*80*) principle, namely, that physiological contour processes underlying the images of parallel target borders interfere with each other.

The production of threshold edges in perception is undoubtedly interfered with by the existence of two closely spaced parallel borders, such as those of the bars. This makes the width of the bars a factor in the determination of visual acuity. (See Fig. 7.6.) When the bars are wide, the opposite borders of the bars themselves are far enough removed

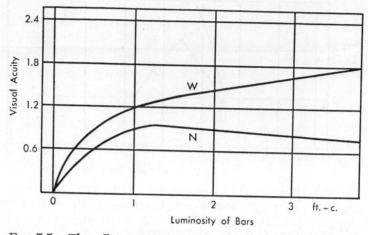

FIG. 7.5. The effect upon visual acuity for varying the luminosity of two bars on an unilluminated background. W is the result with wide bars (1000 seconds); N, with narrow bars (168 seconds) (Fry and Cobb in Bartley, *Vision: A Study of Its Basis*, Van Nostrand, 1941).

from each other to interfere very little. When the borders are close to each other, as in 1, the contour processes responsible for seeing edges interfere with each other as much or more than the smallness of the

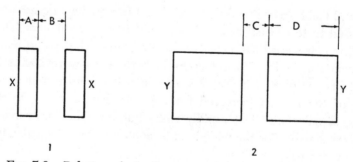

FIG. 7.6. Relation of visual acuity to bar width. Bar widths A and D determine the distances of outer borders XX and YY from the inner borders of the respective bars. Thus those borders as well as the interspaces B and C determine visual acuity.

distance between the bars. But in 2, the opposite borders of the bars in target are far apart and do not elicit contour processes that interfere so much with each other, as in the case of target 1.

FINE LINES

Hecht and Mintz (109) studied visual acuity by using a fine line whose length subtended a visual angle from 12.5 degrees to 19 degrees. This target was presented on a background subtending the same visual angle as the line. With a background range from 0.00000603 ml. (millilambert) to 30.2 ml., the visual acuity varied from 10 or 11 minutes to 0.5 seconds. This was a range of 1320 to 1. Putting these values into the notation given earlier in the chapter, the visual acuity ranged from about .09 to 120. It will be remembered that 1.0 is the order of normal visual acuity with Snellen letters in a clinical situation.

VISUAL ACUITY AND RETINAL MOSAIC

The relation of visual acuity to the retinal mosaic is of fundamental significance. The retinal mosaic is one of the limiting factors in determining the smallest angular separations that can be seen between target elements.

The results that Hecht and Mintz obtained went far beyond the expectations and findings of earlier workers. It was once thought that for two portions of a visual target to be seen as separate, their images on the retina had to be separated by at least one row of cones. If this was to be the case, then, the finest resolution obtainable could be calculated beforehand by finding out the cross-sectional size of cones and their separation, if any. This was done, and hence certain expectations were stated.

Let us examine Fig. 7.7 to see what the retinal mosaic is like in terms of angular subtense. At the top of the diagram, the distances subtended by cones is indicated. At the bottom, the distances in microns ($\frac{1}{1000}$ mm.) are given. In the lower part of the diagram are three short horizontal lines, each representing the width of fine wires as they would be projected in retinal images if the images corresponded strictly to the subtended visual angles. It happens, however, that retinal images are not precise target representations, but instead are somewhat blurred. That is, images are not abrupt, but taper off at their bounds.

The upper curve represents the distribution of the light on the retina in the image of the finest wire, the one represented by the shortest horizontal line, already mentioned. Whereas the width of the line in the image covers only a portion of the width of a single cone, the tapered image covers not only a whole cone, but tapers off over most of the cone to either side of it.

The theory that lies back of visual acuity, or the detection of the line as such, is that in order for a fine-line target to be visible its image must

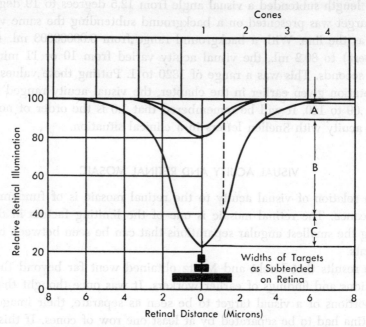

FIG. 7.7. Curves showing relation of images of target to foveal cones. A, B, and C show that the intensities of illumination on adjacent cones are unlike. Cone 1 is illuminated somewhat more intensely than cone 2; although cones 3 and 4 are not so intensely illuminated, the difference between their illuminations is very great (modified from H. Hecht and E. U. Mintz, The visibility of single lines at various illuminations and the retinal basis of visual resolution, *J. Gen. Physiol.* [1939], 22:593–612, Fig. 3).

affect a single row of cones either greater or less than the row to either side of it. That is, for threshold detection, there must be a threshold *difference* between the energy impingement on the central row and its neighbors to either side. Perhaps this difference needs to be no greater than 1 percent, so some authorities think.

The finest wire that can be detected is so fine as to represent a visual angle much less than that subtended by a single cone. According to the diagram, the image of the wire tapers and extends beyond the distance represented by the angular subtense of the wire. The fineness of the wire controls the steepness of the taper and the critical taper is formed by wires finer than one cone in cross section. Were there no taper, a very fine wire would cast an image that would not be so broad as to cover a row of cones. The finer the wire, the less radiation delivered to the one row of cones. Hence, finally, as finer and finer wires were used, intensity would be the prime factor in such wires being seen, and one fine wire would be as visible as another. Once target fineness fell below the width of a cone, no further distinctions could be made in spatial terms. This does not seem to be the way visual acuity relates to target subtense.

TAPER OR BLUR OF RETINAL IMAGE

The discrepancy between visual target and its image on the retina is one factor that is involved in considering the matter of visual acuity. Ideally, the natural image is described as a copy of the visual target. This is not the case. Whereas targets may be said to possess abrupt borders, their images may be otherwise. The images are, at best, somewhat tapered or blurred. There are various optical reasons for this that involve the nature of the mediating tissues.

The laws of chromatic and spherical aberration are generally used to

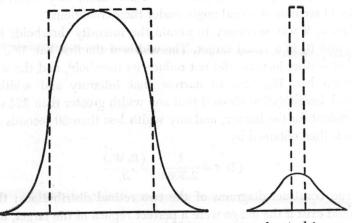

FIG. 7.8.   Relation of target width to intensity of retinal image. Broken lines represent distribution of radiation in target; solid lines, the distribution radiation in image (S. H. Bartley, *Vision: A Study of Its Basis,* Van Nostrand, 1941).

calculate the pattern or degree of blurredness, but such calculations do not take into account the slight oscillatory action of the eye itself, which results in introducing a blur factor of its own. Fry and Cobb (*81*) took this into account by a direct method.

The threshold response to a long narrow line used as a target depends not only upon the intensity of the luminosity of the line but also on its width. It is evident that there is some spread of radiation forming the image. It would be expected that the image would be most intense at its center, and that the threshold of visibility would be determined by a certain minimal intensity of the central region. In Fig. 7.8, the center-to-periphery taper of the retinal image is shown. Reducing the *width* of line, which is already very narrow, would be expected to lower the *intensity* at the center due to the blurring.

Fry and Cobb assumed that center-to-periphery distribution of radiation in the image of a homogeneously intense target would be described by the Gaussian equation:

$$(1) \quad Y = \frac{1}{\sigma\sqrt{2\pi}} e^{\frac{-X^2}{2\sigma^2}}$$

Where Y is the intensity at a distance X from the mean, and σ is the standard deviation or the mean square deviation from the mean of the distribution. The area under the curve between extremes of plus and minus infinity is unity. The problem of these investigators was, then, the measurement of the value of σ. Using whole spectrum ("white") radiation and an artificial pupil with a diameter of 2.33 mm., they found σ to be equal to 44 seconds of visual angle under their conditions.

To find σ, it was necessary to obtain the intensity thresholds for two bars B_1 and B_2 in a visual target. The width of the first bar, W_2, was so great that further increase did not reduce its threshold, and the width of the second bar, W_2, was so narrow that intensity and width were reciprocal. Investigation showed that any width greater than 224 seconds was sufficient for the former, and any width less than 30 seconds for the latter. σ is then obtained by

$$(2) \quad \sigma = \frac{1}{2.5066} \cdot \frac{(B_2 W_2)}{B_1}$$

We can construct diagrams of the two retinal distributions: the one that would exist if the image were a perfect replica of the target, and the other the Gaussian distribution that is being tested for its validity. Since the total amount of radiation in the image is the same regardless of distribution, certain relations between the two are known. The two diagrams are shown in Fig. 7.9, in which the heights of the rectangle and of the Gaussian curve are the same. They are so constructed because it was assumed that the intensity in the center of the image should be the same regardless of distribution. It is known that when the rectangle and the Gaussian distribution are the same height and contain the same area, the width of the rectangle is equal to 2.5066 σ. We shall call the height of the rectangle indicating the intensity B_0, and the width of the rectangle W_0. Thus, W_0 is 2.5066 σ. The width of the base of the Gaussian curve will be W_1, and its height B_1. It is evident that B_0 equals B_1. B_2, as we have assumed, is the intensity of a width of bar so small that intensity and

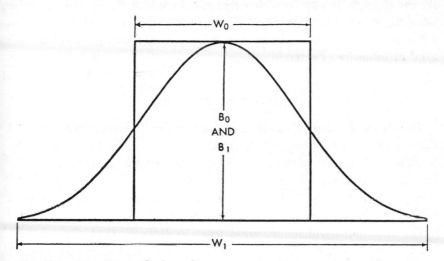

Fig. 7.9. Dimensions dealt with in Fry and Cobb's experiment (from Fry and Cobb, in S. H. Bartley, *Vision: A Study of Its Basis*, Van Nostrand, 1941).

width are reciprocal, and W_2 is the width of such a bar. Thus, according to the hyperbolic relations,

$$(3) \quad B_0 W = B_2 W_2$$

Since $B_0 = B_1$ and $W_0 = 2.5066 \sigma$, equation (2) is obtained when these values are used in equation (3).

For a bar 3000 seconds long, the threshold was obtained when it was 192 seconds wide, and when it was a number of other lesser widths. The minimal width used was one by which it was shown that width and intensity were reciprocal. By substituting in equation (2), the value of σ was obtained. The results coincided with theoretical calculations in such a way as to mean that the distribution of illumination in the image caused by blurring follows the Gaussian equation, whose value for σ is 44 seconds for an infinitely narrow bar under the particular optical conditions tested. It also was taken to validate the assumption that the intensity at the center of the retinal image remains constant for various bar widths at threshold.

Using the fact that the image of an infinitely narrow line is distributed in keeping with the Gaussian equation, it is possible to determine the illumination distribution for targets of various widths, and to demonstrate how width affects the intensity at the center of the image. Intensity and width increase almost proportionally at first, but the relation slowly changes to one in which increase in width finally fails to raise intensity at all. The strength of illumination for any target wider than 242 seconds is 1 troland per sq. mm. of pupillary aperture, and for each c/m² of intensity of external source.

DYNAMIC VISUAL ACUITY

The determination of visual acuity, as so far described, has involved the use of stationary targets, for the attempt has been to ascertain the fundamental spatial relations in the function of the sense cells of the retina. Visual acuity for moving targets has been recently studied, however, by Ludvigh and Miller (168, 169). Visual acuity, under the conditions they used, has come to be called *dynamic visual acuity*.

The conditions which they used were as follows. With the subject's head immobilized, he viewed a revolving mirror that disclosed a target

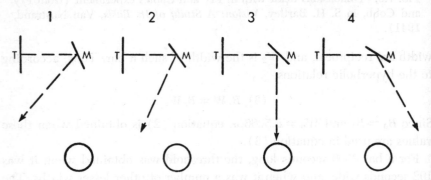

Fig. 7.10.   Diagram to show how a revolving mirror can pass the radiations from a target across the eye and thus produce the equivalent of a moving target. Each circle is the same eye, but at a different instant. In diagrams 1 and 2, the target, in effect, is approaching the eye. In 3, it is in full view; and in 4, it has passed by. M is the revolving mirror. T is the target.

that was effectively four meters from the eye. The rate of revolution of the mirror determined the velocity of the stimulus presentation as it swept past the eye. Fig. 7.10 shows how a revolving mirror provides target motion. The illumination of the target was held at about 25 foot-candles, with a background area that possessed a reflection coefficient of about 85 percent. The angular velocity of the sweep of the radiation beam across the eye was varied from 10°/sec. to 170°/sec. The total duration of the target presentation was 0.4 second in all cases, regard-

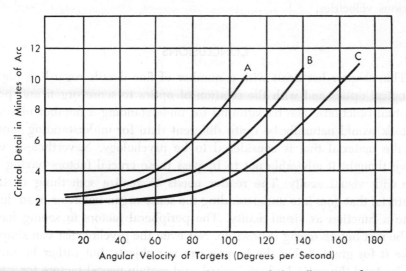

Angular Velocity of Targets (Degrees per Second)

Fɪɢ. 7.11.   Relation between visual acuity and the effective velocity of moving targets for each of three groups: A, B, and C (E. J. Ludvigh and J. W. Miller, *A Study of Dynamic Visual Acuity*, Joint Project Report No. 1, Kresge Eye Institute Contract Nonr 586 [00], ONR Project Designation No. 142–023, BuMed Project NM 001 067.01.01, 1953, Fig. 3).

less of target velocity. The target consisted in a Landolt C, whose open portion was positioned randomly from trial to trial in one or the other of eight clockface positions. Figure 7.11 shows the results. They were found to be representable by the equation $y = a + bx^3$, in which a is a measure of static visual acuity. This, of course, is small when static acuity is good. For high values of angular target velocities, y is chiefly assignable to bx^3, in which b is a measure of dynamic acuity. It is small when dynamic acuity does not decline rapidly as angular velocity is increased.

At an angular target velocity of 20°/sec., the acuity with target motion in the vertical correlated 0.50 with acuity for target motion in the horizontal. With angular velocity raised to 80°/sec. the correlation rose to 0.72, and for 110°/sec. the correlation dropped to 0.59. The fact that the dynamic visual acuities in the two directions correlated as well as they did was interpreted to mean that dynamic visual acuity was largely dependent upon the efficiency of the overall ocular pursuit mechanism rather than upon the strength or behavior of individual muscles as such. The results, too, showed that not all persons with equally good static acuity were similar in dynamic visual acuities for the various velocities.

CONCLUSIONS

This chapter has dealt with a number of fine details regarding physiological optics and with the relation of optics to sense organ and perceptual functions. The background for understanding a number of such details would naturally be quite different than for understanding much of the material that is considered to be psychology. Nevertheless, we have thought it advisable not to by-pass these crucial factors having to do with visual acuity. The reader needs to realize something of the material that goes into understanding the sense-organ behavior in so delicate a function as visual acuity. The peripheral factors in seeing have to be met before seeing is possible. Not even the psychologist can simply take it for granted that the human can see objects, but rather he must understand the optical, physiological, and certain neural factors for such performances.

The beginning student need not be dismayed if he has not understood all of the presentations in the chapter as well as he could wish. He will be doing well if he has found the chapter of service in impressing upon him the need for more people than at present to know about peripheral function in accurate terms. Too much of psychology is made up of preoccupation with "states" and too little with process. While it is to be admitted that knowledge of process is hard to come by, it is nonetheless something that is required for solid explanation of outcome.

Chapter 8

PERCEPTION OF COLOR

In this chapter we are about to attempt to deal with some of the facts of color experience. In times past, the greater proportion of attention to color was given to theories about how the color mechanisms in the eye function so as to provide the experience of the hues of the spectrum. It was as if, in the first place, color was an intrinsic property of a physical object, and the eye simply a detector and the person a captive of isolated outside conditions. Throughout this text we have abandoned the copy theory of human perception, and have put in its place the idea that certain complex energy patterns impinging on the sense organs induce certain kinds of organismic reactions, one aspect of which is our experiences. We have supposed that our experiences are perfectly unique products of the human organism and copy nothing else in the universe.

Nowhere else, in all the study of perception, is it more necessary for us to maintain our understanding of the noncopy relations between organisms and environment than in dealing with color experience. The study of the perception of color is a great deal more than a specification of the wave lengths in the spectrum of the illuminant, be it sun, incandescent lamp, or any other source. The colors we see are in every case a complex end result of several factors: the composition of the illuminant or illuminants, the several reflectances of the visual targets (samples), their spatial relations to each other, the reflectance of the surround or ground, the state of adaptation of the eye, and even the kind of activity the organism as a person is carrying on at the time. Under fundamental and strictly controlled conditions reduced for study in the laboratory, perhaps the learning which one observer versus another has undergone does not greatly enter in, but under everyday conditions it does.

Let us take a look at some examples of color phenomena to see what they are like, and what it is that has to be dealt with. The following are some commonplace situations in which color is seen and is of some interest.

1. Under some illuminations, food is less palatable than in others. In some restaurants, the butter has a definitely greenish tinge. Although we still believe that the butter is yellow, this new color reduces its palatability. The greenish color is a function of the fluorescent lighting of the room.

2. When we want to be sure of the color of certain materials, we try to see them in daylight. We know that materials tend to be a different color under artificial illumination, and we do not know how this color relates to the material's appearance in daylight.

3. When we make a colored photograph of a painting on a wall, we do not "shine light" upon the painting directly with an unmasked incandescent bulb, but set up illumination that is diffuse. We reflect "light" from the matte surface of a bed sheet, for example. The direct "light" would have produced shiny reflections from some portions of the painting, and these might have been nearly colorless, while other parts would not have been "lighted" well enough.

4. If we want to bring out interesting effects in viewing or photographing such colored objects as china or porcelain, for example, we use direct illumination so as to cause reflections and highlights. Diffuse illumination would make such objects look dull and uninteresting.

5. To obtain the perception of an acceptable amount of depth, a scene must be given some illumination contrast. This means that instead of the illumination being diffuse it must be supplied from a single direction. Not only will some portions of the scene be better illuminated than others, but shadows will be produced.

6. Objects appear to be of different colors in accord with the colors in their surroundings. This is not due to colored illumination. If a certain object is placed in front of a white background, let us say, it appears blue-green. If placed in front of a black background, it will appear a light blue. If it is placed in front of a greenish yellow (chartreuse) background, it will tend to be seen as a purplish blue. If the background is a grayish purple, the object will be a brilliant blue.

7. If the illumination of a scene is intense, the shadows tend to be dark and objects lying in them are obscured. In such scenes, we look *at* the shadows. If we walk up closer, we are able to look *into* the shadows and they appear to lighten. With a still closer approach to a shadow it lightens still more and objects within it are seen still better. Under such conditions, it may be said that we look *through* the shadow. I

loses its identity as a shadow, and the low illumination that was the shadow becomes more nearly the illumination level for the scene itself.

8. When we go into dimly illuminated places, the color of objects and surfaces largely disappears. In very dimly illuminated places, even though we can still see well enough to get around, all color is absent.

9. The illumination of a scene definitely controls the viewer's mood, which he generally attributes to the scene. For example, the illumination may come from the sun low in the sky. This changes the distribution of the radiation from the scene, and provides a mood quite different from that at noonday, even though the noon illumination on a "dull" day may be not very brilliant.

10. When one looks at a colored object steadily for a moment, and then turns away to look at a solidly colored surface, such as the wall of a room, he sees the object imaged against the wall. The imaged object is of a different color than the object first looked at. The object seen for a fleeting few seconds is called an afterimage.

Here is a small sample of the countless variety of situations and circumstances under which we see color. Although these examples are of a restricted variety, they do bring up a number of questions in the mind of anyone who thinks about them. No doubt the reader himself has a number of other color situations in mind regarding which questions have arisen from time to time.

THE STIMULUS

The radiation commonly called light possesses several characteristics that play a role in determining perceptual reaction. Photic radiation (light) is wavelike, and is usually composed of a wide variety of wave lengths. This combination generally tends to evoke the experience of whiteness. The separation of these components from one another in an orderly array in accord with wave length produces what we call the spectrum. It is from the analysis of the sensory effects produced by various wave lengths (portions of the spectrum) that our fundamental understanding of the relation between photic radiation and color experience has been gained. Those who study color do so primarily either by way of spectral analysis; by manipulation of various factors, such as juxtaposition of spectral target areas of different sizes and shapes; or by way of environmental situations whose complexity predisposes the experimenter to talk about objects, surfaces, shadows, etc. (all of which are in themselves terms describing various features of the observer's perceptions rather than true stimulus conditions). Thus, very generally, we depart from the mere specifications of the stimulus in describing color effects, for stimulus situations are so complex that we have no other means by which to talk about them than the perceptual efforts produced by them. Thus the visual target (the visual field) is described in terms of objects, shadows, and so on. The color of a given portion of the target is studied in relation to its appearance on the surface of an object, in the object's shadows, or in terms of the illumination of the scene itself.

There are three main variables involved in the radiation itself. They are wave length, total energy content, and spectral purity. In simple situations, wave length goes a long way in determining the perceived hue, that is, redness, greenness, blueness, etc. (See Fig. 8.1.) Total flux

1	PURPLISH BLUE	8	YELLOW GREEN
2	BLUE	9	GREENISH YELLOW
3	GREENISH BLUE	10	YELLOW
4	BLUE GREEN	11	YELLOW ORANGE
5	BLUISH GREEN	12	ORANGE
6	GREEN	13	REDDISH ORANGE
7	YELLOWISH GREEN	14	RED

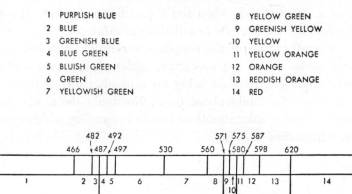

FIG. 8.1. The solar spectrum, in which visible colors are related to the wave lengths that elicit them.

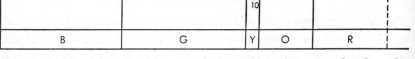

largely determines brightness, although certain wave lengths evoke a greater brightness effect than others. Spectral purity is the main factor in determining whether a given hue is seen to its fullest extent or the color more nearly resembles a gray or verges into some other hue. The hue seen to its fullest extent is spoken of as a fully saturated color. Simple desaturation results in making a color appear more nearly a gray. Hues, in normal color vision, can be produced either by a narrow band of wave lengths, generally spoken of as though only a single wave length, or else by combining the proper three such bands. Normal vision is thus called *trichromatic*. Various defects in vision occur in a small percentage of the general population, and will be dealt with later.

Not all portions of the color-producing spectrum of radiation are equally effective. That is, not all wave lengths are equally able to affect the sense cells. The diagram picturing this relative effectiveness is called a *luminosity curve*. In Fig. 8.2, two such curves are shown. The curve bounding the black area is the curve for high levels of radiation and the other curve is for low levels. It will be noted that maximum ef-

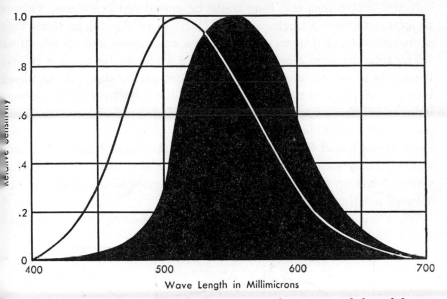

FIG. 8.2. Luminosity curves of the human eye; the contour of the solid area represents the relative sensitivity of the light-adapted eye to the various wave lengths. The other curve represents a shift in sensitivity for vision at lower illuminations.

-fectiveness for the high-level (photopic) curve lies in the region of 550 to 560 mμ, and that the maximum for the other (scotopic) curve lies at about 510 mμ. This shift occurs as the illumination of a room is lowered, for example. It is observed as a shift in the relative lightness or brightness of the various hues in a complex scene.

NUMBER AND NAMES OF COLORS

The question of how many colors there are and how names are related to color experiences is a very important one for us. Evans (72) points out that there are two kinds of color description, although they are quite difficult to distinguish. One set of terms describes color on an absolute basis. It has reference to what he calls the "mental color system." The other set depicts differences between colors and applies directly to the amount and direction of shift in hue, saturation, and lightness. Judd (*133*) indicates that there are ten million such distinguishable color differences that are describable by words. As to actual color names (the first set), there are far fewer than this number. The Maerz and Paul (*173*) color dictionary gives less than 4000, and some of these are only transient names and thus could be considered synonyms. Thirty-six of the terms are single words. A little more than eight times this many are compound terms consisting of a color name and an adjective.

The Inter-Society Color Council devised a scheme for naming colors. It consists of hue names, such as red, yellow, green, blue, purple, olive, brown, and pink. These are modified by the adjectives weak, strong, light, and dark. The term *very* is also included. Furthermore, the terms pale (light weak), brilliant (light strong), deep (dark strong), vivid (very strong), and dusky (dark weak) are also used. Names for intermediate hues, such as yellowish orange, are also used. All told, this system totals up to 319 items. These items were given in terms of the Munsell notations.

When one tries to use these names for designating transparent ma-

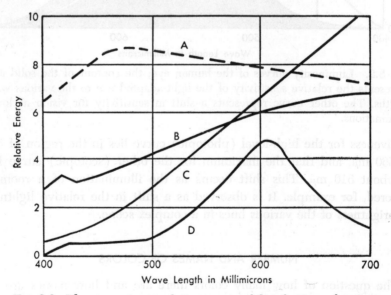

FIG. 8.3. The approximate relative energy of distributions of various sources of radiation within the visible spectrum. A is the sun; B, a mercury arc; C, a tungsten lamp; and D, a fluorescent lamp. The curves as drawn have no absolute relation to each other. For example, curve A could have been set at a different level than shown.

terials, some of the terms have to be changed. This is obvious, for the lighter surface colors run to *white*, and the colors of solutions run to *colorless*.

COLOR SOURCES

Various sources of radiation leading to color experience are available: the sun, carbon arcs, incandescent lamps, vapor sources such as mercury lamps, various fluorescent tubes, and so on. The sources differ from each other in their spectral composition, that is, the proportions of the total output in the various wave lengths. A color source is described in terms of its spectrum. The spectral compositions of the more common sources are pictured in Fig. 8.3.

COLOR SPECIFICATION

The most direct means of specifying the color of some sources is by stating "color temperatures," but the explanation of what is meant by this term would take us too far afield for our purposes.

There are two fairly well-known systems of color specification that involve color samples that bear a systematic relation to each other in terms of hue, saturation, and brightness. The first of these systems is the Munsell, and the second is the Ostwald. In the Munsell (190) system, the three factors varied in the samples are called hue, chroma, and value. These compare roughly to the three variables already mentioned. These are built into a three-dimensional scheme, ordinarily called a color solid, having a vertical black-to-white axis. (See Fig. 8.4.) Radiating from this, the hues are arranged in equiangular spacing. Chroma is defined as the horizontal distance from the axis. Munsell published a color atlas containing two sets of colored paper samples, or "chips," arranged in accordance with various sections through the solid, one in the vertical and the other in the horizontal plane, and systematically numbered. The specification of any test color is given in the form of a numerical statement of where it matches the color solid. The Munsell system as modified (improved) in 1943 is the nearest approach to a color solid based upon the appearance of surface colors. It must be recognized, however, that such a system possesses limitations. For example, all colors we perceive are not surface colors, and all surfaces do not act alike; hence, all color comparisons we are able to make cannot be made directly by consultation of the atlas.

The Ostwald (205) system also employs a color solid—a double cone, that is, two cones base to base. (See Fig. 8.5.) In this solid, the complementary colors (red, green, blue, yellow, etc.) are placed opposite each other around the circumference of the solid. The axis, running from the apex of one cone to the other, is the black-white axis. A vertical section through the Ostwald solid is in the form of two triangles, base

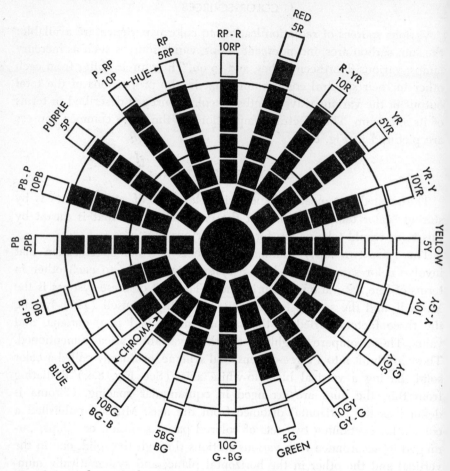

FIG. 8.4. A horizontal cross section through the Munsell scheme of interrelated colors. Although the illustration is in black and white, it is meant to represent an array of colored samples (rectangles). The Munsell notation suggests the hues, such as red, red yellow-red, yellow-red, yellow-red yellow, yellow, etc. All of the samples (when colored) have the same brightness value (value 5/). They differ only in hue and saturation (chroma in Munsell terminology). The present cross section represents the level 5/ in the color plate opposite, which shows a vertical section through the color scheme. It will be noted that all hues do not provide equal numbers of color samples outward from the center. (Courtesy, Munsell Color Company, Inc., Baltimore 2, Maryland.)

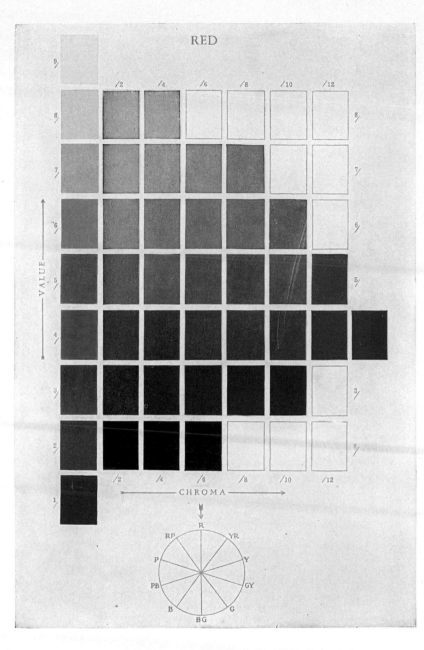

The RED color sheet from the *Munsell Book of Color.*

Whereas Fig. 8.4 represents a horizontal cross section of the Munsell color system at Value 5/, this is a vertical section representing a single hue. The system involves ten such sections. (Courtesy, Munsell Color Company, Inc., Baltimore 2, Maryland.)

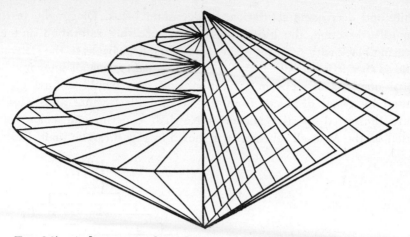

FIG. 8.5. A diagram to show the principle of the Ostwald color solid (reprinted with permission from R. M. Evans, *An Introduction to Color*, John Wiley & Sons, Inc., 1948, Fig. 13.13).

to base, or a diamond. (See Fig. 8.6.) The common portion of the two triangles is, of course, the vertical black-white axis already mentioned. The triangles always represent complementary colors. Diagonally in one direction, the diamond-shaped blocks represent a series of increasing

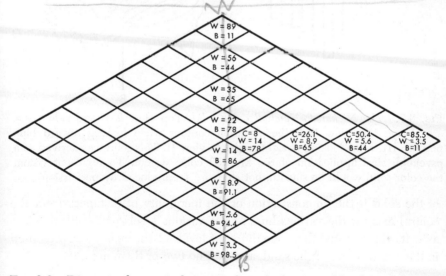

FIG. 8.6. Diagram of a vertical section through the Ostwald color solid. W = white, B = black, C = "full color," that is, the hue aside from white and black. The numbers are the percentages. Just a few are shown for example (reprinted with permission from R. M. Evans, *An Introduction to Color*, John Wiley & Sons, Inc., 1948, Fig. 13.14).

white and decreasing saturation, but constant black. Diagonally in the opposite direction, the blocks represent decreasing saturation and increasing black with constant white. One of the drawbacks to the Ostwald solid is that it is radially symmetrical. In actuality, not all hues involve equal numbers of steps in saturation, and thus would not be represented by equal distances from the vertical black-white axis. This is aptly illustrated by the Nickerson-Newhall experimental color solid based on the Munsell scheme. It is shown in Fig. 8.7. The main feature

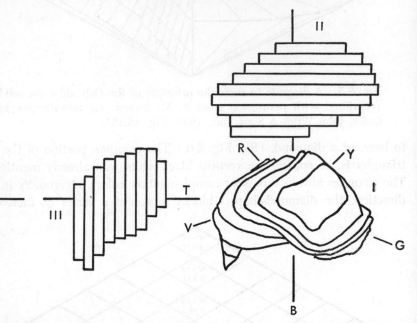

FIG. 8.7. *The Nickerson-Newhall color solid.* Top view is I, and side views are II and III. View II is the elevation contour when looking toward blue portion; III, when looking at right angles to view II. This solid was derived as a psychophysical application of the Munsell color system. To represent vision, the color solid would be smooth, not stepwise (reproduced by permission).

of the solid is the demonstration of the inequality of distances from the central axis for the various hues at the various levels of the black-white axis. It will be noted that nine different levels of this axis are represented in the construction of the solid, and that no two of them are alike.

PHYSICAL PROCESSES IN PHOTIC RADIATION

As was already stated, the stimulus that gives us light and color is a form of radiant energy. Photic radiation from source to the eye may involve several processes, namely, *transmission, absorption, reflection, refraction, diffusion, diffraction,* and *interference.* These constitute all that happens to the radiation, once it has left the source. Some substances *transmit* radiation; it passes through them. Some substances *absorb* photic radiation; radiant energy is transformed within them to other forms, such as heat or mechanical work or chemical processes. Some substances change the direction of the radiation, sending it backward. We say they *reflect* the radiation. If the radiation reaches the surface of the substance obliquely, the reflection angle has the same value as the incident one. Some substances change the direction of the radiation as it passes through them. This is called *refraction. Diffusion* is the process of reflection by a rough surface, or of transmission of radiation through a translucent material. In both cases, rays are sent in various directions in a helter-skelter fashion. *Diffraction* is the modification which radiation undergoes in passing edges of opaque material, or through very narrow slits, or in being reflected from ruled surfaces (surfaces with parallel lines scratched on them), in which the rays produce parallel light- and dark-colored bands. *Interference* is the mutual effect, upon meeting, of two wave fronts. The effect is partial or total cancellation depending upon relative energies, and upon whether the wave lengths are the same or different. In some cases, reinforcement instead of cancellation takes place. Interference bands may be set up by different gratings, the ruled surfaces just mentioned. Most of the foregoing processes can be manipulated to produce color effects.

SUBTRACTIVE AND ADDITIVE EFFECTS

When radiation is reflected, generally, not all wave lengths are equally involved, and thus the surface is seen as colored. Conditions being favorable, the color is, of course, the color expected from the wave lengths reflected. When photic radiation passes into a medium, some of it is absorbed and some passes on through. The color seen is the color expected from the wave lengths passing through. Let us say, the color is green. Now, if this "green light" falls on some surface and it absorbs wave lengths for green and reflects other wave lengths, then the surface will look black. In all cases, as "light" is cast in sequence from one surface to another, the energy distribution is changed, and the total amount of energy is reduced. This, of course, also happens when a series of color filters is used. Each filter stops certain wave lengths and transmits others. When radiation must pass through a series of them, each differing in the wave lengths transmitted, little or none of it may ultimately get through the final filter of the series.

Pigments are substances that selectively reflect radiation, and when one pigment is mixed with another, subtractive effects are produced. That is to say, the mixtures of pigments are seen as darker than the pigments themselves. The proper mixture produces black. Of course, a mixture of a substance seen as white with other pigments tends to brighten the color seen.

MODES OF COLOR APPEARANCE

Colors may be seen in several ways. That is, color may be an aspect of various kinds of perceived situations. These situations have been divided into five classes. They are generally spoken of as *modes* of perceiving colors, and they are the following: (1) the aperture, (2) the illuminant, (3) the illumination, (4) the film, and (5) the object modes of surface and volume.

The aperture mode is the mode in which color is seen without regard to its distance and its being a property of a surface or any object. One of the best illustrations of the appearance of aperture colors is the color that is seen through some optical instrument, such as a microscope or a spectroscope, in which the field is uniform and is not seen to be that of the surface of any object. The same result may be obtained when viewing a spectral target through a cardboard mailing tube.

The illuminant mode is the mode assumed when one views a source of photic radiation, such as an incandescent filament, an arc lamp, or the surface of an opal-glass window of a lamphouse when illuminated from the side opposite the viewer in a darkroom.

The illumination mode is the mode assumed when one detects that the color of a surface is "due to" its illumination, or that the illumination of the room is affecting the color of objects in it.

The film mode of seeing color is produced, generally, by photic radiation falling on the rapidly moving blades of a fan, or an episcotister. The radiation to the eye from a given point in space is thus intermittent. The film is translucent. One sees not only it but also objects beyond it.

The two object modes, those of surface and volume, have to do with the perception of the properties of objects. In these cases, the color seems to be an intrinsic property of the object itself rather than light that falls on it. The seeing of color as a property of a surface is so convincing that at times it takes some peculiar demonstration or explanation to help a person to realize that color is a function of illumination as well as of surface properties.

In other cases, we do not necessarily see the surfaces of objects standing out in distinction, but are able to look through the objects. This is true in the case of vessels of colored liquids. The color which we see is distributed through the liquid and is a three-dimensional affair. This is illustration of the volume mode of seeing color.

Depending upon the mode of viewing it, various properties of color emerge.

PROPERTIES OF COLOR

A number of properties have been proposed for color. The retention of any one of them depends upon how well it can be shown that observers perceive them. Those wishing to study these properties are, of course, interested in how they may be manipulated and thus to what possible stimulus factors they relate. The list given below includes most of the important color properties that have, from time to time, been proposed.

1. Hue	Color quality distinguishing it from all other colors. A function of wave length.
2. Brightness or lightness	The intensive feature varying from light to dark, bright to dim.
3. Saturation	Purity and intensity of hue.
4. Warmth	Thermallike quality, in which red and yellow are warm; blue and green are cool.
5. Hardness	Tactilelike quality, in which red, white, and yellow are hard; blue and black are soft.
6. Affective tone	The attractiveness or unattractiveness, i.e., pleasantness or unpleasantness.
7. Pronouncedness	The ability to stand out as, for example, white or black.
8. Impressiveness	A stimulus quality rather than a perceptual quality, so it would seem.
9. Area	Surfaces seen as green or blue are larger than those seen as red or yellow.
10. Location	Red and yellow give the impression of being near, blue and green to recede.
11. Transparency	Revealing or hiding power of what lies beneath or beyond. This may pertain to the stimulus rather than the perceived hue.
12. Shape	Colors depend on object shape.
13. Flicker	A kind of experience dependent upon intermittent stimulation.
14. Gloss	Color effect produced by ratio of specular to diffuse reflection of target surface.
15. Luster	A perceived surface and intensive property, the origins of which are not clearly understood.

One author, in addition to listing all the foregoing, includes the following: (16) sparkle, (17) texture, (18) volume.

It will be seen from the foregoing list that some of the properties stem from the nature of the radiation itself, some from the nature of the reflecting surfaces, some from intensity factors, some from spacial factors, some from temporal factors, and possibly others from still additional origins, such as the attitude of the observer.

Koffka and Harrower (146) studied visual acuity by means of spectral targets rather than the usual nonselective ones. They reported that visual acuity was highest with targets seen as red, white, or yellow for both figure and ground. It will be noted that these were the hard colors in the list of color properties above. Visual acuity was 'next best for a hard figure on a soft ground, and poorest with a soft figure on a soft ground. To be sure of these conclusions, great care would have to be taken to equate intensities, etc., so that unwanted factors would not vary. It is possible that it is not only the hardness-softness factors that correlate with acuity but also the area or size properties of colors.

Surface colors may vary oppositely or at least quite differently with respect to certain of the properties in the list to which we have just referred. For example, white-appearing surfaces are more pronounced when their total reflection to the eyes is reduced. Black-appearing surfaces, however, rise in impressiveness as total reflection is increased.

In reference to item 9 in the list, it is sometimes said that "hue affects size." This is a figure of speech rather than a statement of literal fact. To say that hue affects apparent size or that apparent size affects hue is to imply that one aspect of perception affects another when they are produced by the same stimulus. It seems preferable to say that the stimulus conditions that produce an experience of given hue more often produce a different experience of size than do those conditions that produce other hues. In other words, we must attribute the end result to the stimulating conditions rather than to perceptions simultaneously produced. To use one perception, or one aspect of a perception, to account for another perception is to use the traditional "cue" theory, and we wish to refrain from this in all cases.

ADVANCING AND RECEDING COLORS

When two colors are seen adjacent to each other, they may tend to lie in different planes. Sometimes this difference is very slight or absent, but at others it is very prominent. This phenomenon is generally attributed to the fact that radiations of different wave lengths have different focal lengths, although it is supposed that other factors may also contribute. It would seem that learning would be a factor.

Radiation from distant target projects retinal images closer to the lens than does radiation from nearby targets. This would seem to form a usable basis for the learning to discriminate. Radiation of short wave lengths (i.e., producing blue) focuses images within the eye closer to the lens than radiation of long wave lengths (i.e., producing red). Since the retinal effect is of the same sort for distances and for wave lengths, it could well be expected that the organism would respond to the two in much the same way.

COLOR ADAPTATION

As one deals with color in either a practical or an experimental situation, he is impressed by two apparently diverse principles. Color is seen to be a facile and changeable thing, depending largely upon the relationship of one part of the scene to another. Two colors seen as juxtaposed are always different than they would be were the stimulus to be simplified so that only one color were seen. It can be said, then, that color is not fixed in its relationship to the direct stimulus that produces it. On the other hand, the properties of surfaces that give rise to color do not seem to change much under a wide variety of illumination colors. They tend to look much the same in most cases regardless of whether the light is artificial or sunlight. Although these effects seem diverse and unrelated, they are both due, in part, to the mechanism of color adaptation.

When one's gaze is fixated on a colored area, adaptation of the eye to the area and its immediate surrounds sets in. Though the appearance of the fixated area does not immediately change, the next area viewed, when the eye shifts position, will be affected. This effect is dependent upon the amount of time the previous fixation was held, upon the intensity of stimulation, and upon the area of the surface viewed. Increase in these factors works toward increase in the persistence of the effect. Full adaptation occurs quite readily if the target viewed is of moderate intensity and if the eye came upon it from darkness. As fixation upon such a target is prolonged, the consequent adaptive effect is more persistent, as demonstrated by the longer time required for adaptation to a new target of low intensity.

This accounts for the production of what we call afterimages. With the eye exposed as indicated for a few seconds to a surface of limited area, and the gaze then shifted to a larger area of lower intensity, the sensitivity just produced by the first area will cause it to appear as an afterimage superimposed upon the second area viewed.

This local color adaptation is generally accounted for as follows. Suppose the eye contains three color receptors, one for red, one for green, and one for blue. A "green" stimulus induces adaptation of the green receptor, thus decreasing its sensitivity to green. Since the figure area does not reflect much blue or red, the receptors for these colors become more sensitive when time is allowed for the eye's adaptation to the white paper to disappear. When the gaze is shifted to a gray square, the effect on the red and blue receptors is greater than on the green one, since gray sends about equal amounts of stimulation for the three colors to the eye. The figure then is seen as purple. One can test this principle by using one or more of the other squares and repeating the process. If a yellow square is used, for example, it will be discovered that this time the spot appears red. This is brought about because the yellow square does not reflect blue. The eye is low in sensitivity to green and therefore red becomes the predominant color.

Thus the local adaptation alters the sensitivity of some portions of the eye so that it becomes opposite to that of the stimulus causing it. In connection with the adaptation we have just described, it can be noted that when the intensity or the percentage of nonselective radiation in a stimulus is altered, the perceived hue is changed. When stimulus intensity alone is altered, the resulting saturation of the hue changes. All simple physical variables by which intensity or other features of the stimulus are changed alter all three variables—hue, saturation, and brightness—to some extent or other.

THE RELATION OF HUE AND SATURATION TO INTENSITY

The relation of perceived hue to intensity of radiation has been studied by several investigators, including Purdy. Purdy (215) used a target with two portions, the intensity relations between which bore a ratio of 10 to 1. A large field was matched with a small field that was less intense. In Fig. 8.8, a typical set of results is shown. The curve shows the amount of discrepancy in wave length between the two fields that had to be used in order to make the two hues match. In the extreme left portion of the graph, it will be seen that the small matching field had to have a slightly longer wave length than the test field. As the wave length for the test field was lengthened, the wave length for the matching field had to be shortened so as to retain the hue match between the two. At a little above 500 millimicrons, the matching field had suddenly to be shifted toward the longer wave lengths. This effect reached a peak in the region of about 525 mμ. From there on, the wave length of the matching field had to be gradually reduced to main-

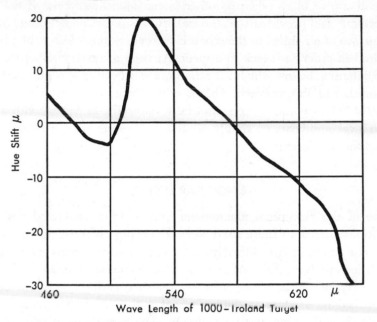

FIG. 8.8. Change in hue produced by a change in intensity from 1000 to 100 trolands. Targets of these two intensities were matched and a wave length shift was found necessary to match the hues (D. M. Purdy, Spectral hue as a function of intensity, Am. J. Psychol. [1931], 43:541–559, Fig. 1).

tain the hue match. In the region of about 575 mμ, the two fields matched when their wave lengths were similar. As longer and longer wave lengths were compared, the wave lengths of the matching field had to be reduced more and more until, as is seen by the graph, the discrepancy became very great.

Abney earlier studied the relation of intensity to hue. He studied a much wider range and came to the conclusion that all hues tend to move toward blue or yellow at high intensities, and toward red or green at low. This conclusion is not contradictory to that derived from Purdy's experiment.

BLACK

What is perceived as black is much more complexly determined than either gray or white. In perceiving black, the adaptation level of the eye is much more crucial. At each adaptation level of the eye there seems to be a point in the lower intensity range below which all intensities will appear black when no other lower intensities in the visual field are present, and provided that the radiation is not at all selective. When the surface of an object in the scene is colored, a much lower intensity is required in order for black to appear. At each adaptation level there is some intensity below which all stimuli, regardless of the hue qualities produced, will appear black. This is what Evans (72) and others refer to as the "black point." It rises and falls, naturally, in accord with adaptation level, and bears no simple relation to those intensities eliciting the perception of whiteness.

BINOCULAR LUSTER

One of the perceptual phenomena that is often associated with the conditions similar to those used to produce binocular rivalry is that of binocular luster. If two diffusely reflecting (matte) targets whose characteristics are very different are used, the phenomenon, instead of rivalry, may be that of seeing a highly polished surface. This can be accomplished by a white-producing target and a black-producing target, presented to the two eyes respectively. The perception produced may be that of a highly polished graphite surface. There are neurophysiological explanations for this phenomenon, but they need not be considered here.

BINOCULAR RIVALRY

Whenever a target is binocularly fixated and corresponding retinal areas stimulated by much the same patterns of impingement, the resulting perception is likely to be not only that of a single surface but also an unfluctuating one. This usual integration of the impressions from the two eyes is called *binocular fusion*. If by use of a stereoscope the corresponding areas of the two retinas are activated by separate targets, or separate portions of the same target, which differ in their spectral characteristics, the contributions of the two eyes may fail to result in a single unfluctuating perception. Instead, the surface seen may tend to alternate between two hues. This alternation is known as *binocular* or *retinal rivalry*. If the two targets involve quite remote parts of the spectrum, fusion tends to be resisted. On the other hand, when two nearby parts of the spectrum are involved, fusion comes easily. Sometimes largely unselective stimuli are greatly dominated or obliterated by the more selective ones rather than combined with them.

DEFECTIVE COLOR VISION

Defective color vision, sometimes called *color blindness* or *anomalous color vision*, is an inherited condition. In it, confusion in the discrimination and naming of the various target portions that give rise to the normal array of color is manifested. The defects in color perception that are possible occur in reference to hue, saturation, and brightness or lightness.

There are three principal forms of color defect. The first of these is total color blindness, or *monochromatism*. In this condition, all hues and saturations of them are absent, but variations in brightness can be detected, of course. The next condition is partial color blindness, or color weakness in which only two distinct hues are perceived regardless of the spectral content of the radiation reaching the eye. This is called *dichromatism*. The third kind of defect is known as *anomalous trichromatism*. This form of defect differs least from normal color vision, which is known as *trichromatism*, since radiation from any properly selected three portions of the spectrum can be combined so as to match a chosen color. In dichromatism, two portions of the spectrum will provide the matches. In anomalous trichromatism, three portions of the spectrum are required to match all colors, but the matches are more variable from test to test.

Whereas there are but three principal kinds of color defects, there is a total of nine subvarieties. They are so complex as to warrant omission of their description. They are named as follows: (1) typical total color blindness, (2) atypical total color blindness, (3) green blindness (deuteranopia), (4) red blindness (protanopia), (5) absence of blue and yellow perception, (6) a weakness for the perception of colors in the short-wave end of the spectrum, (7) green weakness, (8) red weakness, and (9) blue weakness. Some of these forms are exceedingly rare. The most prevalent forms are (2), about 2 percent males and about $\frac{1}{70}$ as many females; (3), 1 percent of males and $\frac{1}{10}$ percent of females; (4), about 1 percent of males; (7), 5 percent of the population; (8), 1 percent.

Tests for Color Vision

Tests for color defects have been standardized; but they tend to have certain limitations, some owing to their length, some to their failure to deal with all the principal kinds of defects, some to the marked difference between them and the conditions of everyday life in which color defect is significant. A description of the eight best-known color tests would be too lengthy and complicated for us here. One of the oldest is the Holmgren yarn test. In it, yarn samples are sorted into the groups in accordance with hue. The samples themselves vary not only in hue but in saturation and in lightness.

Chapter 9

PERCEPTUAL CONSTANCIES

From the perceiver's standpoint, it is nothing unusual and surprising that the objects he sees maintain their characteristics pretty much unchanged under various circumstances. His "common sense" tells him that these characteristics are inherent properties of these objects. Usually, objects generally act as he would expect them to.

This is not the view held by those who study perception from the scientific standpoint. As has been pointed out several times already, objects are constructs of the perceiver. They must be somewhat different for a mouse and for a man. Both react to an energistic universe described by the physicist, which has none of the characteristics experienced by the perceiver. The result for man is a world of objects with various sorts of properties that we are acquainted with. If we forget that these properties are the organism's own creation, we can study them as though they exist apart from man. This is the common thing to do. In so doing we can be artists, architects, merchants, farmers, or any one of the many sorts of person who does not make it his business to understand perception and other aspects of human behavior for what they are.

We are undertaking, however, to "look behind the scenes" on human behavior. In so doing we find that not only is the experiencing of objects one of our problems but also the fact that they maintain their properties so well in spite of the conditions under which they are observed. This characteristic of objects—or had we better say perception?—has been called *constancy*. To use the term constancy does not mean that object properties remain perfectly uniform and unchanged. It only labels the tendency to do so.

Constancy is coupled with another property of perception that might well be mentioned here in passing. It is the property of continuity— not exactly a perceptive property, but still a behavioral property that goes along with perception.

When we look at our car, our house, or a pot of flowers, we believe

171

these are the same items we looked at previously. Continuous confrontment with the stimulus conditions that evoked these experiences is not
necessary. The only requirement from the stimulus standpoint is that
the stimulation is nearly enough like it was previously. When it is, we
take it that we are simply being confronted again with an object that
we have dealt with before. We impute continuity to that which is definitely discontinuous from the sensory standpoint. If that were all, the
matter would not be so complex as it is. We perceive similarities from
occasion to occasion where they do not exist from the stimulus standpoint. To see a piece of paper as white under two different kinds of
illumination is certainly not to be acted upon by the same stimulus in
each.

The property of constancy applies both in spatial comparison and in
sequential (temporal) comparison. In the latter we may be more prone
to call the matter *continuity*, and in the former, *constancy*.

From the common-sense[1] standpoint it may be argued that since all
of us possess such an insistent feeling and belief that objects exist apart
from us and that all we do is to apprehend them and their properties,
we should let the matter rest that way. In fact, the common-sense argument is that since we have this powerful belief in the externality of objects, to deny them is to be foolish and absurd. This very argument can
be turned inside out by asking the common man how he knows that a
certain object exists. He will tell you that he can *see* it, and *touch* it.
Were he to be blinded, or were there no illumination, the object could
not be known (detected, discovered, believed in) visually. Were we to
inactivate kinesthesis (the muscle sense) or the tactile sense, the object
might lose all the rest of its reality. Had a man once "known" about
the object through his senses, he might retain the belief that it still existed; but had he never experienced the object, he would have no way
of ever being sure or even feeling almost sure that it existed.

This argument could be carried on and on. This is not the task of the

---

[1] Common sense has at least two broad, but differing, definitions. On the one
hand, it is considered to be a kind of wisdom the most people have. Were they only
to use it, they would fare the best. On the other hand, common sense is the total of
understandings that develops from the limited variety of experiences that most people
have, including the teachings that were handed down to them. With extended areas
of experience, such as provided by laboratory situations, for example, new conclusions and understandings are called for. Common sense does not cover those situations. This inadequacy is not a part of common sense to recognize. Hence common
sense and "highfalutin" ideas are always in conflict. Formal training is the process
of providing individuals with greater varieties of experience and the attempt to get
the individuals to see that common sense does not cover this more expanded set of
experiences. Science and common sense are thus very much different at many points.

present chapter. The purpose is to provide some experimental information on how constancy operates.

Since there are several sorts of object properties, there are as many sorts of constancy. In the main there are four sorts of constancy in visually perceived objects, namely, lightness, size, shape, and color. It must be understood, however, that the principle of constancy is not confined to visually perceived objects, although it is in vision that many of the most common and outstanding examples are to be found.

LIGHTNESS OR WHITENESS CONSTANCY

In the discussion of brightness discrimination in Chapter 6, much was said that demonstrated lightness constancy. We shall, however, add some examples here. Lightness constancy is to be regarded in terms of the relative weights given two important factors in visual stimulation: the intensity of target illumination by some source of photic radiation, and the amount of reflectance of the target itself. We know that the reflectance of a target does not vary as intensity of radiation is varied. That is, a target always reflects a *constant percentage* of the radiation falling on it when intensity is the only variable manipulated. If the property of lightness was to be dependent upon this factor, then the target would look equally light no matter how weak or intense the radiation reaching it. Were lightness to depend upon quantity of light falling on the target, lightness would vary in keeping with radiation intensity. Lightness does not strictly follow either of these rules. If it followed the first rule strictly, perception would manifest complete "constancy." To the extent that it does not follow the rule, complete constancy is departed from. Most experiments in constancy provide a measure of just how closely complete constancy is approached. Brunswik (45) expressed this in a ratio.

Let us take an example to illustrate what the ratio is like. Suppose we have a target ("gray") whose reflectance is 30 percent, and we have it under an illumination of 10 ft.c. Under a separate illumination of 60 ft.c., we have a group of visual targets ("samples"—cardboard squares, let us say), each having a different reflectance. If the subject chooses a sample with a reflectance of 5 percent to obtain a perceived lightness (grayness) match with the first sample, he would be manifesting zero constancy in his perception. If 100 percent constancy was to be manifested, he would choose a sample having 30 percent reflectance. But let us say he actually chooses a sample that has 20 percent reflectance.

The Brunswik ratio, $\dfrac{(R-S)}{(A-S)}$, would express this in the following way.
R is the subject's response. So, since he chose a sample having 20 percent reflectance, we shall make it the first part of the numerator. For the second part of the numerator we have S, the sample reflectance needed for a match with zero constancy. In this case it is 5 percent. The reflectance of the standard sample is A, and it is 30 percent. Thus we have the ratio as follows:

$$C = \frac{(20-5)}{(30-5)} = \frac{15}{25} = 0.6$$

The degree of constancy is thus 0.6. With this equation, complete constancy would produce a value of 1.0 and no constancy whatsoever would produce a value of 0.0.

Thouless (247) used the logarithms of the S, R, and A, since perceptual response is more nearly in keeping with the logarithm of the photic flux used (that is, the physical intensity of the stimulus) than with the simple arithmetic values. Thouless' ratio is as follows:

$$C = \frac{(\log R - \log S)}{(\log A - \log S)}$$

For our purposes, the essential thing is to understand the basic principle involved in the ratio rather than insist upon logarithmic values. Woodworth and Schlossberg (274) suggest another set of values entirely, a procedure which we shall not describe. It can be said, however, that the fundamental nature of the ratio remains constant in all three procedures, those of Brunswik, Thouless, and Woodworth and Schlossberg.

Involvement of Illumination

Although we shall see that the apprehension of illumination as such is not a necessary factor in producing the kinds of results we are to deal with, it must be recognized that illumination may be involved in various ways in various situations. It must be also recognized that visual results depend in a large measure upon the way illumination is involved in a given situation.

There are several ways that illumination may reach the eye. The use of apertures is one. One way to provide an aperture gray is to set up a *hole* arrangement. A screen is provided with a hole that subtends a few degrees of visual angle at the eye. An illumination source is concealed behind the screen. The illumination falls on some reflecting surface that can send radiation to the observer, as in Fig. 9.1. The hole can be seen as an aperture filled in with a certain gray. The light does not seem to come from a definite surface at the plane of the screen, or even at some distance behind the screen, unless the area viewed through the hole is textured, that is, inhomogeneous. If, however, the observer is predisposed toward seeing surfaces, the hole *may* be seen as a surface.

Illumination may be tapered due to progressive distance from the source. This is called illumination perspective. This effect is often per-

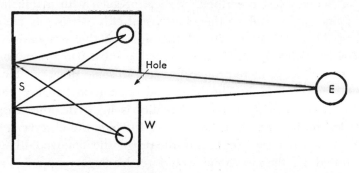

FIG. 9.1. Diagram of illumination arrangement to produce an aperture gray. In this setup, the radiation falls on a surface (the opposite wall of an adjoining room) and is reflected through a hole to the room of the observer, whose eye is E. The hole seen as a gray area is now the target, on a well-illuminated background, W.

ceived as a space dimension. Painters use tapered lightness to give the visual effect of progressive distance away from the viewer.

Illumination may encounter obstructions, in which case shadows are cast. Shadows are areas of diminution of illumination within which object lightness constancy tends to be high. Here again, we encounter the need for distinguishing between the observer's ability to *identify* lightness of objects within the area and actually to see the area or objects of a different lightness than others in the visual field.

When equations (matchings) of lightness between the area seen as in shadow and an area seen as outside the shadow are called for, they are difficult. Let a screen be set up in front of the field just implied, and the two areas viewed through an aperture or through separate apertures, and the match at once becomes much less difficult.

Radiation falls on obstructing surfaces at various angles. These varying *angles of incidence* determine the amount of reflection and as a result function for the observer as factors in seeing various degrees of lightness.

Not only is this so, but the different amounts of reflection enable the perceiver to see a third dimension and objects with volume.

Illumination of an area in the visual field may be intermittent, as when one looks at a revolving fan. Its blades intermittently obstruct and permit a view beyond them because of this motion. Radiation falling on them and reflected to the observer produces what is seen as a film, through which objects are observable beyond. There need be nothing about the visual properties of this film to indicate that it is being produced in the way just described. A sheet of glass with a thin layer of dirt or paint might produce the same visual effect. It is this ambiguity regarding the nonvisual reality of the situation that emphasizes what Ames (5) has pointed out. He has pointed out that perception possesses the nature of a bet or mere prognostication. In some situations the probability of the bet is high. The likelihood of nonvisual reality being in accord with the visually perceived reality is high. In other cases the prognostication is poor. If, in the case of the film, the observer reached out to try to touch it, the poorness of the prognostication would be amply demonstrated, for the individual would get his fingers nipped. Visually, the film was perfectly innocuous. Tactually, it was a very different matter. Touching the "film" was like touching a buzz saw in motion.

In some respects interrupted radiation functions essentially the same whether a beam from a radiation source is being interrupted, or whether reflections are interrupted, as in the case of the moving fan blades. The ratio between the period of interruption and the period of transmission or reflection determines the quantity of radiation reaching the eye in a given period, and thus the lightness or brightness seen. A film, however, is produced only when the radiation source is on the same side of the moving blades as the observer so that there can be reflection.

Constancy and the Perception of Illumination

In Chapter 6 it was pointed out that under some conditions the perceiver is able to make a distinction between the properties of a target surface and the photic illumination it receives. One might be tempted to say that there is a causal relation between being able to perceive illumination as such and the perception of lightness constancy, or color constancy. MacLeod (171) points out that we must not conclude that the perception of illumination as such is an essential condition for the operation of color or lightness constancy. He and a number of other investigators look upon the perception of color and lightness constancies and the perception of illumination as two products of some more fundamental factor. In fact, very definite constancy phenomena can be produced that are not dependent upon the perception of illumination.

Shadows

Long ago, Hering pointed out that if a black line is drawn around the edge of a shadow, the shadow as such will disappear. The shadow area will take on the appearance of a dark surface.

This fact was used by Kardos (134), who used an encircled shadow with a small disk at its center. He showed that when the shadow was encircled, the disk appeared darker, in contradiction to the laws of color contrast that would be expected to operate in this situation. He also found that the effect was relatively independent of the area of the field, and would occur as easily with a white encircling line as with a dark one. Thus one cannot use the line as a factor in the explanation by saying it produced a lightness contrast effect. The preferable explanation is that conditions that produce shadows make them operate as special forms of local illumination. Accordingly, the disk shifts toward greater lightness in line with the laws of lightness constancy. When the shadow is turned into a surface, it is seen as darker, but in the brighter illumination that falls on it. Whatever the explanation may be, the change from shadow to surface color in the Kardos experiment is not to be doubted.

MacLeod (171) repeated Kardos' experiment in the following manner. A circular white line, 5 mm. in width, was placed on an upright surface seen as black. A circular shadow was cast so that its penumbra coincided with the line. A penumbra of a shadow, it will be recalled, is its tapered or less-dark outer border. In MacLeod's setup the area was seen as a luminous black surface bordered by a white line. The area looked like a piece of velvet, or like a black hole cut in a surface. When he shifted the surface on which the shadow fell, to dispense with the white encircling line, the area simply became a shadow, and was not so dark as it was to begin with.

In the center of the shadow, a rotating disk whose two components, 'white" and "black," could be manipulated was introduced. Consultation of Fig. 9.2 will help to understand the setup. Two disks, C_1 and C_2, are shown as being propelled by motors that lie behind screens of low reflectance (black). A is also a low-reflectance surface. E_1 and E_2 are shadow-casters for the radiation source D. The observer is O, and views the setup through aperture F.

When observers were given the chance to observe the visual field produced by the foregoing conditions, they found it quite difficult to say what was what. The shadow cast by E_1 was encircled by the line already mentioned, and the shadow cast by E_2 was not. In every case, the encircled shadow and its central disk were perceived as definitely darker than the comparison target formed by the shadow of E_2 and its disk. The unencircled shadow was more difficult to localize in distance. In other cases, the shadows were seen as being at different distances.

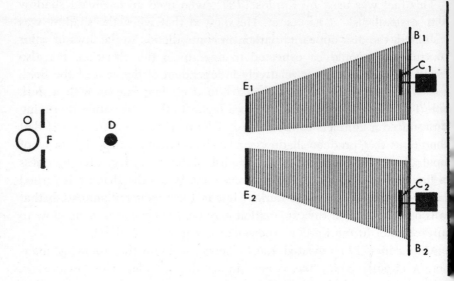

FIG. 9.2. MacLeod's arrangement for studying lightness constancy. A, uniform low-reflectance surface. B_1, B_2, low-reflectance cardboard screens. C_1, C_2, color wheels. E_1, E_2, shadow casters. F, observation window. O, observer's eye. D, radiation source. (R. B. MacLeod, Brightness constancy in unrecognized shadows, *J. Exper. Psychol.* [1940], 27:1–22, Fig. 1).

About 60 percent of the 38 observers perceived no special or anomalous illumination. The summary of findings for the experiment as a whole were that (1) a definite difference in lightness was described for the two targets even when neither one of the two shadows was perceived as shadow; (2) the difference remained despite full explanation of the setup to the observers.

It would seem that MacLeod showed that the perception of anomalous illumination conditions does not lie back of all lightness constancy results. MacLeod concluded that the phenomena in question could be handled better by referring them to organization of the visual field, and that the concept of "constancy" is of doubtful value in studying such situations as illustrated by the present investigation.

MacLeod's conclusions are in contrast with the usual "cue" explanation of the nature of visual perception. It will be recalled that in other places in the text the fallacy of prevalent cue theory has been pointed out, for it consists in using one perception to help explain another, when the very same stimulus field is responsible for both of them. Here, in the case at hand, MacLeod has shown that lightness constancy has not depended upon the "cue" of illumination.

The Contributions of the Perceiver

In many experiments in lightness constancy, and in the other forms of constancy as well, all observers do not see alike. This divergence in results reminds us that the observer brings something to the occasion. Sometimes this is labeled *past experience*, sometimes *set*, sometimes *attitude*, sometimes *knowledge* of the situation. None of these labels are descriptive of the actual mechanisms at work, but they all do indicate that the observer is not a fully neutral or passive system that is acted upon from without. Certain predispositions of the observer have to be taken into account here as in every case in dealing with perception. Just what weights the stimulus conditions and the predisposing factors within the observer have must be determined by experimentation. From appropriate experimentation some sorts of generalizations are to be expected. Much more work is necessary for us to arrive at desirable ones.

SIZE CONSTANCY

In size constancy, we are dealing with the ability of the observer to perceive metric size ("true" size, or the size determined by using a meter stick) regardless of target distance or other factors that might be expected to interfere. Metric size of target, and the awareness of the observer that the object constitutes a smaller and smaller part of the visual field as its distance from him increases, must be distinguished.

All visual targets subtend visual angles, small or great. Certain distant large targets subtend the same visual angles as certain near small ones. The visual field need not be structured for an object to be seen at a given distance; but when structured, the field determines largely the distance at which the object is seen. In keeping with this field structure, objects are likewise seen as metrically small or large. To perceive size in this way is something different than to note analytically that the portion of the total visual field occupied by the object is small or large.

An object may be seen as a familiar object, such as a tree, a playing card, a thimble, and so on. When it is seen as a member of a class of objects whose range in size is rather limited, it is also seen as a large, medium-sized, or small object of its kind. One aspect of the perception of the object is *identification* and the other is the *appreciation of size*. Some persons who attempt to explain the perception of size use identification as a crucial factor. It will be recognized that this principle has been discussed before as a logically unjustified procedure, for it is making one aspect of perception explain another. The two aspects are but two end results stemming from a common origin, and to account for them the common origin must be discovered. It is a slightly different procedure, however, when a contribution of the organism other than a perception is taken to be a crucial factor in producing a perceptual end result.

Perception of object size follows one set of laws in an unstructured field and a different set in a structured one. This is to say that when the object in question is the only thing in the visual field, the field contributes nothing to object identification. Hence, from the stimulus standpoint, broad field properties cannot be called into use. The only thing that is structured is the small region which constitutes the object itself. This leaves the object to be almost any size. Lack of field structure leaves object location indefinite also. The object may be near or far away. Despite this indefiniteness as far as stimulus contribution is concerned, the observer does not fail to perceive. It only means that the organism itself has to put more into the matter. The organism simply acts as though one of the several alternatives were true. Perception proceeds as though a choice had been made, as though a premise had been used or an assumption had been instantly employed. We do not know what the process actually is. We only know that perception proceeds *as* if the above were true. No marked delay, no antecedent conscious process, takes place. Perception is just as straightforward as though the stimulus situation had furnished all the determinants necessary.

The laws that govern visual perception of size when the field is structured stem from the field itself.

The most fundamental and comprehensive description of the visual field is Gibson's texture-gradient concept, which he uses to describe three-dimensional space perception. For this the reader is directed to Chapter 10. We shall not give the description here. It can only be said that the visual field is conceived to exist as a textured expanse. The texturing of the field is of such a character as to determine the distance factor of perceived objects (segregated portions of the field) as well as their direction and size. Thus, according to this view, one must not confine his search for the controlling factors of object size to the characteristics of the object itself. That is, no restricted portion of the field possesses the necessary and sufficient factors for size determination. The field as a whole must be taken into account. The contribution of the observer himself must also be taken into consideration. This contribution exerts varying influence, depending on the stimulus field.

Size Constancy and Great Distance

The perceived size of an object does not diminish in keeping with the retinal image of the target as it recedes in the distance. Few persons suppose, however, that the perceived object size does not diminish at all when the target is placed at great distances. At certain distances the target subtends visual angles so small that the object is scarcely visible. It is then that the second of the two above-mentioned modes of perceiving size comes into prominence. Size now may come to mean the occupation of an insignificant portion of the total visual field. Extremely small size and bare visibility may now become synonymous. Before this happens, the object might very easily be supposed to be becoming smaller. This is to say that size constancy is generally thought to break down for targets removed to great distances. For targets outdoors in contrast to those in rooms, apparent size would be expected to taper off long before disappearance into the horizon. This general outlook on size constancy was investigated as follows.

Gibson (86) exposed upright stakes in a flat unfurrowed field, one at a time, at various distances. These stakes ranged from 15 to 99 inches in height. A row of comparison stakes was set up at a little distance from the subject at right angles to his line of regard. Each was of a different size, and the stakes were numbered from 1 to 15. As a distant test stake was exposed, the observer was to indicate with which of the sample stakes it compared closest in height. The observer could even say "smaller than 1" or "taller than 15." Hence, no preclusion was made for range in perceived heights.

The trials included different sizes of stakes at different distances in random combinations. Each observer made 150 observations. Averages of the perceptions were computed for the different stake sizes, distances, and observers. Let us look at what the observers did in perceiving a 71-inch stake, the one that compared to comparison stake number 12. At 12 feet, the mean perception was 71.9 inches, with a standard deviation of 1.8 inches. At 672 feet, the mean perception was 75.8 inches, with a standard deviation of 7.3 inches. At nearly a half-mile (2352 feet), the mean result was 74.9 inches, with a standard deviation of 9.8 inches. For four other distances the results were comparable. Since at one-half mile, the 71-inch stake was almost invisible, but was still perceived just about as nearly correctly as those much nearer, the question of diminution of size constancy with distance is answered. Distance essentially has little to do with size constancy. The object remains its "true" size just so long as it can be seen at all. On the other hand, something else happens to the perception of distant targets. The heights of the stakes become more and more indeterminate as distance increases. This is evidenced in the increase in variability of reports as distance increases.

Gibson and Henneman (86) investigated the perceived size of targets and distances between them in a thoroughly cluttered room. The results indicated that size constancy for objects and constancy for perception of distances between them followed the same principles. Thus it can be said that the same concept of constancy applies to interobject distances as it does to object dimensions. This would tend to lead us to conclude that constancy is a *field* property rather than simply a *thing* property, thus obviating the need for special explanations for constancy based on some uniqueness in perceiving objects. It is easier to comprehend how a part of a field is subject to the principles that govern the field than it is to understand how field items obey laws of their own in isolation. It does not seem appropriate to resort to mysterious intrinsic properties, or to cues with all the logical objections we have pointed out as applying to them. Consideration of total sets of factors acting in organized ways is also more appropriate than reliance solely upon the "contributions of the observer" in the form of learning and past experiences.

The foregoing investigations are among the most significant in all the realm of size-constancy studies. Most other studies in this area have to do with manipulations in field structure surrounding the specific target used, but too many of them in no systematic way.

Size Perception in an Unstructured Field

We have already mentioned that size perception in an unstructured field is a different matter than in a structured one. In fact, it is so different that certain experimenters disclaim the virtue of using unstructured fields for the study of any of the features of perception. As we pointed out, however, it does demonstrate the fact that perception is possible when little is given by the stimulus. Although it can be shown that the organism is so constituted that it can proceed somewhat on its own, we cannot as yet be sure of arriving at many laws regarding just what direction perception will take under such field conditions. As one example of perception in an unstructural field, the following card demonstration is given. If a target comprising a rectangular blank card is the only visual differentiation provided in a dark room, it may be perceived as almost any size. It may be seen as a small rectangle nearby, or a large rectangle far away. Both may produce the same-sized retinal images. Since it is only the retinal image and the contribution of the perceiver himself that determine the perceptual end result, object size is dependent upon the *distance* at which the object is projected in perception. Size and distance are reciprocal for any fixed retinal image. The observer sees the object as being of a certain size and at a certain distance. All that we can show is that the two are related to each other, as would be expected from the trigonometry involved in target size, target distance, and the retinal image produced. The pivotal factor is retinal image size, for that is the only fixed thing as far as the stimulus is concerned. If a playing card is substituted for the blank card, then one more of the factors becomes determined. The observer "knows" the size of playing cards. Thus with retinal image size fixed, the object size fixed, distance is determined. The object seen can be seen at only one distance, unless it is possible to conceive of giant playing cards and miniature ones. A rare observer may be able to act as though looking at a giant playing card; and if so, its distance is increased. Or he may be able to act as though looking at a miniature. If so, its distance from the observer is diminished. Nevertheless, the experimenter cannot obtain these results by merely asking all observers to "imagine" that the cards are giants or dwarfs. The more facile observers may be able to do so, but most of them may not be. Likewise, the experiments can never predict when some observer is going to see something in a way all his own. All we can say is that what he does is lawful. The fact that the observers have this latitude is the troublesome thing. We cannot tell when some new factor will enter, and we cannot always control the factors we intend to.

We are now ready for another indoor example of size constancy. Holway and Boring (*120, 121*) compared two circular targets: one fixed in position, the other posed at various distances. The fixed target was 10 feet from the observer, whereas the movable one varied from 10 to 120 feet. The fixed target was seen as a disk of light, the diameter of which was controlled by an iris diaphragm. The variable target was adjusted so as to subtend a visual angle of one degree at each position used. The observer's problem was to adjust the stationary target in diameter so that it appeared to be the same size as the movable target.

What is spoken of as the "law of the visual angle" requires that the movable target be increased in size as it is placed farther and farther away, so that both it and the fixed target subtend equal visual angles if the two objects are to appear equal in size. The "law of size constancy" requires that, regardless of distance, the size of the movable target should remain constant in order for the two objects to appear constant in size. In Holway and Boring's experiment, then, the movable target should remain unchanged in size as it was moved to greater distances if the law of size constancy was to hold. If the two objects appeared equal to begin with, then moving the one target to greater distance should not upset the original apparent equality between the two in size.

These two laws represent the opposite extremes that the results could take. If the size of the comparison target was represented on the vertical axis and the distance of the movable target on the horizontal axis, as in Fig. 9.3, the relation of the results to the two extremes represented by the laws could be shown.

In the figure, the horizontal line expresses the law of the visual angle since the movable target is adjusted to subtend constant visual angle regardless of distance. Accordingly, the size of the fixed target must remain constant so as to match it, and the line in the graph must be horizontal.

The top broken line represents the law of size constancy. For, since the movable target is held at a constant angular subtense of one degree, it is actually enlarged, as it is made farther away. The fixed target must also be enlarged to maintain the original match when constancy operates.

Holway and Boring found neither extreme to hold in their study. Four different observing conditions were employed. The results are shown in the four curves lying between the two extremes. The lowest of the four represents the results with one-eyed viewing with an artificial pupil and with a reduction tunnel to eliminate the operation of certain extraneous field factors.

Obviously, monocular viewing eliminates stereoscopic factors and should work toward the perception following the law of visual angle. With binocular viewing, that is, with conditions in which stimulation is least simplified, the law of size constancy is expected to operate most forcefully. The results, of course, were a compromise between the two.

Various degrees of size constancy have been found in the behavior of children and animals. It has also been found that "attitude affects the results." It was found that a "betting" attitude favored the obtaining of size constancy.

One other author's results seemed to show that departure from the law of the visual angle is dependent upon the elevation of regard. Boring (30) found, too, that eye position was the influential factor in ac-

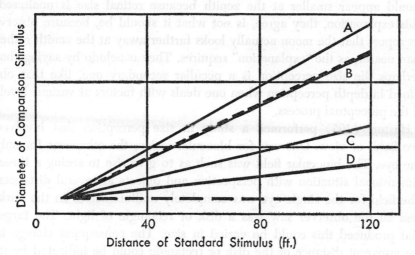

FIG. 9.3. Relation of diameter of comparison target to distance of the standard stimulus for the conditions in Holway and Boring's experiment. The diagonal dashed line shows expectation of size constancy. The horizontal dashed line shows expectations according to the law of visual angle. Curve A is for binocular viewing; B is for monocular with natural pupil; C, monocular, artificial pupil; and D, monocular, artificial pupil, and reduction tunnel (C. H. Graham, "Visual Perception," in S. S. Stevens (ed.), *Handbook of Experimental Psychology,* John Wiley & Sons, Inc., 1951, p. 873, Fig. 2).

counting for the well-known "moon illusion." This so-called illusion is the fact that the moon looks to be much larger when it is low in the sky (i.e., near the horizon) than when it is overhead. Boring and colleagues manipulated every factor that they could conceive of in attempting to account for this effect, and finally Boring ended up by concluding that the essential factor was the raising or lowering of the eyes. Even the movements of head and neck were ruled out as causal factors.

Since the days of Ptolemy it was thought that the size effect was dependent upon apparent distance, in which case the moon looked nearer when at the horizon. To study the phenomenon, Boring and colleagues used a setup intended to simulate moon viewing conditions. They used an artificial moon which they could place overhead, or at the horizon. Woodworth and Schlossberg (274) deduced that elevating the eyes tends to produce a slight reflex divergence to the eyes, increasing the tension necessary to maintain the proper convergence of the two eyes. This is thought to be a "cue" for seeing the moon at a decreased distance. If the moon was to be nearer at the zenith than at the horizon, it should appear smaller at the zenith because retinal size is unaltered. This explanation, they agree, is not what it should be, because observers report that the moon actually looks farther away at the zenith rather than nearer, as the "explanation" requires. They conclude by saying that perhaps the size perception is a peculiar secondary one, like that obtained in depth perception when one deals with factors at various levels of the perceptual process.

Hastorf (105) performed a study in size perception that involved two fields of view. One was for binocular vision; the other was for only one eye. The binocular field was such as to give rise to seeing a three-dimensional situation with perspective and objects at several distances. The field for the single eye was completely unilluminated. In the darkness all the observer saw was a disk or rectangle of light. The target that produced this could be varied in size. The consequent change in the apparent distance of the disk or rectangle could be indicated by its localization relative to the perceived items in the binocular field. The binocular field contained four posts distributed at intervals of one foot. These were the comparison items to which we have just alluded.

The monocular field was a projection screen on which the disk or rectangular target already mentioned was projected. This screen was at the same distance from the observer as the third post in the binocular field. A Clason projector provided a target that varied in size without developing a consequent blur in contour.

According to the experimenter's instructions, the disk of light in one set of observations represented a ping-pong ball; and in another set, a billiard ball. In two different sets of observations, when the rectangle was used, it represented a calling card or an envelope, respectively. In all cases the observers were to set the target (disk or rectangle) at a size necessary for the seen object to be at the distance of post number 3 in the binocular field while using the monocular and the binocular fields at the same time. The supposition was that the binocular field gave third-dimensional perception and could be used as an indicator for the distance at which the object was seen by the one eye using the monocular field. The readings compared pretty well to what would be expected from the visual angles that would have been subtended by the actual objects, that is, billiard ball and ping-pong ball. These balls, of course, are of different sizes and thus required different adjustments of the target size.

In the third part of the experiment, the size of the target was set at the mean reading given for the ping-pong ball. The observer was then asked to locate the distance of the object seen, by telling where it was in relation to post number 3. Nothing was said about whether the target in this case was a ping-pong ball or a billiard ball. It was true, however, that the "ball" which the observers had just been dealing with was a "billiard ball." The disk was reported beyond post 3, as would have been expected, for the target was too small to be at post 3 if the object was a billiard ball. Implied in the experimentation is the assumption that the observers would be still behaving as if looking at a billiard ball. Implied in the behavior is the principle that behavior follows certain "assumptions" the observer makes.

The author felt that he had demonstrated that there is something "assumptive" about perception that heretofore had not been too well recognized or demonstrated. While this is not one of the more usual forms of investigation of size constancy, it certainly involves the continuity and constancy principles.

Summary

In the foregoing, you have been given examples of the very best work in the study of size constancy. It will be seen from them that field properties, eye posture, and the "contribution of the observer" work in curious combinations to produce the results from situation to situation, and that the factors just mentioned are not all of the same weight or even present in all cases.

SHAPE CONSTANCY

The third aspect of constancy is shape. Shape is one of the very things that enables us to identify objects or distinguish them from each other. Shape as pertaining to objects and shape as descriptive of the various regions of the visual field are to be distinguished from each other. Take, for example, the top of a table. We perceive it as rectangular. We say that shape belongs to the table. Rectangularity is ascribed to the table top regardless of the position of the table with regard to us. On the other hand, we know that the "shape" presented to the eye may be any one of an infinite number, depending upon the table's position with regard to us. It should be obvious, then, that perception is involved in distinguishing what is the shape of the table top, and what is the shape of that portion of the visual field segregated off as table top. Were the perceiving organism unable to make this distinction, it could not react as we find it now able to do. It might act as though the visual field was a single plane, the frontal plane, with all events occurring within it. Thus, if we were to present such an organism with a target (a three-dimensional table top) and tip the target in various directions one after the other, the organism would not see a single entity being moved about in three-dimensional space, but rather a region of a two-dimensional field constantly changing shape. If this constantly changing shape was to be seen as a single entity, it would be credited with being quite elastic or pliable rather than being rigid, as we now see table tops to be.

An operational convenience for our purposes is that of distinguishing between shape as a consideration that may involve a two-dimensional geometry, or a three-dimensional one. In any case, even if only two-dimensional, it may involve one or more orientations from occasion to occasion in three-dimensional space. As an initial but not a final label, we may speak of this shape as *real shape*. It is only real in the sense that perception makes it have continuity, and assigns it to an object. The second item of consideration is shape in terms of shape in the frontal plane. This shape we can call a frontal-plane projection of real shape. To understand what is meant here, if you are not familiar with such terms as frontal-plane projection, see Fig. 9.4. From it, it should be seen that the tilted target makes an image on the retina as if it was another-shaped target in the frontal plane, instead of the target it is. So, for convenience, all targets may be referred to the "projection" they make in the frontal plane. In keeping with this principle, we may say that the frontal-plane projection of a circle, when tilted out of the erect position (more strictly, tilted out of the frontal plane), is an approximate ellipse. Actually, in some cases, as we shall show later, the perceiver cannot tell whether what he sees is an ellipse in the frontal plane or a circle tilted out of the frontal plane. Keep this general principle in mind throughout our discussion of shape constancy.

Along with this, it must be understood that targets in this sort of study will be described in terms of Euclidean geometry. This is about as great a distinction between stimulus specifications and perceptual specifications as we are able to make. There are times when such a Euclidean term as "square" or "triangle" is unfortunately both a geometrical term and a perceptual term. We have pointed out in several other connections before that it is necessary to try to have a language that pertains to the stimulus (impinging energies) and a different language that pertains to details of perception. This caution needs to be reiterated here, for it is easy to think of real objects in terms that are only descriptions of perceptions. The nearest we can come here to describing external reality,

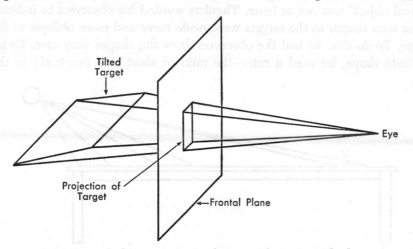

FIG. 9.4. Frontal plane projection of a target lying in a tilted position with reference to eye. Naturally, such a projection may be of a different size and shape than the target, but will compare to the shape of the image projected onto the retina.

the targets used, is to indicate their geometrical properties. This is a compromise or a descent from the ideal of having a way to specify spatial factors (or whatever they may be) in wholly nonperceptual terms.

Regression to the "Real Object"

A good place to begin our discussion of shape and shape constancy is with Thouless' (247) work. His very first study consisted in presenting observers with a disk target and a square target. One or the other was placed on a long table and viewed obliquely by the observer from a fixed viewing position. Obviously, as the position of the target was shifted farther and farther out along the table, it was viewed more and more obliquely. Obliqueness of view produces a different-shaped retinal image than does the normal view (view at right angles to the plane of the target). For convenience, Thouless called the target the real object (R). The resulting retinal image, with its varying shape in relation to obliqueness of viewing conditions, he called the stimulus object (S).

As has been pointed out in other places in the text, we can deal with targets in two ways as observers. Either we can identify them as objects or we can deal with some object property. In this case, it is the property of perceived shape as abstracted from identity that is the issue. In the experiment, it was obvious to the observers that they were dealing with a disk and a square, at different times, so the identity of the "real object" was not at issue. Thouless wanted his observers to indicate the seen shapes as the targets were made more and more oblique to the eye. To do this, he had the observers draw the shapes they saw. To indicate shape, he used a ratio—the ratio of short axis (vertical) to the

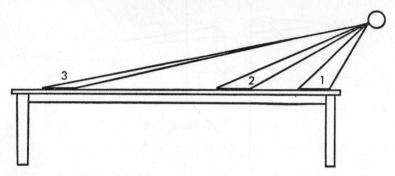

FIG. 9.5. *Thouless' experiment.* E is the eye. Items 1, 2, and 3 are the target positions. Shifting the target from one position to another changes its effective shape (frontal-plane projection), and varies the visual angle subtended by one dimension.

horizontal or long axis of the form they observed. Obviously, the shapes which the observers saw in looking at the circular target obliquely were approximate ellipses. Consult Fig. 9.5 for the schema that applies to the study at hand. Target T subtends a much smaller visual angle at position 3 than at position 1.

The drawings of the observers were measured in terms of the ratio given above, and found to represent a seen shape (phenomenal shape) somewhere between the shape of S and the shape of R. This shape Thouless called the phenomenal object (P). To provide a numerical way of expressing the relation of P to R, he used the following ratio that is reminiscent of the ratio described in the earlier part of this chapter in connection with the Brunswik ratio.

The ratio which Thouless used was:

$$\frac{\log P - \log S}{\log R - \log S}$$

This he called the *index of phenomenal regression*. He labeled the perceptual behavior phenomenal regression to the real object. This implies that there is some fixed intrinsic entity called the real object, and that it has some influence upon what is perceived. We are hard put to it to conceive of the real object meant here as being anything other than either (1) a concept or (2) a perceived object to which the perceiver is led to attribute a more ultimate form of reality than the perception of shape referred to the frontal plane. What reaches the eye is a pattern of photic radiation that corresponds to the shape (geometry of S), whereas R is both a perceptual object and a conceptual one. Thouless is assuming that whatever it is that gives rise to the experience of circularity or squareness, regardless of the angle of viewing the target, is the real object, something that has some uniqueness and indestructibility.

It is necessary for us to go farther and describe some other sorts of investigations. These involve conditions through which a further look at the idea of real object can be had. For this purpose, several investigators have used targets in unstructured fields. To accomplish this, the targets were luminous and were the only observable items in a dark room.

Further Experiments

Nelson and Bartley (*196*) used three such targets. They were outlines of a circle, a 4 x 5, and a 3 x 5 luminous ellipse. These were oriented in several positions: (1) in the frontal plane, that is, upright; (2) at a 22.5-degree tilt from the vertical, away from the observer; (3) at a 45-degree tilt; and (4) at a 67.5-degree tilt. Thus there were 12 different kinds of presentations used. These, of course, were given in random order. In Figure 9.6, the results are shown. Phenomenal or perceived shape is represented on the vertical axis of the graph, and stimulus shape (shape of retinal image) is represented on the horizontal axis. Were there to be a direct correspondence between the two, the results would fall on the diagonal straight line shown in the graph.

The authors used the same kind of notation as described for Thouless' investigation, and likewise obtained their data through observers' drawings. It will be noted that the data lie along the line, but not in perfect fashion. It could be said that in general the observers behaved as if they saw all the targets in the frontal plane. In other words, it was the stimulus shape that was followed in the perceptions.

It cannot be insisted that the departures from perfect correspondence to S in the data are slight regressions to the real object. The "real ob-

jects" (targets) in this investigation were not always circles. One would
not know which real object to refer the data to.

It will be remembered here that a target forming the same given retinal image may be an ellipse or a circle, for a tilted circle will provide
the same "projection" in the frontal plane (that is, same visual angle) as
a certain ellipse.

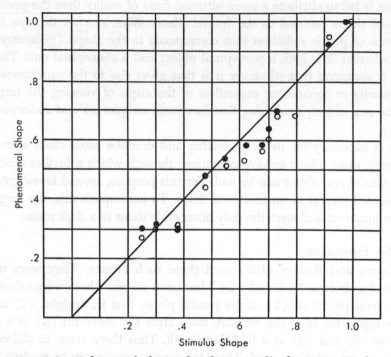

FIG. 9.6.   Relation of observed (phenomenal) shape to stimulus
shape in an unstructured field. Shape in both cases is measured by
the ratio of the vertical to the horizontal dimension (T. M. Nelson
and S. H. Bartley, The perception of form in an unstructured field,
J. Gen. Psychol. [1956] 54:57–63, Fig. 1).

It is obvious that the observers had no way of "knowing" which was
the case in any trial. They could have seen the target as either one.
One would have made as much sense as the other. It just did not turn
out that the 24 observers acted as if it were tilted circles they saw.

In Fig. 9.7 another set of data for observer behavior with ellipses and
circles at various tilts is shown. These findings are taken from the work
of Miller and Bartley (184) in which the field was structured. In this
case the targets were cardboard circles and ellipses placed on a tilt

board whose limiting edges were hidden by a reduction screen. For the arrangement, see Fig. 9.8.

It will be noted from this lighted-room experiment that the perceptions were much different than those obtained in an unstructured field. The phenomenon that Thouless called "regression to the real object" seemed to be involved. But since there were several "real objects" in-

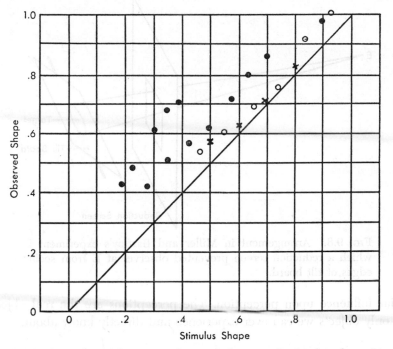

FIG. 9.7. Relation between observed shape and stimulus shape in Miller and Bartley's experiment; see Fig. 9.6 for comparison (T. M. Nelson and S. H. Bartley, The perception of form in an unstructured field, *J. Gen. Psychol.* [1956], 54:57–63, Fig. 2).

volved and since the observer had no way of "knowing" what the targets were like, the concept of real object is not a suitable one. In this experiment there were five ellipses and one circle, and they were presented in four different positions (one erect and four tilted). Even this investigation began to demonstrate that the concept of real object has limited usage in dealing with perception of shape and shape constancy. The findings obtained in an unstructured field make even more obvious that the real object as an indestructible entity existing outside the observer and describable in perceptual terms is a fiction. We do "carry around with us" concepts of objects, such as circles, diamonds, triangles, and so on. We are impinged upon by certain photic energies and we do see objects tallying with our object concepts. But in trying to understand visual perception we cannot begin with the idea that there are real objects, outside of the experiences we have, and that they have some pe-

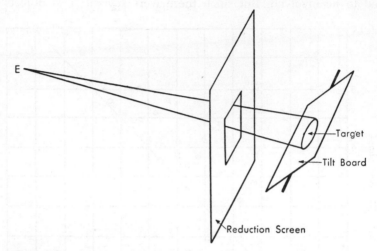

FIG. 9.8.   Arrangement in Miller and Bartley's experiment in which a reduction screen prevented observer at E from seeing edges of tilt board.

culiar influence upon perception. The perceptions are the real objects, the only objects we can ever experience and directly know about.

Perception of Tilt

Another type of observing problem needs to be brought in, namely, the task of reporting upon perceptions of tilt. For this, we shall consult the findings of Haan and Bartley (*100*). In their work, the same stimulus conditions were used as were used in Nelson and Bartley's (*196*) study. In this case, however, the observers were asked to report on perceived tilt. Figure 9.9 shows us the results. In it, phenomenal tilt (perceived tilt) is plotted against stimulus (target) shape.

The three solid curves, beginning at the upper left and descending toward the lower right portion of the graph, represent the cosine functions for various shapes (minor-major axis ratios) in relation to actual tilt. In other words, the left-hand curve represents the cosine function for an ellipse having a 3 x 5 shape; with no tilt from the vertical, such an ellipse presents a 3 x 5 shape (0.6). When the ellipse is tilted a full 90 de-

grees from the perpendicular, then it presents a zero shape. The middle
curve represents a 4 x 5 ellipse (0.8), and the right-hand curve represents a full circle (5 x 5, or 1.00).

The first thing that can be said about the findings is that most of them
lie between the limits expected of a 3 x 5 ellipse and a full circle. But
if we were to ask what is the real object that is functioning in the

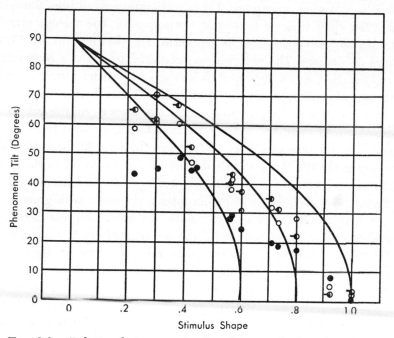

Stimulus Shape

FIG. 9.9.   Relation between stimulus shape and phenomenal tilt.
Shape is defined as the ratio of the vertical axis to the horizontal axis
of the stimulus (L. E. Haan and S. H. Bartley, Apparent orientation
of a luminous figure in darkness, Am. J. Psychol [1954], 67:500–508,
Fig. 1).

experiment, it would be found that no positive answer would be appropriate. There is no sensible answer, except to say that whatever the observer sees is real—real to him—and that there is no other necessary single reality toward which perceptions must regress. Here again we see
that the concept of regression to the real object does not apply, and if
used at all it has to be confined to Thouless' investigation, or the like.
In this connection it may be stated that, in the Nelson and Bartley experiment, telling the observers that the objects were circles at various
degrees of tilt, when asking for shape reports, influenced shape very little. Of course, it could not be ascertained how thoroughly the observ-

ers were made to "believe" that the targets were "circles," but at least
the potential bias was offered, and it did not make much difference in
that particular experiment.

We shall conclude the experimental portion of the discussion of shape
constancy by describing one of Stavrianos' (233) experiments. This experiment consisted in having the observer tell which of a group of seven
rectangles was seen as a square. These rectangles ranged from those that
were taller than wide to those just the opposite. The surface carrying
these rectangles varied from being vertical to having tilts of 15, 30,
45, and 55 degrees. The observer was required to adjust a rectangle at
his right so that its tilt appeared to be the same as the surface carrying
the group of rectangles already mentioned. The observer was also to
tell which of the rectangles was seen as a square. As the actual tilt
of the standard increases, the comparison target deviates from it progressively in the direction of lesser tilt. Also the error in shape matching
increases as the tilt of the standard increases. With no tilt of the standard, the chosen rectangle is very nearly a square. As tilt becomes greater,
the rectangle chosen as a square becomes a rectangle with greater and
greater height with reference to width. In some respects Stavrianos
showed the same principles as did the experiments of the other workers. There was, however, a failure to corroborate some of the expectations made beforehand. One of these was to the effect that a reciprocity
would exist between perceived inclination (tilt) and perceived shape.
It is not certain that the most appropriate experimental conditions were
set up to test this idea, so that failure in strict corroboration is not to
be taken as final.

Another very prevalent concept found in some quarters must be mentioned. It is the idea of goodness of form. This idea stems from Gestalt
theory. Some shapes are said to possess properties that others do not.
By this is meant that when stimulus conditions anywhere nearly approach the characteristics for the production of the perception of such a
form, this form will emerge. It is as though the organism was prone to
perceive this form rather than just something somewhat similar. This is
a difficult idea to test and substantiate, hence it has not reached the status that many other ideas in the study of shape perception have.

While it is difficult to come to grips with the contribution of the organism in producing perception as we find it to be, it is nonetheless certain that the organism does contribute by ways of learned sets, align-
ments, expectancies, bias, or what not. Haan and Bartley introduced the
concept of "assumed object" (A) into the discussion of their study in

line with what Hastorf (*105*) did in dealing with the relation of perceiving size and distance.

Operational Aspects of Perceiving Shape

Certain aspects of the task of perceiving the shape presented to the eye (i.e., the frontal-plane projection) should be mentioned at this point. When a person attempts to draw just what he sees when he is looking at a tilted circular target, he is put into conflict. At one instant the most obvious feature of his looking is that he is looking at a tilted circle. The stimulus field is so structured that he perceives this with no doubt. If he was to picture on paper what he saw, he might even draw a circle, just as he would say that it was a circle. This act would be one of mere identification. But he not only sees a circle; he sees that it is tilted. How is he to picture that? Common experience has given almost every adult in our culture some information of how to approximate this. The usual person will draw a kind of rough ellipse. Were the person not to attempt exactness, he would get his task over with in a hurry and with satisfaction. But if exactness is intended, the observer looks again and again, and each time he looks he is disturbed by not being able to break apart the necessary features of the situation. Instead of readily being able to see a frontal-plane projection of the circle, he sees a circle tilted. It is *as if* he runs his eyes out along the surface of a tilted circle and, before he knows it, what he is drawing looks, on paper, more like a circle than the needed form of ellipse. Hence, we may say that the regression which Thouless talks about is actually something that accompanies seeing *tilt* as well as seeing a circle. The visual field is so structured that tilt and shape are bound together. As soon as field conditions do not lead to seeing tilt, the frontal-plane projection can be represented on paper without too much trouble. Real objects, as something which the experimenter presents as targets, do not exert intrinsic factors of influence upon shape perception.

COLOR CONSTANCY

Color constancy is the final form of constancy that we shall deal with. Much of what has already been said in Chapter 6 and in this chapter on the other forms of constancy applies to color constancy.

General Conditions of Color Attribution

The observer does not always know when he sees a colored surface whether spectral illumination or differential reflection is the cause. The radiation (illumination) may be from a restricted portion of the spectrum, or the surface of the target may reflect only the restricted band of wave lengths producing the color that is seen.

Cramer (63) set up a situation which well illustrates this. He papered the walls of a corner of a room to produce a uniform color and then illuminated the walls by a concealed source of nonspectral illumination. The walls then appeared to be illuminated with colored lights, though somewhat less saturated than the walls themselves. Thus a compromise situation was set up, for a part of the perceived color was attributed to the illumination and a part to the walls.

In a different occasion, Cramer projected lantern slides on a "yellow screen." Houses that would have been seen as white on a "white screen" retained their original whiteness. The yellow of the house in the scene was attributed to the yellow illumination. When the slide was thrown out of focus, the white house lost its object color (whiteness) and also its three-dimensional appearance. With extreme malfocusing, the scene became simply a cluster of various hues, with no object color remaining.

In another case, a "blue" square appeared as gray when projected onto the yellow screen. This is how it should have appeared, for complementary parts of the spectrum were being mixed. In contradiction to this, a "blue" dress of a child appeared blue but was perceived as in yellow illumination.

In the foregoing we have given some examples in which color constancy occurs and some in which it does not. It is now our task to inquire into the physical conditions of color constancy to see whether the perception of things (objects) is always tied up with color constancy. We shall be asking whether color constancy can arise without what we have earlier called the "contribution of the perceiver."

The Physical Basis of Color Constancy

Each scene of reflected radiation, i.e., each target surface, possesses a so-called object color. This is its property of modifying the radiation falling on it by means of absorbing some wave lengths and reflecting others. This is a virtually fixed characteristic and plays some role in determining color constancy, although in Cramer's illustrations the role is not great.

If a target is viewed sequentially under two different illuminations, or two identical targets are viewed concurrently under two different illuminations, producing two consequent surface-color perceptions, they tend to be similar but not actually identical. This is another way of stating

the compromise already described in Cramer's first example. The similarity of the perceptions is favored by the identicalness of the target surfaces, while the dissimilarity of the perceptions is favored by the differences in the two illuminations.

Another way of illustrating the influence of the reflectance of the target is to compare the effect of doubling it and of doubling the intensity
of illumination. When illumination is doubled, little difference is made;
whereas when reflectance is doubled, a great difference is made in the
color of the surface viewed. In both cases the total radiation leaving the
target surface for the eye is the same. Consequently, one cannot expect
to alter surface color greatly by spectral changes in illumination unless
they are extreme in comparison with the spectral selectivity of the target
surface.

Naturally, the principle just described pertains to a faulty appreciation of the illumination level of a scene. Photographers must be aware
of this, else they will underexpose a stage scene containing great contrasts and overexpose a flat outdoor scene.

Physiological Color Mechanisms

Visual adaptation enters into the determination of color and color constancy. By far the majority of situations met with from day to day provide for the visual mechanism to adapt for variations in illumination, the
result of which is in the direction of maintaining color constancy. This
is to say that adaptation works in the direction of minimizing both lightness variations and chromatic variations, and thereby promotes color
constancy. The most common example is that a target that looks white
in daylight does not look yellow when seen under ordinary incandescent
illumination once the observer is adapted for that illumination. Exposure to the incandescent radiation induces adaptation more to the yellow
than to blue, for the radiation is blue-deficient. Hence there is greater
blue sensitivity of the retina and a "white" target looks white.

Although it is not established that the process of color contrast is a
retinal affair, it is generally taken to be either that of a very fundamental physiological process—one probably more basic than color constancy.
Hence in the cases in which color constancy and color contrast are similar, the constancy is attributed to the contrast process.

Let us say, for example, that if a target which appears reddish is illuminated by radiation which is the complement of the reflectance of
the target, i.e., "green," the target will be achromatic if there is no background associated with it. Let a background which is spectrally nonse-

lective (i.e., "gray") be now used and also illuminated by the same "green"; the target will resume its original reddish color. This is an account of simultaneous color contrast. The retinal induction from the illumination was effective in restoring the original color, a result that failed when there was no target surround to reflect the "green" to the eye. This same general effect is supposed to operate to some degree or other in many other situations where the target reflectance and the illumination are not merely complementary or reciprocal to each other. On the other hand, the same principles in certain cases work in the very opposite direction.

Factors at the Perceptual Level

The two sets of factors for producing color constancy that have just been mentioned do not account for all of color constancy. Authorities include what they call "interpretive" factors, or "psychological" factors. These are difficult to come to grips with, and their descriptions are rather unsatisfactory. Much more needs yet to be done to make the laws governing the higher neural processes tangible and respectable. The most that can be said at present is that color constancy, as influenced by these higher processes, is enhanced by all the factors that can be used to enhance the object character of the portion of the field looked at. Visual resolution of spatial microstructure of a target tends to result in it being seen as a surface rather than a film, a volume, or an aperture, and the likely accompaniment of this is color constancy.

The investigations that have enabled the most comprehensive outlook on color phenomena and thus on color constancy are those of Helson (112, 113). His work argues for a simple underlying mechanism that accounts for the many diverse phenomena of color vision under all conditions. Helson has been able to conclude that theories of color perception that attribute more or less independence to reflectance and illuminance; that disjoin color constancy, color contrast, and adaptation; and that attribute different behavior of these mechanisms to surface and film modes of color perception are based on restricted or distorted conditions of investigation.

Among Helson's conclusions are the following. Targets above the reflectance to which the observer is adapted take the hue of the illuminant. Targets below this adaptation take the hue complementary to the illuminant hue. Targets close to the adaptive reflectance appear either colorless (achromatic) or greatly reduced in saturation. Targets appearing least saturated are those near the adaptation reflectance, and this adaptation shifts with reflectance of surrounds. The mere alteration in surrounds was able to change nearly all the hues he used. The hues that will be constant, those that will shift toward illuminant or to the complementary hue, depend upon their relation to the reflectance of the surround.

The "adaptation reflectance," or the achromatic point, is established in accordance with the viewing conditions at the time rather than with daylight illumination, a factor not acting at the time. Helson also asserts that effects often attributed to the "pressure of other objects in the field" or to unspecified organizational factors can likely be attributed to alteration in "adaptation reflectances" brought about by variation in target and surround reflectances.

The question of what actually remains constant under spectral illumination has received two quite extreme answers. One is that all nonselectively reflective targets remain colorless in nonspectral illumination, and the other that constancy is zero for targets with selective reflectance in spectral illumination. Some investigations have supported these generalizations, but they have done so only because they dealt with restricted conditions. Different setups or more pervasive surveys have produced exceptions. Helson states that nonselective targets near the achromatic point remain colorless in nonspectral illumination, whereas others do not. Selective targets whose color in daylight is close to the illuminant color, or complementary to it, tend to retain their hue if they are of low reflectance. In some cases nonselectively reflective targets may look colored and some selectively reflective ones may look uncolored in spectral illumination. By an appropriate shift of surround, a target can be shifted from being colorless to its complementary color or to the color of the illuminant.

Among the many virtues of Helson's investigations is the fact that he made his manipulations with neutral targets, i.e., those not seen as familiar objects whose "natural" colors lie within a limited range. All of the higher-level personal factors were eliminated or reduced to an insignificant minimum. Hence we can take his several generalizations as representing the basic processes that are in operation. All other phenomena that appear to be contradictions to these generalizations are only cases in which some higher-order process is so strong as to transcend what would be provided when only the basic factors are in operation.

Adaptation Level

No doubt a much better understanding of the constancy phenomena would be achieved by the reader were he to give some consideration to what Helson (112) has called the *adaptation level*. Helson has pointed out that various authors recognize the universality of such terms as attitude, frames of reference, standard, norm, anchor, etc., in the attempt to explain behavior. He has stressed, at the same time, the total lack of any quantitative formulation that expresses the general idea in these terms so frequently used. It was this lack that instigated his attempt to arrive at some general quantitative expression usable in experimentation. The result was his formulation and the concept of *adaptation level*. Adaptation level can be defined operationally in terms of the stimulus eliciting an indifferent or neutral response. Adaptation level can be quantitatively determined, since it is this neutral point that defines the frame of reference within which behavior takes place.

Helson has arrived at the following equation, which we hope the reader may understand after some explanation:

$$P = K(Xi - A)/(Xi + A)$$

In this equation, P stands for a just noticeable difference, a concept described earlier in the book. Xi is a "judgment" of a stimulus or, shall we say, the perception evoked by a stimulus. Naturally, both P and Xi are to be dealt with in numerical terms. A is the adaptation level itself, and is the point about which the whole frame of reference hinges. The constant K contains the Weber fraction appropriate for the modality in which the response is being made.

In the equation just given, if $Xi = A$, then $P = O$. This is to say, when the response is to a stimulus having the value of the adaptation level itself, then P is zero; i.e., there is no just noticeable difference.

It must be further understood that responses of the reacting individual are not given in quantitative units representing j.n.d.'s. Any numerical scale may be used, as one pleases, instead of j.n.d.'s.

Helson has shown that the latter possibility is satisfied when two conditions are met and adhered to. The first of these is that K must be the maximum value in the numerical scale used, and that if a P value other than zero is to represent the response, when the stimulus is at the adaptation level, its value must be $\frac{K}{2}$. The second condition is that if the subjects give their responses in *qualitative* forms that are to be converted into a numerical scale, these categories must be such as to preserve linearity between qualitative and quantitative scales. Helson has shown that the value of K that establishes the numerical scale can be selected arbitrarily, and that all K's yield the same value of A, so long as the two foregoing conditions are met.

This short statement of the concept of adaptation level and its formulation may not be very intelligible to all elementary students of perception. That is, not all readers can be expected to feel satisfied that they can apply the equation. This is not necessary to begin with. Our attempt here has been to show that a workable quantitative formulation has been produced. Those who pursue the matter of understanding human behavior farther will want to become better acquainted with the concept and its relevancy, not only to perceptual behavior, but to behavior that is studied from other aspects.

Chapter 10

SPACE PERCEPTION

The study of space perception is the study of perceptual behavior as it relates to size and shape of items and to their distances and directions from each other and from the observer. The sighted person has the apprehension of an outwardness, an extensional domain surrounding himself and in which there are other objects. Both they and he can move within this experienced domain. It is not alone something that can be directly experienced; it can be conceived of when no sensory information is being involved at the moment. When a person uses the word space, he may often be referring to what he and others are conceptualizing at the moment, such as the distance from their homes to places of employment, the shape of the earth, the relation of the earth to other planets and sun. Much of our spatial response is not perceptual but conceptual.

Man has not merely conceptualized space but he has devised methods of dealing with it. He has developed standard ways of talking about it. Geometry and trigonometry are good examples. The use of geometry has become so customary that we impute the features dealt with in geometry to being the very attributes of space itself. Euclid, two thousand years ago, developed the geometry we use even nowadays. It is a common-sense geometry, for it is a convention that follows quite closely the way we experience things. One of its axioms is that a straight line is the shortest distance between two points. It includes other axioms which we feel are "correct," and we would expect that axioms contradicting them would be absurd and untenable. It must be recognized that Euclid's is but one of several geometries, and furthermore that some of the axioms of these systems do contradict those of Euclid. Mathematicians do not think they are absurd ideas; for with them they can construct whole systems of geometry, and with these geometries they can solve some of the problems of today that are impossible with Euclid's geometry. This should be a very solid demonstration, to those who have not heretofore realized it, that geometries are man made and need not follow or corroborate direct experience. We may add that many of the problems facing physicists today are those quite outside the domain of everyday direct experience.

As psychologists, we have two facts to face—space as experienced, and space as conceptualized. We must be well aware of this when we are dealing with space in the one way and in the other. We must have ways of interrelating the items involved in the two modes.

To deal with space as a convention, or as a conceptual frame, we shall employ Euclid's geometry. It is relevant, however, to point out here that non-Euclidean geometries have been employed by advanced scholars to describe certain features of space perception, and one of these has been able to describe certain aspects better than Euclidean geometry. We shall not get to the point of describing the experiments involved, however.

As we all know Euclidean geometry describes space as an extensional domain made up of three coördinate dimensions. Two of these describe a plane in which right and left, up and down, can be handled.

In perception, the perceiver is the reference point in the space domain. In vision, for example, the plane or two-dimensional field is vertical, and at right angles to the line of regard. This plane is called the frontal plane. Space as a volume involves a third dimension that is parallel to the line of regard, that is, at right angles to the frontal plane. Structuring space in this stepwise fashion has brought about certain difficulties in dealing with visual space perception. These will be dealt with later in the chapter.

SPACE PERCEPTION DEFINED

We have already pointed out that space is conceived to be an extensional domain within which the sighted observer finds himself, and to which he refers as externality. All movements of organisms are thus events that take place in space. Since this is the case, one may ask whether all motor behavior is to be interpreted as space perception. Most persons would probably answer in the affirmative. That is to say, they would claim that if an animal can successfully get around in space, it possesses space perception of some order or other.

It is helpful in this respect to recognize two orders of behavior rather than one. One order would be movement about in space without any instantaneous organization of the behavior in relation to space as a total domain. In this case, there would be just a happenstance random movement, such as in the case of the amoeba. Such an organism need not return to any single fixed place. All that is necessary is to be able to deal with what is close by. It needs to behave merely in terms of what is encountered as food, for example. A different form of restricted behavior may also be found in higher organisms. It can be characterized as a sequential reaction to item after item in the space domain without an appreciation of the domain as a whole at any given instant. It is a form in which the animal does have to deal repeatedly with certain items in space. The animal does have to find its way about. This would be a form in which only mechanical contact with externality is needed. Such contact cannot directly deal with portions of the domain at a distance from the body. It can deal directly with only restricted portions of the space domain at any single instant. The resultant relation to externality is therefore purely a sequential affair.

The second order of response is the response to space as a whole—to the *extensional domain as a domain* rather than to single bits of it. It is this form of response which we shall call true space perception. These two forms will be described in more detail later in the chapter.

SENSE MODALITIES AND THE SPACE DOMAIN

It is our next task to examine the various sense modalities to see which of them could be expected to provide for true space perception. We must not take it for granted, to begin with, that hearing, touch, kinesthesis, and so on, each through its own processes, will provide for space perception. Certain criteria have to be met before this can be expected. They would seem to be the following. (1) A modality would have to provide for a direct ordinal relation between central nervous organization and points in space. This would imply a kind of receptor mechanism wherein large portions of the extensional domain would be represented. This representation would not be a copy, but it should involve an ordinal relationship. For the receptor mechanism to play this role, it must be affected by radiation rather than solely mechanical contact. It must deal with structures in space at various distances. (2) This representational relation must be a simultaneous one. The various points in space must be related to the neural activity pattern at all instants rather than brought about by mere sequential "exploration." The representation of the extensional domain in the sense organ must be carried into the central nervous system. Such representations are called cortical projection areas. (3) The modality must include a means whereby motor reaction patterns are incorporated into its functioning. For a sensory modality to be related to space, as already indicated, it must be related to the motor system in an orderly way. Movement and kinesthetic information from movement must be integrated with the sensory input into the modality in question.

The Muscle Sense

Kinesthesis informs the possessor of the static and changing conditions of muscles, and therefore of the position and activity of the body and its parts. For the sighted individual, body movement is experienced as something spatial.

In the brain, the muscles as motor organs are represented by a kind of spatial representational area, called the motor area. The body senses, including pressure and kinesthesis, are represented in a projection area, called the somesthetic area. These areas could be expected to integrate the items of movement and contact sensitivity, respectively, that otherwise would exist as isolated independent units. All movements of the body could be expected to be related to the body as a whole, and thus *sensitivity* of position and movement of body parts could be expected to be related to the body as a whole. In a way, then, the body could be looked upon as a miniature space domain of its own, as far as kinesthesis and pressure are concerned.

Demands for locomotion or posture would be met in relation to the situation as it pertains to the body as a whole. This would be expected to be the case even without the contribution of other sense modalities such as vision.

There would be such a thing as a tactual and kinesthetic memory. This memory would play the role of enabling the organism to utilize isolated and sequentially obtained bits of information in an organized way. Learning to get around in space or to move body members in successful and predetermined ways would thus be made possible.

Let it be recognized, however, that in this description we have intentionally implied nothing in favor of the organism's apprehension of the external space domain as such. Our description has been only one of accounting for consistent action in response to body contact with items in space through exploration, learning, and memory. We can conclude that the kinesthetic modality is not a direct informer of the structure of externality. Body movements are relative to the gravitational field, to the terrain on which one walks, and to the surface upon which one sits or lies. All involvements of the muscle sense are sequential, and provide successive bits of information rather than a simultaneously overall appreciation of space. It cannot be said, therefore, that the muscle sense is a true space sense.

The Visual Sense

We shall ask about vision next. How does the visual mechanism relate to externality? In the first place, vision is a modality whose receptor mechanism relates to externality at various distances from the body. The retina receives an orderly representation of the pattern of externality through photic radiation. The radiation reaching the eye comes from all points in almost half a sphere at each instant. This representation is relayed in an orderly fashion to the visual projection area of the cortex, and the representation is also shunted off to motor centers of the brain wherein appropriate muscular movement directives are organized. Part of the muscular system is built right into the visual sense organ itself. The postures of the eyeballs are a part of the orderly overall reaction to the space domain itself. The eyes are not passive but rather become part of the mechanism for manipulating the organism's relation to the domain. Integration of seeing and moving is furthered by eye movements as well as by the movements of the head and body.

It can be said, therefore, that vision satisfies the criteria set up and is a form of true space perception. Vision provides a space frame, and, in turn, visual perception takes on its full form through the operation of such a frame.

In Chapter 4 it was pointed out that when a given modality is directly activated by stimulation of its own sense organs, the end result is not only the experience belonging to that modality but also the elicitation of associative imagery. Visual imagery is elicited when the muscle sense is activated. This means that muscular behavior is guided by visual imagery, even when the person is blindfolded or adventitiously blinded. Movements made in such persons are those made in a space world. The relations between space, vision, and movement must necessarily become very intimate through this developmental procedure.

The Auditory Sense

Hearing is a kind of perception that in the sighted is thought of as a space sense. When you and I hear something, what we hear is in reference to some point in space. The sounds we hear generally "come from" somewhere. Despite this appearance of hearing as a space sense, an examination will show that it is not.

The sense organ in the ear is sensitive only to differences in intensity and wave frequency and timing. Intense acoustic impingements produce louder sounds than weak ones do. High frequencies are heard as having a different quality (pitch) than low frequencies. There is nothing about the construction of the arrangement of the receptors themselves to correspond with any feature of space, as in the case of the retina. There is no space-related projection area in the brain for hearing. The only factors in hearing that have anything to do with space are the shape of the outer ear and the presence of two ears instead of one. The two ears are affected intensively in accordance with whether the acoustic source is to one side of the ear or the other, or whether directly behind or directly in front of it. Binaural phase relations in the wave fronts from some acoustic stimuli provide somewhat of a differential. These factors help to prove a gross relation between the space location of the source, and when taken by themselves cannot be expected to establish an appreciation of externality as such. Sounds do not fill a domain with detail, as do sights.

The chief result possible with a mechanism such as this is that the listener is enabled to turn his head toward the source by reason of the fact that in so doing he is adjusting his head so that the two ears are receiving the same amount of energy, or that the acoustic waves are put into similar phase. Even this behavior does not necessarily establish, for the congenitally blind, that sounds "come from outside."

Sighted individuals, on the other hand, whenever they hear a sound, may experience it as somewhere outside of themselves, in space. It may be thought that this constitutes evidence that hearing is a space sense. But it must be cautioned that this localization is provided for in the first place by the existence of a space frame for which the visual sense is responsible. Sound, when localized, is heard in a visual space frame, not in an auditory one. Audition is not a sense that by its nature can give us an initial appreciation of the space domain. The appreciation it does provide is one that is based on the operation of vision.

The Tactual Sense

In the tactual or pressure sense, we have the fourth candidate for a space sense. What we have already said about kinesthesis applies to touch. We have already coupled them together in some things we have said. They belong quite together, and much of what can be said about one can be said about the other.

The visual modality remains the only sense modality that inherently contains the mechanisms which relate the organism to its surrounds in such ways as to enable us to call it a true space sense. Other modalities operating by themselves or collectively could not provide the necessary relations between organism and surrounds to give us an appreciation of externality.

THE POINT OR AIR THEORY

The conventional and classical way of accounting for human visual space perception is to begin with a point and proceed as if all space was made up of an aggregation of points. This is in line with the old analytical-sensation outlook on perception. Perception of two-dimensional space is considered possible by the operation of simple optics, because the retina is, in effect, a two-dimensional surface upon which two-dimensional space can be represented or copied. It is the third dimension in space that gives the conventional space theory its trouble. The third dimension is not conceived to be representable on the retina, since it is only a two-dimensional manifold.

Two kinds of factors, called "cues," have been resorted to. One kind includes the peripheral factors: the convergence of the two eyes and ocular accommodation. Since the amount of convergence is lawfully related to target distance, this factor could become a learned cue for distance. Accommodation or focusing of the eyes is also expected to be a cue for distance, for accommodation is a muscular effect which varies lawfully as distance of target is manipulated.

The second kind of cue has been the monocular cue. There are about seven of these usually listed. We shall not discuss these at length, for we have pointed them out previously as examples of using one aspect of perception to explain the other concurrent aspects. For example, interposition and elevation are two monocular cues that are commonly given. To describe interposition is to describe what the observer sees, rather than merely to tell of the metric features of the stimulus. If one object is *seen* interposed between the observer and another object, then the object partially covered is seen as farther away. By the method of resorting to these cues, the observer's appreciation of the visual field is built up, as it were, bit by bit. In this way of dealing with the relations between the stimulus and the response, nothing is provided to begin with in the form of a description of overall field structure whereby to account for the roles played by restricted portions of it.

THE TEXTURE-GRADIENT CONCEPT

The texture-gradient concept of the essential nature of the organism's visually perceived surrounds, although implied to some extent in what artists and draftsmen have been doing for centuries, is a recent development. It is embodied in a recent book by Gibson (86) that describes the nature of the visual world. The concept is an answer to the puzzle experienced by those who for many decades have asked how it is that the organism can perceive the third dimension. Whereas the first two dimensions which define a plane can be represented on another plane, such as the receiving surface of the retina, the age-old question asked how the third dimension could be represented. The reasoning underlying the question was to the effect that it would require a three-dimensional space. This question was seriously asked again and again despite the fact that artists and draftsmen had been representing three-dimensional objects and space relations on two-dimensional surfaces for several centuries.

The texture-gradient concept implies that all surfaces function as components of a macrotexture of the visual field as a whole. Many surfaces are themselves physically differentiated in some way so as to be seen as textured. So in one way or another the whole visual field is textured. The texture possesses various effective characteristics in keeping with the orientation of the surface with reference to the viewer. The surface which lies in what we call the frontal plane, i.e., the plane at right angles to the line of regard (usually vertical to the earth), provides an undistorted retinal image. That is, there is practically a one-to-one relation between it and the image.

All other surfaces, i.e., all those lying outside the frontal plane, form tapered textures in the retinal image. The viewer looks at such surfaces obliquely; and it is well known that when this is the case, the farther end of such a surface is geometrically more oblique to the viewer than its near end. A good example of this is the floor that one stands upon. As one looks down at the floor near one's feet, the floor lies almost in the frontal plane. As one views the floor farther and farther away from one's feet, the obliquity increases. If one looks out along a long hall, the yonder end seems almost to be at eye level and the texture of the floor covering is finer and finer as distance increases. There are, of course, two reasons for this: first, the increasing distance; and second, the increasing obliquity of viewing it. The difference between viewing in the frontal plane and viewing an oblique surface is pictured in Fig. 10.1. In it the two surfaces are marked off in equal spaces by lines running from the surface to the eye. The projected image of the oblique plane (the floor surface) is a tapered texture in the retinal image. Fig. 10.2 shows the same sort of situation as viewed by the perceiver. The one

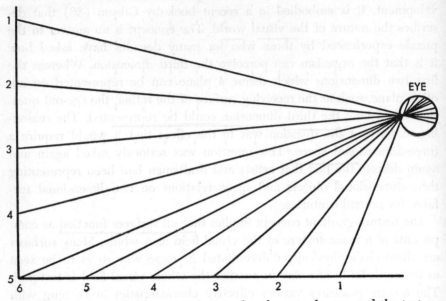

FIG. 10.1. Relation between orientation of surfaces to the eye and the texture they present to it. Frontal-plane surfaces present a uniform texture when the target field is uniform. The same surfaces oriented obliquely present a graded texture.

texture is seen as the yonder wall, and the tapered texture is seen as the floor extending from near the viewer to the yonder wall. The term perspective applies to the scene. But the term refers not only to perception but to the techniques the artist and draftsman use to produce the kind of perception we are dealing with here.

In fact, there are four items to which the term perspective generally refers: (1) the target (the three-dimensional visual field), (2) the two-dimensional representation of a three-dimensional visual situation, (3) the retinal image, and (4) the perception. In common practice the term perspective is most used for (1), (2), and (4). It would be helpful if we made some restriction upon our usage of the word. Let us use the term only for (4), the perception. Let us use the *third dimension* to describe the target (1), *foreshortening* to describe the arrangement in a two-dimensional representation of a three-dimensional object (2), and the form and composition of the retinal image (3). Thus we see perspective and can produce it by presenting a three-dimensional target, or a foreshortened two-dimensional representation of the original target.

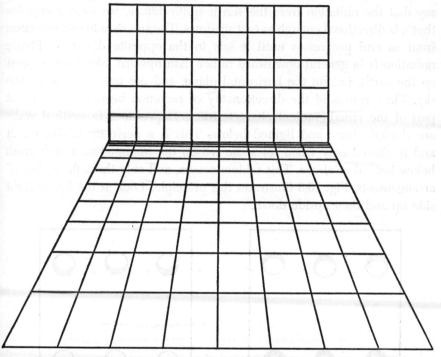

Fig. 10.2. The appearance of the surfaces dealt with in Fig. 10.1.

Both of these presentations produce essentially the same sort of retinal images, which also may be spoken of as being foreshortened when they represent planes oblique to the line of regard.

The second major realization involved in the texture-gradient concept is that the visual world (outdoors) is divided by a horizontal line called the horizon. The texture gradient, or taper of the ground (field below the horizon) and the sky (field above the horizon), runs in opposite directions. Faraway positions of the field, both in sky and on land, are of fine texture. These two gradients of texture meet at the horizon.

In all that we have just said we have been describing a definite and lawful relation between features of the three-dimensional domain called space and the representation of it in strictly geometrical terms on the retina. This description is a sufficient answer to the question of how it can be that the organism can appreciate the three-dimensional visual world.

There are still more features to the texture-gradient concept. One of these is that the organism lives in a world in which photic radiation is not perfectly diffuse but instead is directional. Even though at times we say that the radiation from the sun is quite diffuse, we must recognize that it is directional enough to cast shadows. The sun rises in one direction from us and progresses until it sets in the opposite direction. Photic radiation is in general downward rather than upward. Shadows are cast on the earth, i.e., on the horizontal plane, and not upward toward the sky. Thus, results of the directionality of radiation become an inherent part of the visual-gradient characteristics. Depressions in vertical walls are shaded above and lighted below. This is a perfectly lawful result and is altered only when for some reason the illumination comes from below instead of above. This seldom occurs, and only through "artificial" arrangements. Fig. 10.3 illustrates this principle. Look at the figure right side up and then upside down.

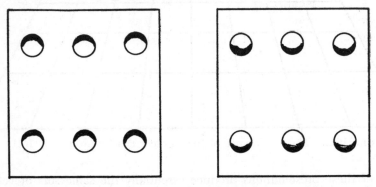

FIG. 10.3. Diagrams to show the relation between direction of illumination and consequent shadows to the perception of bulges and recesses. The left-hand diagram contains recesses; the other contains bulges such as are exemplified by rivet heads.

There are still other features of the texture-gradient concept to be pointed out. According to it, the elements of vision, or the starting points in considering visual behavior, are not *points*, as in the air theory, but are *edges, corners*, and so on, the abruptions formed by the junctions of various gradients. Visual objects differ in complex ways by reason of differences in gradients.

Much of the material of the present chapter will be descriptions of the relations between perceptual end results and the way that the images on the two retinas differ from each other. The two retinas are neurally connected to the central nervous system in such ways as to function properly only when the two eyes are coördinated posturally.

In general, it may be considered that the texture-gradient concept of the visual stimulus field is useful in both one-eyed seeing (monocular vision) and two-eyed seeing (binocular vision). The proper interaction between the two eyes (good binocular vision) provides for a more precise use of the texture gradients of the visual field. Thus binocular vision does not supersede monocular, but only makes better use of the visual stimulus complex under certain conditions. On the other hand, when the two eyes do not work together properly, a less effective vision than monocular vision results.

THE VISUAL ANGLE

One of the simple geometrical facts applying to the relation between targets and retinal images is the visual angle. The visual angle is the solid angle subtended by a target at the eye. Thus the target can be specified in terms of the visual angle it subtends, rather than by telling its metric dimensions and its distance from the observer. There is a fixed relation between the visual angle and the size of the retinal image, and thus instead of specifying the metric size of a visual image it is customary to give it in angular terms. An image subtending a given angle possesses a metric size, and covers a given number of retinal elements, depending upon the density of their distribution in the given part of the retina.

When the phenomenal size of an object depends simply upon the visual angle subtended by the target, it is said that the "law of visual angle" is being followed. In this case, for instance, doubling the visual angle would be expected to double the size of the phenomenal object.

Under some conditions the law of the visual angle is quite closely followed, and in others it is widely departed from. The widest departure consists in the production of no change in the phenomenal (perceived) size of the object when visual angle is varied. In such cases, maximal *size constancy* is said to obtain.

The law of the visual angle provides for an unlimited number of targets differing metrically and in geometrical location producing the same perceptual end result. That is, such targets will all provide for

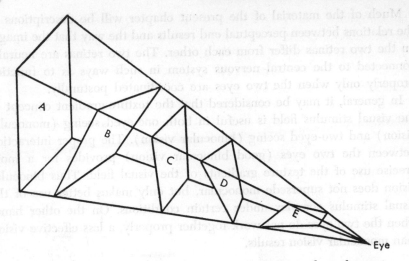

Fig. 10.4. Diagram showing that an unlimited number of targets may subtend the same visual angles at the eye. The targets are A, B, C, D, and E.

seeing the same object. This one is illustrated by Fig. 10.4.

All the plane targets, A, B, C, D, E, and an infinite number of others of various sizes and at various distances will subtend the same visual angles. Unless there is further structuring of the visual field to alter results, these targets will be seen as the same object when one is presented at a time.

EQUIVALENCE IN STIMULUS SITUATIONS

An infinite number of external situations may be visually *equivalent;* that is, they may look exactly the same from the observer's point of view. The example given earlier (page 182 f.) of a luminous rectangular target, presented in a dark room, is a case in point.

A still better example of equivalence is provided by the distorted rooms of Ames. He showed that an endless series of rooms of various shapes will look like a given rectangular room (a "normal" room) just so long as certain conditions in their construction are satisfied. First examine Fig. 10.5. You will notice that the room looks rectilinear and in every way normal, but there seems to be something the matter with the sizes of the faces of the two persons seen looking through the windows. The person to the left is smaller than the person to the right.

This difference would be expected only if one were literally smaller than the other, for the windows of the room appear to be of equal size. The two persons seem also to be equally far away. It is very puzzling why the two persons differ in size, for human faces do not generally, if ever, differ as much in size as these do.

We may now turn to the construction of the room. In B of Fig. 10.6, a normal room with two side windows and two back windows is shown.

FIG. 10.5. View of a distorted room with two persons looking in windows (drawing from photograph in M. Lawrence, *Studies in Human Behavior*, Princeton University Press, 1949, p. 89, Fig. 10).

As part of the diagram, we have pictured the position of the single eye to be used in viewing the room. From the eye, dotted lines are drawn to show the visual angles subtended by the windows and the corners of the room. These lines may be also considered as *lines* of *direction*.

The distorted room is shown in A of the figure. The same lines of direction are used for the features of this room. Since the walls are in a different position than those in the normal room, the windows have to be of different sizes so as to subtend the proper visual angles and lie in the same directions as they do in the normal room.

It will be noted that the back windows are larger than they are in the normal room, and that the left window is larger than the right one. The two circles are meant to represent the heads of people. Hence, if one person looks in at the right window and the other at the left window, the two persons' heads and faces will be of very different apparent sizes, since the windows are of the same apparent size and the two faces subtend different visual angles. This difference in angular

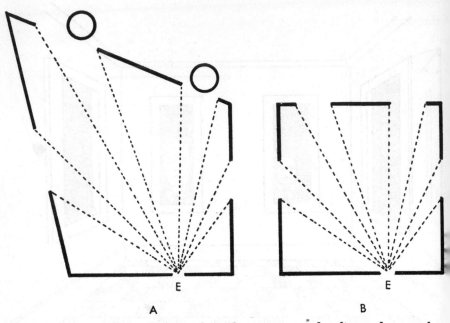

A   B

FIG. 10.6. Floor plans of a normal rectilinear room and a distorted room, the windows in both subtending the same visual angles at the eye, E. The circles represent similar-sized objects that may look unequal in size in this context.

subtense is brought about by a difference in the distances of the two faces from the viewing position.

The distorted-room diagram in A of Fig. 10.6 is only one of the types of rooms built by Ames. In the present one, the distortions are those necessary to make the room appear normal when viewed from a point to the right of the center of the near wall. Only the lateral distortions are pictured in the diagram, but vertical distortions are also involved to compare with the lateral ones. These are shown in diagram A of Fig. 10.7. A second type of distorted room is shown in diagram B of the same figure. The viewing point for the second room is at the midpoint of the near wall rather than off to the right, as for the first room.

When the distorted room of the first type is large enough for people to stand upright in it, a further test can be made. When one person stands against the rear wall on the left, and another person stands against the wall on the right, they do not look equal in size. In fact, if the room is photographed, the photographs of the two persons are not equal in size. This is brought about by the fact that the person to the left is farther away than his partner to the right. The use of distorted rooms for monocular viewing certainly demonstrates exceedingly well the operation of the law of the visual angle.

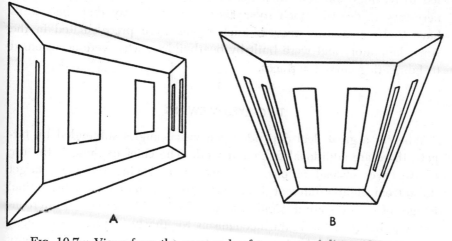

FIG. 10.7. Views from the open ends of two sorts of distorted rooms.

The basis for the whole set of effects in the present example is the preclusion of factors other than the law of visual angle from operating. This is not the case in common situations, and thus very startling results are achieved here. The first factor is the adoption of a single fixed point for viewing the presentation. The presentation is a situation that provides for the seeing of planes or surfaces at discernible orientations from the point of viewing. What is seen is a room with a back wall in the frontal plane. Moving the target planes does not change the overall appearance since the visual angles that provided, in the first place, for the perception of a rectilinear room are maintained in the new target called the distorted room. All that is necessary to make something look smaller than would be expected is to place it farther away from the perceiver. This is most readily done by moving one end of the wall of the room farther away. Thus, when an object of fixed size is placed against a feature of the new wall (itself enlarged), the old object looks small. Really, it is small for two reasons: (1) it subtends a smaller visual angle than it would when closer to the viewer, and (2) it is smaller relative to a fixed feature of the viewed scene than a second metrically equivalent object (a second face). To put the matter in brief terms, the visual field was so structured as to preclude size constancy for the test targets used, and to promote size constancy for items following the law of the visual angle.

Rooms properly distorted for binocular viewing have also been made. Since the two eyes view a room from two different positions, room form has to be quite different than the form for one-eyed viewing. It is not necessary to describe such rooms here, except to say that their walls have to be complexly curved. Such rooms were precalculated in the Ames laboratory and were built by boatbuilders, who were accustomed to fabricating curved surfaces.

TWO-EYED VIEWING

Whereas a great deal depends upon visual angles subtended by targets, there are additional factors at work. The chief of these is the use of two eyes instead of one. The two eyes viewing the same target do so from slightly different directions, and as a consequence the retinal images of the eyes are dissimilar. Coupled with this are neural interconnections between the brain mechanisms for the two eyes. These interconnections are such that various kinds of integrations in brain activity are brought about in accordance with the differences in the two retinal images.

Differences in the forms of the two retinal images are produced by confrontment with situations in the external space domain. The organism learns on the basis of the orderly relation between retinal images and properties of the space domain. This learning is the development of experiences of size, location, distance, etc., and the ability to react in lawful ways to externality. Hence any condition, whether artificial (done by lenses) or not, that produces the image differences produces the appropriate experience of some three-dimensional scene. All that remains for the experimenter is to learn what external three-dimensional situations produce what retinal images in the two eyes. Once this is known, the experimenter can produce substitute situations and use them as laboratory presentations. In accordance, then, with the laws pertaining to such matters, he can produce predictable experiences whether common or bizarre.

Let us depict some of the more simple and fundamental features of the relations between targets and retinal images. Fig. 10.8 demonstrates the simple fact that the retinal images of the two eyes differ from one another when a simple target is shifted out of the frontal plane. The figure also shows that the two halves of the target are not

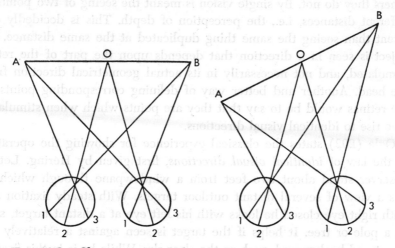

FIG. 10.8. Changes in internal proportions of retinal images produced by changes in orientation of target. AOB is the target. Images are signified by 1, 2, 3. In the left-hand diagram, 1–2 equals 2–3; at right, it does not.

necessarily represented by two equal portions of the retinal image when this shift is made.

THE HOROPTER

The horopter is the aggregation of points within the visual field at which a target is seen as single in binocular viewing with the eyes in a given position. All other points lie outside the horopter. There are many horopters; for as the two eyes shift from converging (pointing toward) upon a given point to converging upon a point nearer or farther away, the horopter is a different one and has a different shape.

The apparent frontal plane (horopter) changes shape depending upon the fixation distance. If the observer's eyes converge upon a distant point, the horopter tends to be geometrically convex toward the observer. If he fixates at a suitable lesser distance, the apparent frontal plane is a geometrical plane. At a still nearer distance, the apparent

frontal plane is concave toward the observer. The points on the horopter
are said to stimulate corresponding points in the two retinas. By definition, the points on the two retinas which, when stimulated simultaneously, always give rise to single vision are said to correspond. In certain
cases, noncorresponding points give rise to single vision and in certain
others they do not. By single vision is meant the seeing of two points at
different distances, i.e., the perception of depth. This is decidedly different than seeing the same thing duplicated at the same distance. An
object is seen in a direction that depends upon the part of the retina
stimulated, and not necessarily in its actual geometrical direction from
the head. Another and better way of defining corresponding points on
the retinas would be to say that they are points which when stimulated
give rise to identical visual directions.

Ogle (202) states the classical experience for showing the operation
of the law of *identical visual directions,* first given by Hering. Let an
observer stand about two feet from a windowpane through which he
has a view of several distant outdoor targets. With steady fixation and
with right eye closed he looks with his left eye at a distant target, such
as a pole or tree. It helps if the target is seen against a relatively unstructured background, such as the clear sky. While he is in this fixation
posture, let a mark be placed on the windowpane in line with the eye
and target. Now let the left eye be closed and the right eye opened
and pointed toward the mark on the windowpane. While so doing, let
the gaze pick up a distance target in line with the mark and the eye.
Now let both eyes be opened and directed (fixated) upon the mark
on the window. Once the images are "fused" and the observer sees the
mark as a single one, he can also see the two targets in line with the
mark. This means that one sees all three items in the same forward
apparent direction, despite the three geometrically different directions
from the observer.

RETINAL DISPARITY

Images from target points that do not fall on corresponding points on
the two retinas are said to be *disparate,* and in monocular vision would
result in two different experiences involving two different perceptual directions. The farther the points are away from the horopter, the greater
the disparity. Disparities can be of two sorts, vertical and horizontal.
However, it is the horizontal disparities that underlie the stereoscopic
perception of third dimension.

Disparities can also be spoken of as crossed and uncrossed, as shown in Figs. 10.9 and 10.10. Fig. 10.9 shows the separate images of an outdoor scene with the horizon and a roadway leading to it. The vanishing point is labeled V for each image. In Fig. 10.10 the two images are fused, which means that the eyes are fixating upon the vanishing point

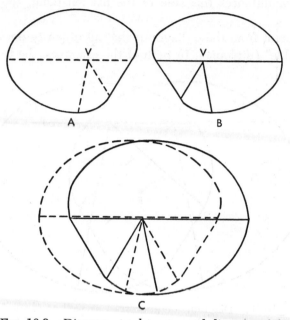

Fig. 10.9. Diagrams to show crossed disparity. A is image of field and fixation point on the left eye. B is the same for the right eye. When both diagrams are placed so that the fixation point is the common point, representation of material for the left eye near the fixation point lies to the right (dotted line). Material for the right eye lies to the left. This is the form of retinal-image disparity that is called *crossed* disparity (J. J. Gibson, *Perception of the Visual World*, Houghton Mifflin, 1950, Fig. 48).

of the road. The two V's fall on corresponding points on the two retinas, in this case the two foveas. It will be noted, however, that certain portions of the rest of the two images do not coincide. Failure to coincide represents disparity. The kind shown in this case is crossed disparity. At the level of the fixation point, disparity is absent, but above and below this line disparity begins and progressively increases. In this gradient, the left eye's image is displaced to the right, and the right eye's image is displaced to the left. This is why the disparity is called crossed disparity.

For fixation on a point nearer than the horizon, the portions of the two images at the level of the fixation point will be made to coincide. But there will be disparity above and below this level, as in the previous example. For distances this side of the fixation point, the disparity is crossed.

It is apparent from these diagrams that all disparity does not lead to "seeing double" (diplopia). In both of the examples, the two eyes were

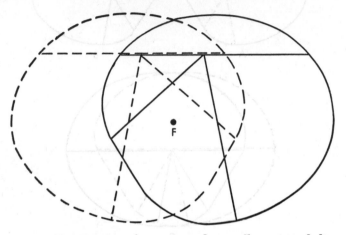

Fig. 10.10. Diagram for uncrossed as well as crossed disparity. Uncrossed disparity is produced by target elements beyond the fixation point, F (J. J. Gibson, *Perception of the Visual World*, Houghton Mifflin, 1950, Fig. 48).

converged on some point and thus a part of the visual field was being represented on corresponding portions of the two retinas. The target involved in the fixation was the target that the individual was attending to. Retinal disparities progressed from the level of fixation upward and downward. Disparity was the basis for perceiving various distances.

On the other hand, when no portions of the two retinal images are made to coincide for the targets viewed, there is no basis for disparity gradients, no basis for seeing singularly what is being looked at, and double vision occurs.

The topic of double versus single vision is so complex that it cannot be covered here. No single rule can be given to the beginner in understandable terms that would enable him to predict regarding double vision and the mere result of seeing third dimension. A very common demonstration of double vision can be produced by holding up one's index fingers at eye level. The one is placed about 5 or 6 inches from the eye and the other at 12 to 15 inches. If one looks at the near finger, there are two far fingers, one on either side of the near one, but of course at a greater distance from the eye than it. If one looks at the far finger, the near finger is doubled. This sort of result is much different than when one extends his arm outward and then looks at any given point out along it. In no case is any part of the arm seen as double. Thus in some respects (certain geometrical respects) the two situations are alike, but in certain others they must be different. These differences may be both external and something pertaining to the organism's own learning.

ASYMMETRY IN RETINAL IMAGES

Inasmuch as the two eyes converge when they point toward near targets and do not converge when quite distant targets are viewed, students of vision have at times supposed that the kinesthesis that would be involved in positioning the eyes would be a "cue" for the perception

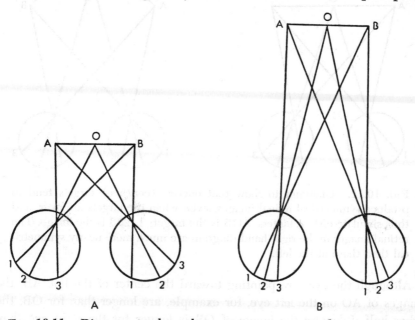

FIG. 10.11. Diagrams to show that convergence varies the amount of asymmetry in the retinal images. See Fig. 10.8 for another basis for asymmetry. AOB is the target; 1, 2, 3 is the image. In the left-hand diagram, 1–2 is unequal to 2–3; at right, the two are almost equal.

of depth (third dimension). Workers have not been too successful in providing tangible evidence that convergence, with its consequent kinesthetic innervation, does provide a basis for discriminating third dimension and distances.

There is, however, another factor that is brought into play where convergence is varied. Convergence varies the amount of asymmetry of the retinal images. Fig. 10.11 will indicate how this is involved. In diagram A the two eyes are fixated on a near target. It will be noted that the images of the two eyes, though alike, are internally asymmetrical.

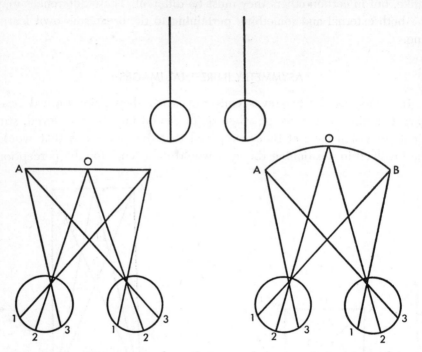

FIG. 10.12. Diagrams to show that curved (concave) targets tend to produce symmetrical retinal images, even when the targets are near, and thus simulate distant targets. AOB is the target; 1, 2, 3 is the image. The retinal images in the right-hand diagram are much more nearly symmetrical than those at the left.

Although the eyes are pointing toward the center of the line AB, the images of AO on the left eye, for example, are longer than for OB, the other half. Likewise the image of OB is longer for the right eye than is the image for AO. Were the eyes to be pointed toward a very distant target, this inequality (asymmetry) would be reduced to the vanishing point. Thus, in keeping with target distance, the images may vary from having no asymmetry at all to having considerable asymmetry. By use of a curved viewing field, such as is shown in Fig. 10.12, the images of a scene painted on it may be made to look far away. A large factor in producing such an end result is the one just mentioned. The scene on the curved surface tends to be imaged on the two retinas with much less if not zero asymmetry. This technique is often used in museums for the distance features of animal habitats.

TILT IN THE THIRD DIMENSION

Another example to show the relation of ocular activity, externality, and visual perception is the case of viewing a luminous line in a dark room. The question put to the perceiver is whether the line is vertical or tilts in the third dimension. Actually, the line when out of the vertical may or may not be seen as tilted.

Let us ask about the retinal images produced by a vertical-line target. Fig. 10.13 shows the retinal images. It will be noted that the images are

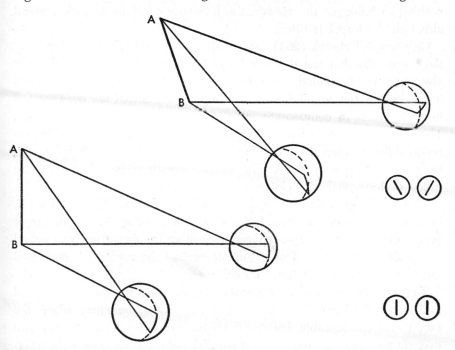

FIG. 10.13. Diagrams showing positions of retinal images for a vertical-line target and a tipped-line target. In the former case, the images are vertical, and in the latter they are rotated laterally outward at the top for a line target whose top is tipped away from the eye. AB is the line target.

parallel to each other, and are vertical. It must be remembered that since there are two eyes involved and they are separated horizontally, the "views" obtained by them are convergent ones. That is, they are slightly like side views rather than views from straight ahead.

If the line target is now tipped, this change affects the retinal images in a manner that would not happen if there was only one eye involved and it viewed the line from straight in front. With single-eyed viewing all that would happen to the retinal image would be a foreshortening. If the line was to be tipped nearly to the horizontal position, the line would become very short. It would approach being a mere point.

With the slightly sidelike views of the two eyes converging toward the line, the retinal images would undergo not only some foreshortening but also some rotation. The rotation produced in the two eyes is in opposite directions from the vertical and thus is a case of retinal disparity, already discussed. This disparity is the stimulus basis for seeing the line tilted.

If the line target is a luminous one in a dark field, so that there is nothing to influence the viewer, the line may continue to look vertical although the target is tilted.

Ogle and Ellerbrock (203) studied the perceptual effects produced by the target situation just described and found that the observer did not always see the line tilted when the target was tipped, at least not unless it was greatly tipped. They came to the conclusion that the eyes rotated in their orbits to compensate for the rotations of the retinal images. The proper rotations of the eyes prevented the images from falling on points different than when the line target was vertical and therefore the target was seen as vertical. The eyeball rotations just described are called cyclofusional or cyclotorsional movements.

That the kinesthesis from cyclotorsional movements did not, in itself, become interpreted in some fashion as indicating a change in target position is then an example of how insensitive the organism is to actual eye position. It is a kind of argument against the organism's supposed use of convergence as a "cue" for distance.

To preclude the use of binocular vision (i.e., the production and utilization of different images in the two eyes), one may place the target at a considerable distance from the eyes, in which case the two eyes do not converge but take up parallel pointing positions with reference to the target. Thus single distant luminous lines would always be somewhat indeterminate in their positions.

STEREOSCOPY

Stereoscopy has to do with the principles underlying the production of third dimension in binocular vision. Some visual fields seem three-dimensional for reasons other than those we are about to describe. On the other hand, the dissimilarity between the images in the two eyes, and the differences in location of the images in the two eyes, play decisive roles in the perception of the third dimension.

Fig. 10.14 is a diagram that indicates where various points in space are projected on to the retinas of the two eyes when the eyes are in a

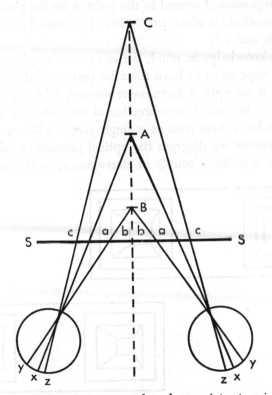

FIG. 10.14. Diagram to show how points at various distances are projected onto the retina at various distances from the fovea. Point A is the fixation point. Point B is nearer, and point C farther away. If one substitutes a stereogram, SS, points A, B, and C would be represented by points a, b, and c on it. Points a, b, and c are projected onto the retina as points x, y, z.

given position. When the two eyes are fixated on a common point, the images of points nearer or farther away than the fixation point are located as indicated in the figure. The fixation point is A and it is projected on the fovea of each eye. The point beyond the fixation point is C and it is projected onto the nasal portion of each eye. The point nearer than the fixation point is projected onto the temporal portion of each eye.

The line SS represents a plane that cuts through lines from points A, B, and C. Actually, the line represents the frontal plane. On this line, it can be seen that near points such as B are represented by points outward (lateral) to the fixation point A. Likewise, points more remote than A are represented central to the point A on the plane. These points then may constitute a *plane projection* of a three-dimensional situation (points A, B, and C).

With this knowledge in mind, we can construct pictures or diagrams for a stereoscope so as to have them be perceived the way we wish. A stereoscope is an optical instrument through which a separate target for each eye is viewed. The redirection of the radiation from the targets is such as to have them seen as a single target with an enhanced third dimension. Before we diagram the optical principle used in the stereoscope, let us examine a couple of stereograms, as shown in Fig. 10.15.

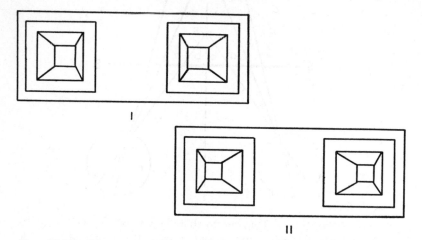

Fig. 10.15. *Two stereograms.* The components in the targets of the top one are so shifted that they will be seen as a truncated pyramid. In the bottom stereogram, the shift is in the opposite direction. The targets will be seen as a hallway.

In stereogram I, the two pictures (targets) are so constructed that they will be seen as a truncated pyramid with its small portion (apex)

toward the viewer. This is because the small squares are shifted toward
the center of the target. The results are as indicated by the findings from
point B, Fig. 10.14. In stereogram II, the opposite is true and the picture
seen is one of a long hallway through which one looks to the doorway
at its far end.

Fig. 10.16 indicates the optical principles of the stereoscope. It will
be seen that the light is redirected by the prism lenses so as to simulate
different origins than the actual ones.

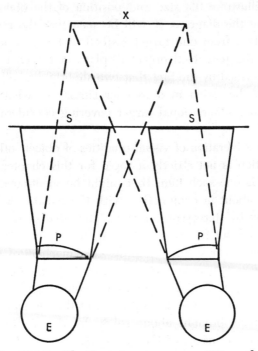

FIG. 10.16.   *The Brewster stereoscope.* EE are the
eyes of the viewer. PP are the prisms that redirect
the radiation from SS, the stereogram items, so
as to enter the eyes as if coming from target X.
Since the radiation is coming from such a direction, and this is common for both eyes, a single
picture is seen.

At this point, a rule of thumb is helpful. Parts of the visual field
("points") look to be where they would be if radiation came straight
from them to the eye. This rule is pertinent, for we shall be using lenses,
prisms, mirrors, etc., to change the direction of the radiation from what
it was as it left the target. This rule is a recognition of the fact that it

does not make any difference how many times radiation is redirected between its leaving the target and reaching the eye; it is only its direction as it enters the eye that counts. In diagraming the radiation and its redirection (refraction), the rule is used by projecting outward from each eye to indicate the direction of radiant origin and to determine where these directions for the two eyes intersect. The intersection is the point from which the radiation seems to originate. When this rule is applied, one chooses the borders of a target for use in diagraming. In that way one can illustrate the size and position of the phenomenal object.

In examining the diagram, it will be seen that the radiation is as if it was originating from one target instead of the two actual ones. We may add that the perceived object displays enhanced third dimension. This is accomplished by the fact that two slightly dissimilar targets were projected onto the retina in a manner similar to what would be the case when a three-dimensional target covering considerable distance is viewed.

While the consideration of visual qualities of objects other than shape, size, and location is not strictly a topic for this chapter on space perception, there is one such item that might be mentioned here. It is an effect brought about in conjunction with the enhancement of apparent third dimension by stereoscopic means. The effect is that of having the objects that stand out from each other at the various distinctly different distances change their surface qualities and mechanical character. Targets that are seen as people with bodies of flesh and blood tend to turn into stone-hard objects. What is pliable becomes rigid.

This would seem to be some indication of the intimate relation of the widespread effects brought about solely by the manipulations of the forms of the retinal images of the two eyes.

FURTHER MANIPULATIONS OF DISPARITY

Binocular disparity may be manipulated by three instruments, which we shall describe. Attention to how these manipulations are produced will further aid in understanding space perception. Among other things, it ought increase the reader's assurance regarding the assertion that the structure of visual space (what is seen external to oneself) is precisely controlled by the nature of the retinal images of the two eyes in relation to each other.

The stereoscope that was described earlier was the kind that Brewster invented many years ago. Wheatstone invented a different sort in which

mirrors instead of prisms were involved. In the following description of
the telestereoscope, we have an application or modification of the Wheatstone principle. Figure 10.17 shows the principle of the telestereoscope.
The target, T, is viewed by reflection from two sets of mirrors. The first
set, M and M, receive radiation from the target from two widely separate

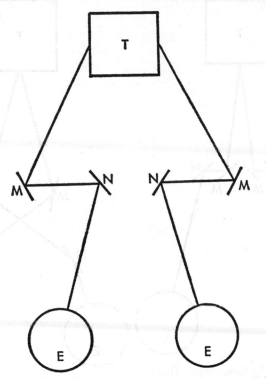

FIG. 10.17. *The telestereoscope.* This is essentially
Wheatstone's stereoscope modified for viewing a
single target. The distances between mirrors M
and N can be made quite great, so that the two
"views" of target T can be diverse. This enhances
the disparity, and therefore the appreciation of
third dimension. The system is one that, in effect,
increases the distance between the two eyes, EE.

positions. These "views" will be quite different, owing to the fact that
they will be more like side views. The reflections of the target are
picked up by mirrors N and N, which are close enough together to be
used by the eyes in a somewhat converged position. Thus the eyes with
their normal separation and in a quite usual posture of convergence will
be receiving radiation from a target as if they were widely separated

The amount of retinal disparity is, of course, enhanced. This enhancement functions to increase the depth of the target, that is, its third dimension. Where the telestereoscope is used to view distance targets, the separation of mirrors M and M may be as much as several feet. In

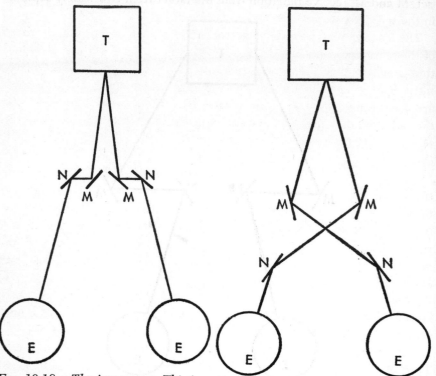

FIG. 10.18. *The iconoscope.* This instrument produces effects just opposite to those of the telestereoscope in Fig. 10.17. By means of the iconoscope the effective separation of the two eyes is minimized, and thus disparity in the two retinal images of the same object is reduced. T is the target; MM and NN, the mirrors redirecting the radiation to the eyes, EE.

FIG. 10.19. *The mirror pseudoscope,* an instrument for interchanging the "views" obtained by the two eyes, and thus reversing the disparities of their retinal images. T is the target; MM and NN, the mirrors redirecting radiation to the eyes, EE.

this way the precision of third-dimensional location is greatly enhanced. This principle has been used for range finders, which are used in connection with sighting of guns.

The difference between a telestereoscope and Wheatstone's stereoscope is this. In the telestereoscope, a single target is reflected to mirrors

M and M. In the stereoscope, mirrors M and M are replaced by separate stereograms. That is, at one mirror M there is a picture, and at the other mirror M there is another picture, a slightly different view of the same target or scene, as in the case of Brewster's stereoscope. Also, between items M and M the distance is greatly reduced from what it is in the telestereoscope.

The iconoscope is an instrument for producing effects opposite to those of the telestereoscope. The iconoscope minimizes binocular disparity and thus would reduce the appreciation of the third dimension. The instrument is diagramed in Fig. 10.18. In it, two sets of mirrors (or prisms) are used. Mirrors M and M are placed as close together as possible and the radiation they pick up from the target is directed to mirrors N and N separated by the usual amount to re-direct it to the slightly converged eyes.

The third instrument is the mirror pseudoscope (Fig. 10.19). It is so constructed as to reverse the disparity that would occur with the naked eyes or with the two instruments just described. The left eye is made to receive what the right eye would ordinarily receive, and the right eye is made to receive what the left eye would receive. This reversal of disparity makes far targets look near and near targets look far. It will be recalled (page 222 f.) that targets farther away than the fixation distance produced uncrossed disparity and targets nearer produced crossed disparity. From this it can be understood that crossing and uncrossing disparity has a third-dimensional effect in visual perception.

With a pseudoscope a convex target can be made to look concave. This, of course, is just one aspect of the reversal of distances of parts of the target from the eyes.

VISION WITH SIZE LENSES

One of the means for manipulating the shapes of retinal images, and thus the perception of objects and spatial relations, is the use of *size lenses.*

All of the lenses that are commonly used in everyday affairs are *power lenses.* Power lenses focus radiation and form images. Because of this, they are limited in their use for certain experimental purposes in dealing with space perception. When they are used in certain ways, they produce the perception of blur. In many cases, this is contrary to what is needed. Power lenses are of several shapes, such as biconvex, plano-convex, biconcave, plano-concave, and so on. In every case, the two faces of the lens are not parallel or concentric. (See Fig. 10.20.)

A kind of lens whose surfaces are concentric is the size lens. The simplest size lens is in the form of a plane piece of glass curved about a single axis, as shown in Fig. 10.21. Since the lens has a single axis of

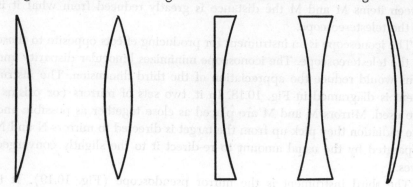

Fig. 10.20. Various common forms of lenses (power lenses).

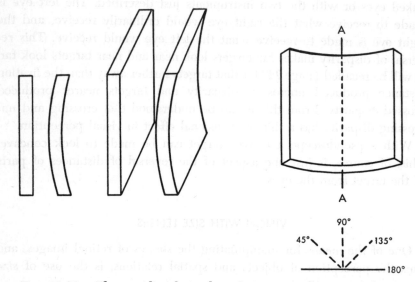

Fig. 10.21. *The meridional size lens.* It is essentially a curved section of originally plano glass. It does not focus radiation as does a power lens. Its axis is designated as A, A. Its axis position in use is designated as 45, 90, 135, and 180 degrees.

curvature, it is designated by the meridian used as the axis. Meridians are designated in degrees, beginning with zero at the left horizontal (9 o'clock on the face of a clock). The vertical meridian is 90 degrees, and the horizontal meridian to the right is 180 degrees. All designations fall within this range. Size lenses of the description just given are called meridional size lenses. On the other hand, a lens formed by cupping a piece of plano material is called an overall size lens. Meridional size lenses magnify the retinal image in the direction at right angles to the axis of curvature.

If a meridional size lens is worn in front of one eye, the image in that eye is magnified in one direction. Thus the image in one eye will differ, in one direction, from that in the other. The combined retinal pattern for the two eyes simulates, to some extent, what it would when some natural three-dimensional target is viewed. The natural target simulated is one quite different, of course, from the one actually involved at the time. When an axis-90 size lens is worn in front of the right eye, certain unique perceptual end results are produced.

The Leaf Room

One of the best target situations to use for studying space perception with size lenses is a leaf room. A leaf room is a small room, let us say, a cube of about seven feet, open on one end. It is called a leaf room because, typically, it is covered on the inside (ceiling, walls, and floor) with theatrical leaves (artificial leaves) to break up the familiar linear stimulus features produced by corners between walls, ceiling, etc. (See Fig. 10.22.)

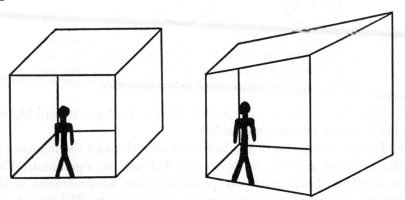

FIG. 10.22.   The leaf room, as it is metrically and perceptually seen when an axis-90 size lens is worn in front of the right eye.

When an observer stands at the open end of a leaf room, with an axis-90 lens in front of the right eye, the room's appearance is greatly changed from normal. The room no longer appears rectilinear. The back wall is no longer in the frontal plane. Its right side is farther away than the left. Although the observer is standing at the midpoint between the two side walls, they no longer appear to be equidistant from him. The wall on the right is much farther away than the left one. The ceiling slopes upward to the right, and the floor slopes downward to the right. The leaves are larger in the right half of the room than in the

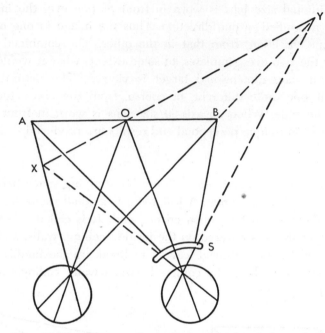

FIG. 10.23.   The psycho-optical principle of the axis-90 size lens worn on the right eye. Target AOB is seen as XOY, since the lens redirects the light in one meridian so as to enlarge the retinal image in that dimension.

left. All of these differences are manifestations of a taper toward bigness on the right and littleness on the left.

So far, the description of the leaf room viewed under the influence of a size lens may seem to be interesting but not too significant. What does it tell us about space perception? It is one demonstration of the ability to manipulate space perception experimentally. The use of size lenses in still other situations indicates the considerable sensory conflict that can thereby be engendered, and that personal insecurity can be evoked. Manipulation of these situations brings out that not only can pure sensory results be obtained but also other results that could be called emotional and social. Actually, the use of the lenses may be one potential way of studying personality differences.

The optical features of wearing an axis-90 size lens in front of one eye are depicted in Fig. 10.23. In this diagram, the rule of thumb regarding perceived direction is again employed. The image in one eye is elongated, and this participates in changing the perceived directions or locations of the limits of the target. The new directions are such that the left side of the target is brought closer and the right side is moved farther away than normally. The diagram forms a basis for understanding how the wearing of the lens produces the perceptual results just described.

Use of Oblique Size Lenses

If two size lens are to be worn, they must be rotated to oblique positions, such as is suggested in Fig. 10.24. In such cases, the magnifica-

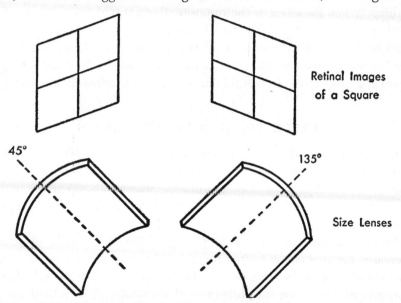

Retinal Images
of a Square

45°

135°

Size Lenses

FIG. 10.24.   Diagram showing the manner in which two size lenses worn obliquely distort the retinal images of a square target (By permission from *Beginning Experimental Psychology*, by S. H. Bartley, Fig. 32. Copyright, 1950, McGraw-Hill Book Company, Inc.).

tions are oppositely oblique in the two retinal images, and this is reminiscent of the oblique tilts of the two line images described on page 227. The perceptual effect of wearing oblique size lenses is to tilt the appearance of the floor either upward as one views it obliquely or to tilt it downward. Which it will be depends upon whether the axes of the lenses are rotated inward or outward at the top.

When the rotation is inward, the tilt is upward; and when the rotation is outward, the tilt is downward. The amounts of tilt are dependent also upon the field conditions in general, including the distance of the targets ("surfaces") viewed. The farther away the targets, the less the tilt. Instead of tilt the appearance turns into a change in apparent size and elevation. When size is magnified, motion is increased. When size is diminished, motion is reduced. This effect pertains aptly to water surfaces containing waves.

If the observer is in a boat affected by the actual waves, the boat is buffeted about in accordance with the size of the waves. If it turns out that the mechanical effect of the waves and the visual effect do not tally, a perceptual conflict is produced. When the waves are smaller than would tally with the buffeting of the boat, the result is very disturbing. When the effect is the opposite, there is said to be less trouble. Little waves never toss boats much, whereas an observer may stand on solid land and not be tossed at all while looking at big waves. Hence, the big-wave, little-toss situation is natural, whereas the other is highly novel and productive of possible uneasiness and possible motion sickness.

EFFECT OF INSTRUMENTAL MAGNIFICATION

It is to be recognized that in all the cases in which binocular vision was manipulated, the manipulation was accomplished by varying the characteristics of the retinal images in some way or other. Various optical devices, not yet mentioned, have been useful in making these manipulations.

One of the devices is the field glass, or binocular, which, of course, increases the size of the retinal images. When one attempts to manipulate visual input to the eye, one of the first considerations is whether or not, and in what way, the instrumental manipulation of retinal images compares with any that are produced in natural (unaided eye) situations. This principle applies in the attempt to understand the effects produced by wearing binoculars. Fig. 10.25 will show the ways the retinal image is altered internally as it is increased in size.

It will be seen that when a three-dimensional target is brought closer to the eye, the image undergoes not only a size change (enlargement) but also a change in internal proportions. In contrast to this, when an image is increased in size by enlarging the target, all parts of the image are increased proportionally. That is, if a target is doubled in size, all factors of the retinal image are double in size. Therefore, the two natural manipulations, while comparing in what is done to the overall size of the images, differ in what they do to image composition. The instrumental manner of enlarging retinal images is similar to the mere doubling of target size.

Since the instrumental manipulation increases all portions of the image by the same ratio, all portions would be doubled by a 2-power instrument. Using these doubled dimensions on the retinal portion of the

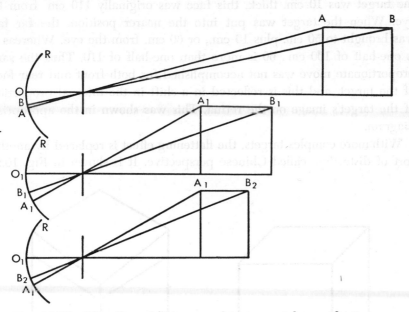

FIG. 10.25. The effect of distance and instrumental magnification on the retinal image. Decreasing target distance increases retinal-image size. So does instrumental magnification. The latter increases all parts of the image proportionally, whereas the former does not.

diagram, we have $O_1 B_2 A_1$ instead of $O_1 B_1 A_1$. If we project the point B_2 outward, we find it reaches line $A_1 B_1$ of the target at B_2. If we drop a perpendicular down to the base line, we have a target with less than the thickness of the original.

Let us turn from this to asking how the target actually looks when viewed through a 2-power binocular. We find that the target appears to have a reduced third dimension. This could well be called a *flattening effect*. Turning back to the diagram, we see that we have accounted for this flattening effect by showing what was done to the retinal image by the binoculars as they magnified it.

The secret of the difference between enlarging images by a shift in distance of the target and by simply enlarging the target is this: when we bring a three-dimensional target closer to the eye, we do not shift all parts of the target by the same relative amounts, although all parts are brought nearer by the same absolute amount. Let us take the following example. If a target, whose front face is 100 cm. from the eye, is brought to 50 cm. from the eye, we say that this face is now one-half as far away as before. But what about the far edge of the target? If the target was 10 cm. thick, this face was originally 110 cm. from the eye. When the target was put into the nearer position, the far face was brought to 50 cm. plus 10 cm., or 60 cm. from the eye. Whereas 50 is one-half of 100 cm., 60 is more than one-half of 110. Thus the same proportionate move was not accomplished for both front and rear faces of the target, and this is reflected in a shift in the internal proportions of the target's image on the retina. This was shown in the appropriate diagram.

With more complex targets, the flattening effect is replaced by another sort of distortion, called Chinese perspective. It is shown in Fig. 10.26,

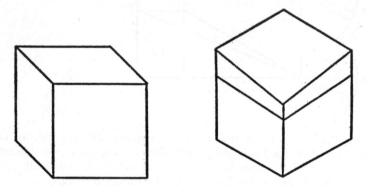

Fig. 10.26.   A cube and a solid with Chinese perspective.

wherein it will be seen that the top and bottom edges of a cubical form no longer look parallel. This effect can also be accounted for by the diagraming procedure, but we shall forego it here.

CHEIROSCOPIC DRAWING

Throughout our discussion of perception, we have been attempting to point out that perception is a creation of the perceiver rather than a process of copying or reproducing externality. In no other example of perceptual behavior is this better exemplified than in *cheiroscopic draw-*

ing—the drawing one does in the attempt to trace what he sees in a stereogram. The word *cheiro,* or *chiro,* is the Greek stem meaning hand. Cheiroscopic drawing is thus possibly thought to be a demonstration of eye-hand coördination. It is far more than this, as we shall presently see.

It will be recalled that a stereoscope is a device whereby two targets are presented to the observer, one to one eye, the other to the other eye, in such a way that only a single object or scene will be perceived. The two targets are plane projections of some three-dimensional situation, as viewed by the two eyes, each from a little different position than the other. Appreciation of depth or three-dimensionality is enhanced by such a technique.

To refresh your memory, turn back to Fig. 10.16. In it, you will see that the radiation from the two targets (stereograms) enters the eyes as if originating from a single target somewhat more distant than the stereograms.

In the cheiroscopic drawing, one stereogram is omitted. Instead of it, there is a blank surface on which to draw. The observer, looking into the stereoscope supplied with only the one stereogram, does not experience ("know") which one of the eyes is being presented with a target. His task is to trace the object seen (let us say, a line drawing). If the stereogram supplied is on the right, he uses his left hand. If the stereogram is on the left, he uses his right hand. He begins his task by moving his pencil into the field of view, on the side opposite the stereogram. As he draws, his experience is simply of tracing the lines he sees. When he is through, he may take his head out of the stereoscope and look at what he has done. He finds he was drawing somewhere on the blank supplied the "nonstimulated eye."

Let us examine the diagram in Fig. 10.27. From it, you will see that only one eye is being supplied with radiation to form a retinal image. The other eye is supplied with a blank. Despite the fact that the pencil traces on a blank area, the perceiver sees himself trace the lines of a figure. Certain visual-training specialists in optometry state that the target furnishes "input," and the drawing demonstrates "output." They say vision *is* output; that is, perception is output. This is another way of stating what we have been saying from chapter to chapter, and what we said at the beginning of this section; that is, that perception is a creation of the observer.

To put it more specifically, the drawer has put on paper what he sees, giving it a size, shape, and position in accordance with the information supplied by one eye. This information is simply photic radiation reaching the one eye from a certain direction. The direction of the perceived object does not have to tally with the direction of the radiation, as one might have supposed. It is the perceiver who not only creates the *object*, upon being stimulated as described, but who also creates its *size*, its *position*, and its *distance* from him.

We shall now examine what various perceivers do when they are given the cheiroscopic task. As a first guess, one would suppose that within

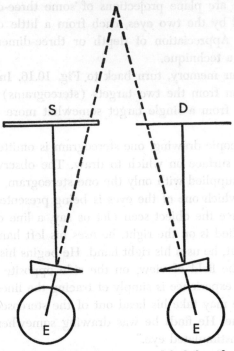

Fig. 10.27.   A stereoscope modified for cheiro-scopic drawing. S is the usual left-hand stereo target, and D is a blank drawing surface. EE are the viewer's eyes.

limits of reasonable accuracy the drawer would "reproduce" the target presented by the stereogram. If the target is a square, one would expect the drawer to make a square. If the square in the stereogram is two inches on a side, the drawing should be the same. If the square is located at the center of the stereogram, the drawing should be at the corresponding place on the blank. These expectations are often far from realized. Instead of being identical to the stereogram, the drawing may differ considerably in shape and/or size, and may be in a position on the blank other than the one expected.

Several possibilities are shown in Fig. 10.28. In some cases, the drawing is nearer to the diagram in the stereogram than it should be. Sometimes it is farther away from it than it should be. Sometimes it is of an entirely different size, as in the middle example.

That these discrepancies could occur might well puzzle anyone who conceives of the situation in conventional terms; that is, as if the drawing represented "input." The drawing is simply a representation of what is seen, and how far away it is seen. Some people see objects as farther away than would be expected from the location of the origin of radiation reaching the eye. The seen object ("output") does not tally with the "structure of externality" as far as photic radiation is concerned. To put the matter into conventional but nonscientific parlance, the observer

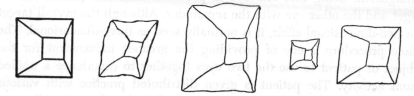

FIG. 10.28. Various samples of cheiroscopic drawings of the target shown on the left.

does not see the object where it is. One observer may see it as farther away, and another may see it as nearer.

Likewise, the observer may not see the object as the size it would be expected to be from what we know about the target. Cheiroscopic drawing is one of the best demonstrations of this, when the drawing does not match the target in size or in position. It is by such a drawing that a vision expert can tell whether the patient has a "visual problem." A "visual problem" is the general name given to the condition of visual inefficiency existing when the person does not quickly (directly) and accurately locate objects in space. His whole behavior is shot through with inaccuracy, secondary corrective movements, and so forth, when space localization is shown to be faulty by such tests as cheiroscopic drawing. When we say that an observer is dealing with "objects in space," let us remember, we are not reverting to the common implication that space is populated with solid external objects in a physical sense. We do posit an externality that is structured by various energistic activities such as photic radiation, and that we must cope with them as if they were what we, in perception, experience from their impingements upon our sense organs. Do as best we can, so far we have not fully gotten away from the description of externality in terms of our perceptions. But to forget that *objects* as such do not exist outside our experiences, after we have once asserted them to be items of perception, would be to have made our assertion all for nothing.

If the observer's drawing is located closer to the stereogram target than it should be, he is seeing objects closer to him than he should. Visual-training experts have means of correcting such discrepancies. A variety of exercises is employed with more or less success. Many of these consist in moving targets that are actively followed with the eyes. Some of these targets are polarized (reflect polarized radiation to the eyes). One portion of the target is polarized in one way, and the other polarized in another. The patient wears polarized glasses, the overall result of this arrangement being that one eye is provided with one portion of the target and the other eye with the remainder. Although the overall target is a two-dimensional affair, it is normally seen as three-dimensional. The whole procedure is one of providing the greatest inducement for the subject or patient to use the two eyes together to experience a unified visual activity. The patient is given distributed practice with various active instrumental targets until he can do what he originally was unable to do, or did incompletely or with difficulty. He is periodically re-checked for improvement, and ultimately he is found to have shifted from seeing objects out of keeping with target locations and distances to seeing them in positions that tally with target locations.

The cognizance that certain vision experts have given to the role of space perception in the individual's daily life, including very intelligence itself, is the chief attainment in the visual-remedial arts of the day. Much of such remedial practice, on the other hand, has not passed the use of eyeglasses to improve visual acuity, and thus has not reached the point of dealing with space perception as such.

THE VAN ORDEN STAR

Another clinical device that involves one of the same general principles as the original form of cheiroscopic drawing is the Van Orden Star. The Van Orden Star is what a drawer produces when he follows instructions in using the following device. From a headrest, such as is used in a stereoscope, the observer or patient sees a well-illuminated field. Far out to the right is a perpendicular row of dots or tiny squares. On the left is a similar row. The observer or patient is given a pencil in each hand and instructed to put the point of the right-hand pencil on the top dot in the right-hand column, and the point of the left-hand pencil on the bottom dot in the left-hand column. He is also instructed to look straight ahead as if looking out into space. The object of this is to get him to relax convergence to the point of having his two eyes point in parallel directions, if possible. With his gaze fixed in this fashion, he is to bring the pencil points together so that they touch. Thus, from the right hand a line will be drawn diagonally downward toward the left, and from the left a line will be drawn diagonally upward to the right. After the pencils are brought for the first time to where they appear to touch, the same act is repeated. The second trial begins with the right-hand pencil at the second dot from the top of the right column, and the left-hand pencil at the second dot from the bottom of the left column. Successive dots are used in successive trials until all are used. To make the matter clearer, turn to Fig. 10.29. In Fig. 10.30 is a normal

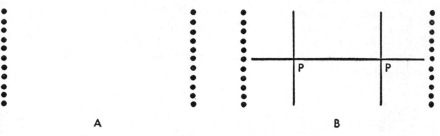

A   B

FIG. 10.29. The material for drawing a Van Orden Star. A is the blank with its dots as points of origin for drawing. B is the template that indicates the normal points, PP, at which the patient's drawing lines should terminate (by permission, Keystone View Co.).

drawing of a subject in A, and in B a template is superimposed on a drawing to show where the lines made by the subject should have converged. The vertical lines of the template indicate the interocular distance (that is, distance between the centers of the two eyes or between pupil centers when the eyes point in parallel). The horizontal line shows the levels of the two eye centers when the subject is looking straight ahead.

Figure 10.30 helps explain why the lines should converge at the intersections of the horizontal and vertical lines, and shows what would be expected if the subject did not position his eyes parallel but converged them slightly instead. With some convergence, the drawn lines would overshoot the intersection of the lines on the template, and thus converge at points closer together than they should.

Figure 10.31 shows several other examples of drawings of various kinds of patients and what they symptomatize.

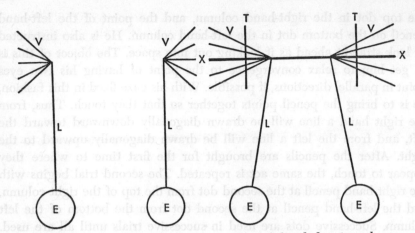

FIG. 10.30. *The Van Orden Star.* In the left-hand drawing, the two eyes have parallel axis positions. The star drawings of the patient should be as indicated. Were the eyes not to be parallel but converged, the lines would converge more nearly toward the center of the field. VV are the parts of the star. LL are the lines of sight (axis) of the eyes, EE. The intersections of TX, TX indicate the convergence points of the normal star.

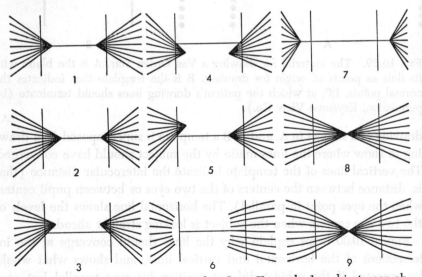

FIG. 10.31. Drawings of Van Orden Star. Example 1, subject sees object too close; 2, closer with one eye than the other; 3, sees objects too close and develops neck tensions; 4, sees objects too close, develops back tensions; 5, vertical imbalance in vision; 6, poor distance acuity; 7, sees objects too far away; 8, alternating vision; 9, another sort of alternation (R. S. Byall, Interpretation of the Van Orden Star, *Visual Training at Work* [1955], 4:21–28).

In the Van Orden Star drawings, we have a device for finding out something about a person's spatial reactions, whether they locate objects too near, or too far away, or whether both eyes act alike.

FIGURAL AFTEREFFECTS

In recent years, the study of perception has included what are called *figural aftereffects*. Although he was not the first to study the phenomena of figural aftereffects, Köhler (*142, 143*) was perhaps the one to name the phenomena and devote the most attention to them. The aftereffect phenomenon was originally studied in vision; now certain afteraffects in other sense modalities are being studied in somewhat the same ways, and are also called figural aftereffects, implying that the very same principle is being dealt with in each modality. Since the aftereffect has to do with perceiving objects, their sizes, locations, and so on, it has to do with space perception and will be dealt with here rather than elsewhere in the text.

Among the first to report a phenomenon that later has become known as a figural aftereffect was Gibson (*85*). He reported that if a subject viewed a curved line for a time, and then was shown a straight line, he saw a line curved in the opposite direction. The effect, of course, was attributed to something produced in the perceiver by the initial observation.

The general procedure used to obtain aftereffects by Köhler (*143*) and collaborators is as follows. A figure called the inspection figure (I) is viewed for some seconds, or even several minutes, with as steady fixation as possible. As soon as the figure (target) is removed, a second or test figure (T) is presented. The features of what is seen are reported upon immediately. T consists in two parts: one that is repeated and thus casts an image on the same portion of the retina as occupied by the image of A, and one that occupies a fresh retinal area (see Fig. 10.32). Despite the fact that the two portions of T are geometrically identical, they are not seen as being identical. The prestimulated portion of the retina gives rise to a smaller perceptual object than the portion of T, whose image falls on fresh retina. It is also seen as farther away than this portion, and its borders appear to be less black. Aftereffects have also been studied stereoscopically (*254*).

To explain such effects and those produced by the many planned variations in the conditions, Köhler used what he called a field theory. This theory was stated in electrical terms, and was meant to be a kind of neurophysiological statement for the basis of the phenomenal effect. The terms used, however, were those uncommon among neurophysiologists for dealing with neural activity. We shall not go into the details of the theory here, but simply point out that Osgood and Heyer (204) produced what they believed to be an adequate accounting for figural aftereffects by using conventional neurophysiological principles, processes which are the stock and trade of current neurophysiology.

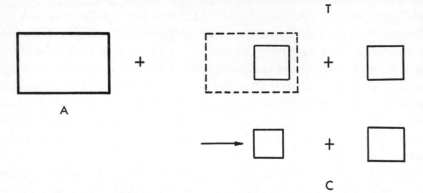

Fig. 10.32. *Figural aftereffects.* A is the inspection figure; T, the test figure, with the inspection figure shown in dashed lines. The crosses are the fixation points for the conditions. C shows the perceptual results from viewing the test figure. The two squares are seen as unequal in size, and unequally distant from the fixation point.

Wertheimer (259, 260) has busied himself with a variety of figural aftereffects, including tactual aftereffects. He is not concerned with deciding between the explanations of Köhler and of Osgood and Heyer, but with determining the relation of figural aftereffects and measures of metabolic function. He has postulated that marked figural aftereffects should be associated with certain metabolic characteristics measured by certain well-known indicators, and weaker figural aftereffects should be associated with reduced or opposite metabolic characteristics. So far, he believes he has shown considerable relation between the two in the direction postulated.

The conventional explanation of visual figural aftereffects is complex and lengthy, and possibly has no place in the present "elementary" description of perception. Needless to say, however, it would seem that a precise enough study of the effects in relation to known retinal and optic pathway structure and function would help us to understand contour processes in the nervous system.

Figural aftereffects are somewhat reminiscent of the effects studied by Werner (256) and by Bartley (12), described in Chapter 6. Both they and the figural aftereffects in vision have to do with the emergence of edges and their modifications. One of the main differences is that for figural aftereffects to become manifest, much longer time intervals must be involved.

OCULOMOTOR MECHANISMS

Since oculomotor mechanisms play a considerable role in determining the nature of visual perception, space perception in particular, we shall give some attention to those mechanisms here. There are three distinct oculomotor mechanisms: (1) the pupil, which manipulates to some extent the amount of radiation reaching the retina, and optically the depth of field; (2) the muscles of accommodation that aid in regulating the shape of the lens, and therefore the focusing of radiation onto the retina; and (3) the extrinsic muscles that regulate the postures of the eyeballs (convergence) so that the two eyes point to the target being dealt with. Since the person himself is generally unaware of these activities, or cannot willfully control all of them, it would be easy to think that they are not a part of perception. Since oculomotor activities do not usually involve awareness and conscious decisions on the part of the owner, the behavior is said to be reflexive. To put these activities into the category of reflexes, however, does not preclude their being perceptual, just so long as they are a form of discriminatory behavior. The reader can be well assured that they are discriminatory. All three mechanisms are linked together so as to provide for certain necessary optical features for seeing. The accommodative and convergence mechanisms, in particular, are linked together so that the conditions that call for a certain amount of accommodation call for a certain amount of convergence.

Accommodation

Accommodation is the refractive state of the lens and depends upon its shape. Although the act of seeing is considerably more than the production of an appropriate refractive state forming a maximally "sharp" image on the retina, it does generally include this act. How lacking in "sharpness" an image can be and still be usable by the owner is a question. The emmetropic ("normal") eye can produce its maximally sharp image when parallel rays enter the eye, and it can likewise focus optimally on the retina when the radiation originates at nearby targets as well. This is to say, the lens in such an eye is highly variable in shape. The greatest distance from which the radiation from a target can be properly focused on the retina is called the *far point*. In the emmetropic person, this distance is infinity. In the near-sighted or myopic person, the far point is not infinity but some finite distance, let us say, within twenty feet. In all persons there is a point that marks the nearest a target can be placed and still be clearly seen. This is called the *near point*. In the far-sighted or hyperopic person, the near point is often scarcely within arm's length; whereas in the normal 10-year-old, the distance is about 7 cm. As age increases, the near point recedes. At 25 years of age, it is typically about 12 cm.; at 40, it is 22 cm.; at 55, it is 51 cm.; and at 70, it is often 400 cm. As the person progresses from child-hood, the far point typically moves closer and closer. The linear distance between near point and far point is called the *range of accommodation*. The difference between the refractive power of the eye (measured in diopters) in a minimally and a maximally accommodated condition is called the *amplitude of accommodation*. The lens is said to be maximally accommodated when it is adjusted to image the nearest target possible upon the retina. The lens is said to be minimally accommodated when it is adjusted to image the most distant target on the retina. The strength of a lens in *diopters* is the reciprocal of its focal length expressed in meters. Thus a lens of 1 diopter will focus parallel rays at a distance of one meter. If the lens was to focus them at one-half meter, the dioptric power of the lens would be 2. Supposedly, there are four sources of accommodation: (1) a tapered pattern of stimulation on the retina, as from a poorly focused image; (2) the convergence of the two eyes, for the greater the convergence the nearer the target, and thus the greater the need for accommodation; (3) the tonic, which is the accommoda-tion produced by the normal tonus of the accommodative muscles; and (4) the proximal, the added tonus engendered when the target is per-ceived to be quite near, for example, within arm's length.

Convergence

When the person attempts to respond to a visual target, his eyes con-verge upon it. We say he fixates it, and by this is meant that the optical axes of the two eyes point to some portion of the target. On the other hand, responding to a target may involve exploratory movements of the eyes as well as fixations. Normally the eyes maintain what are called conjugate positions at all times with reference to the target viewed. This is to say, they point to some portion of the target, not to some point nearer or farther away. If the target is quite distant, the optical axes of the eyes are parallel. As the target is brought nearer, convergence of the axes sets in and increases as the target is brought still progressively nearer. Supposedly, this activity is brought about under the supervision of a fusion center in the brain. How the action is brought about is not specifically known.

Convergence is regulated not only by the fusion center but by several other factors. There is supposedly a certain amount of tonic convergence. The relatively passive tone of the several extrinsic eye muscles is such that the eyes are somewhat converged. A third factor is the state of accommodation of the eyes. The fourth factor involved in convergence is the proximity of the target.

Convergence, like accommodation, is measured in diopters, but in this case it is in *prism diopters*. One diopter is 1 cm. deviation of the eye produced at a distance of one meter. For an interpupillary distance of 60 mm., the optical axis of each must deviate (converge) 3 cm. (i.e., one-half of the interpupillary distance) in order for fixation of a target regardless of its distance. If the target is one meter away, each eye converges 3 prism diopters.

Views on Oculomotor Behavior

The whole science of visual care, whether it involves optometry or ophthalmology, hinges on several concepts regarding the relation of oculomotor activity to the behavior of the person as a whole.

The classical viewpoint, represented largely in the concepts developed in the days of Helmholtz, holds that vision is primarily a matter of optics, fixed anatomy, and a number of fairly stable reflexes. Accordingly, the person is what these reflexes collectively make him. They develop as a feature of general neurological maturation and are not to any great extent trainable. The seeing process is primarily an optical process in which the principles of optics, eyeball size and shape, muscle size and length, participate to provide a certain net result. Sometimes the eyeball is so long that the radiation comes to a focus slightly before reaching the retina; sometimes it is so short that radiation does not quite come to a focus upon reaching the retina. In these cases, myopia (near-sightedness) and hyperopia (far-sightedness), respectively, result.

Myopia is rarely, if ever, present at birth, but develops later on, particularly in the early years of schooling. Newer views with regard to vision are very different from the old. The essential difference lies in the trainability of vision. Some current views recognize that the human being has to learn to see. This learning, we should say, is twofold: a motor learning and a development of comprehension of the environment, the most significant feature of which is its spatial aspect. Motor learning and this comprehension must go hand in hand.

The reader must be cautioned, however, that if learning is involved, there are two alternatives. It can be inefficient or anomalous or efficient and adequate for the demands put upon the individual. It can go wrong as well as right. Since these two possibilities exist, the logical conclusion arrived at by some is that growing individuals, as a routine thing, may need some help (training) in order that the seeing process may develop as it should. A still further consideration enters the picture; namely, that the visual demands made upon most individuals in our time are far greater than those put upon previous generations. This makes training necessary when it otherwise might be by-passed with relative impunity.

We have given you just a few facts regarding oculomotor behavior to give you the assurance that seeing is motor as well as sensory, and that the two factors must work together. The very highest comprehensional processes that the individual is capable of are part of the seeing process and should efficiently control the needed motor activity. So long as the motor and sensory integration is not what it should be, space perception is distorted; the person's body mechanics is ineffective and he cannot meet the demands put upon him. Actually, we are coming to the point at which we have to train the general perceptual processes of men to carry out the objectives of our culture. We can design and make the necessary machines, but we do not always have men adequate to operate the machines. This will be the case so long as we do not realize that the perceptual processes are those that regulate the features of our environment, and that these processes are not at their best without sophisticated training.

There is another point to be mentioned here in regard to knowledge about physiological optics and the motor factors of the visual mechanism. It is that adequate investigation of visual perception cannot be made without this knowledge. We find, here and there in the literature, studies that betray the investigator's ignorance. We find that he makes wrong deductions from his findings, not to say performs the wrong operations. This would not be the case had he realized that physiological optics and a background in oculomotor mechanisms are essential for working in the area in question.

Chapter 11

PERCEPTION OF MOVEMENT

There are many forms of the perception of movement. The two main classes are the experience of the movement of the person himself, and movement of something external to the person. Both of these forms of movement may be produced by stimuli undergoing displacement or by those that are stationary. Movement produced by the first kind of stimuli has generally been called *real* movement, whereas movement produced by stationary stimuli has been called *apparent* movement. Since in both cases the movement meant is the *experience* of movement rather than movement defined physically, we shall call both real movement and apparent movement *phenomenal* movement. We shall say that these are two forms of phenomenal movement, although they are not always to be distinguished by their experiential qualities. They are simply experienced movement evoked by two separate sets of conditions.

Various sense modalities participate in the experience of movement, and for this reason we shall examine what this participation is. Conventionally speaking, there are visual movement, auditory movement, tactual movement, kinesthetic movement, and movement based, in part, on the action of the vestibular mechanism.

In movement, there is a peculiar interrelation between space and time, when time is defined both as a perception and as a convention (clock time). To the extent that some external object is experienced to move, the experience is often predominantly spatial. When movement is primarily that of bodily experience as in touch and kinesthesis, the experience may be experienced predominantly as sequential.

There are some forms of movement that we shall deal with elsewhere. In Chapter 14 the subject of muscle movement will be dealt with, and in Chapter 15 the role of the vestibule in body movement will be discussed. In the first of these two chapters, the emphasis, of course, will be upon the sensory stimulation produced by muscular action. In the second of the two, the experiences and other reactions to passive movement will be given the major attention. This being the case, the major considerations in the present chapter are those of visual, tactual, and auditory movement. Well-structured movement involves an appreciation of the space domain and hence involves the visual modality, at least by way of imagery. When we say the movement is spatial, perhaps it is well to inspect certain curious movement experiences that may throw doubt on the assertion.

Among the great variety of phenomenal movements which the normal person may experience is the kind illustrated by the following. If a person looks steadily at a vertically moving belt on which there are seen alternate transverse stripes of white and black, he will see that the bands continue to move for a short time after the belt is stopped. Although the best experiential description is certainly that of movement, it can be said that the stripes do not go anywhere. But since the stripes do not actually behave so that one can clearly follow their displacement and progress, the movement experience is not in the fullest sense a spatial phenomenon. On the other hand, it is undoubtedly a sequential one. It is the experience of something happening in time. Thus, we have here a visual experience that lies on the borderline of not being spatial according to what we have already said about space perception in Chapter 10.

VISUAL MOVEMENT

Real Movement

Real movement is the experience of movement based upon something being displaced in the world outside the observer, or the experience based upon the displacement of the observer in a stable environment. Since in this section we are dealing with visual movement, we are confining our considerations to visual experiences. Displacements of the sorts just mentioned involve displacements in the images on the retina.

It is appropriate to classify the kinds of image displacements that may occur, for they are not all of one simple sort. The diagrams in Fig. 11.1 show the various essential forms of displacement of images on the retina. The first of the five forms is the whole-field image moving across the retina. This occurs in the unwitting jumplike eye movements employed in reading a line of print. With this form of image displacement, there is no experience of anything in the external environment either in motion or still. The second form of image displacement is the displacement of a portion of the total image, while the image of the field in general is stationary. This is produced when a restricted target is displaced laterally (i.e., in the frontal plane), with the eyes stationary. In this case,

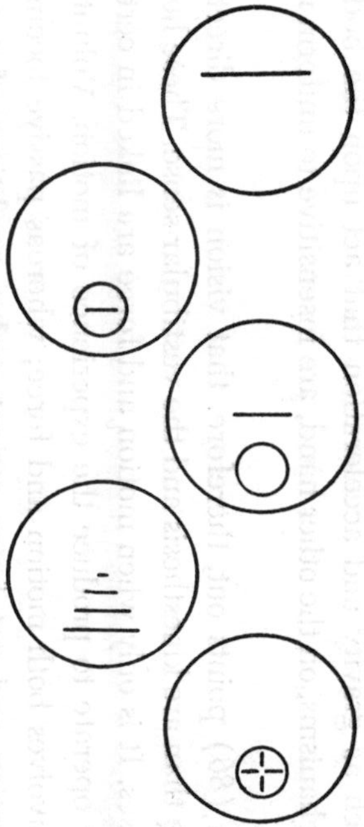

FIG. 11.1.

Mode of Retinal Motion	Physical Situation	Perception of Objective Movement
Rigid motion of the total image	Saccadic eye movement in stationary environment	None, perception of a stable world
Rigid motion of a delimited image	Stationary eyes, target moving frontally	Target moving frontally in a stable world
Rigid motion of the image except for a delimited part	Pursuit movement of eyes with target moving frontally	Target moving frontally in a stable world
Deformation of total image	Movement of head in stationary environment	Movement of self in stable world
Deformation of a delimited image	Stationary eyes with target moving in depth	Target moving in depth in a stable world

(J. J. Gibson *The Perception of the Visual World,* Houghton Mifflin, 1950, p. 132).

one experiences the movement of an object in a stable field. The third pattern of retinal change occurs when the eye follows a target that is moving in the frontal plane. In this case, the image of the visual field as a whole moves, while that of the pursued target remains fixed on the retina.

The fourth kind of retinal change occurs when the head or head and body are moved and nothing is displaced in the external environment. In this case, the retinal image of the whole field tends to be deformed. Images of targets close by move across the retina most rapidly. The targets progressively farther and farther away move less and less. Hence, there is an internal rearrangement of the target field as a whole. The impression in this case is one of self-movement in a stable world.

The fifth case is one in which nothing but a restricted target moves in the third dimension. In this case, the target image grows or shrinks in size and may change somewhat in shape. The perception is of an object moving in the third dimension, while the environment stands still.

The displacement of the total image or some part of it occurs in each case because there is a lawful relation between what happens on the retina and the photically relayed events outside the organism. Although there may be certain features of reaction that intrinsically flow from these retinal events, the organism acts, as we find it in the adult stage, by reason of having been exposed repeatedly to these consistent relations between retinal activity and external events.

Acceleration Versus Motion

The perception of *motion* of the body seems to be best mediated by vision, whereas the perception of *acceleration* is best mediated by kinesthesis. Kinesthesis is a product of the operation of force. The retina is totally insensitive to forces such as acceleration acting upon or within the body. The semicircular canals and otolith organ are very sensitive to forces such as gravity and acceleration that act upon the body. These same mechanisms, on the other hand, are insensitive to uniform motion of the body.

Gibson (86) points out, therefore, that vision is more directly a motion sense than are kinesthesis and the vestibular sense. These he calls the force senses. It is only when motion and force are linked in certain ways that they operate to produce the experience of motion. Voluntary locomotion involves both motion and force; whereas passive locomotion involves motion and not force, except under conditions of acceleration. Very peculiar end results sometimes occur, depending upon how the two forms of stimulation are coupled.

Take, for example, the case in which a person drives his car into an angled parking place, and just after he has come to a stop another car pulls into the space alongside. A possible result for the first driver who restricts his visual field to glancing at the second car is to feel as though he is in motion. A mere instant before, he supposed that he had come to a dead stop. But at this instant there is relative displacement between his car and the car alongside. This relative displacement gives rise to perceived motion, but not in an ordinary way. The motion sets in without any application of force that is characteristic of all acceleration. The acceleration force factor is lacking and its absence distorts the usual sensory input to the central nervous system. The usual innervations contain vestibular and kinesthetic components. It is perhaps on account of the absence of these that the experience of visual motion of oneself is very peculiar. In fact, the experience contains a definite aspect of uneasiness. One might call the experience a twinge of sickness. The main twinge is over with in a second or two, but the aftereffects may last for some time. It possibly can be said, then, that not all motion sickness is brought about by contributions from the vestibule, but that some may result when usual contributions are absent when they ought to occur.

A bit of the same momentary uneasiness is likely to occur when a train on the next track begins to move. One sees his own train moving instead. But here again there is some sort of uncertainty and possibly some uneasiness. The experience carries, at least, a kind of ambiguity. Again, a usual sensory component may be lacking. It is the kinesthetic stimulation that vibration of active motion would set up. Since one's own train is motionless, there is not the least basis for the usual muscular factor underlying the motion one sees. Lacking the jolting, vibrations, and so on, the movement is fantastically smooth and a bit "unreal." One is quickly led to look around in other directions to try to make sure whether it is his own train or the other one that is moving. The answer to the question of how one came to see visual movement in the first place lies in the structure of the visual field. The railroad car seen through the window is seen as a portion of overall stable externality, whereas one's own car is taken to be a restricted portion of the environment more or less identified kinetically with oneself.

Direction of Flow

When the perceiver moves about in space, the visual field changes in accordance with the relation between direction of locomotion and the perceiver's direction of gaze. Obviously, the common description consists in statements regarding objects getting nearer or farther away, or about moving past objects. Another way of dealing with the matter is to consider what happens to the retinal image in various cases. Essentially what happens is a shift of pattern across the retina, and Gibson calls this *flow*. Descriptions of flow then tell what happens on the retina.

In Figs. 11.2 and 11.3 the directions of flow are indicated for two different conditions. In the first figure, the directions of flow are for the

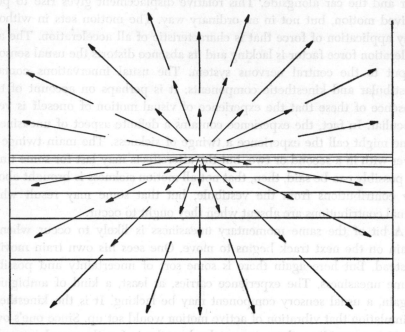

FIG. 11.2.   A diagram to indicate the direction of flow of the textured field, made up of land and sky during an observer's forward motion, particularly when off the ground, as in an airplane.

eye looking straight ahead as the perceiver moves forward. In the second they are for the eye looking at right angles to the direction of motion (in this case, looking to the left). It will be noticed that in the first diagram the flow is upward for positions below the horizon and downward for positions of the field representing sky. These directions are exactly opposite to what one might expect, but this is because the retinal image is "upside down." The rate of flow is least near the horizon and greatest near the observer. The same thing is true with regard to rate when the observer is looking at right angles to the line of his motion. The direction of flow in this case is parallel to and in the direction of motion of the perceiver.

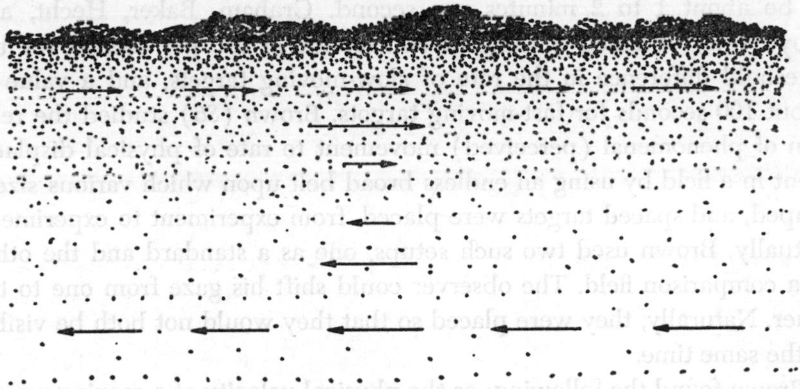

FIG. 11.3. The direction of flow of the textured field (land), when looking to the left and fixing a point in the field midway between the observer and the horizon.

There is still another condition that might well be mentioned and that is the sort of flow involved when one looks to the side, i.e., at right angles to the direction of motion, and fixates a point on the terrain *between* himself and the horizon. This point becomes the point beyond which there is flow in the direction opposite the perceiver's own movement, and on this side of which the flow is in the direction of body movement.

All of this may seem confusing, but the reader will be helped if he simply visualizes the direction in which objects move past him as he moves.

Movement of Perceived Objects

So far, we have been describing the overall changes in the retinal images and the overall perceived effects during motion of the field, or of the observer. We now come to considering the perceptual features of seen objects in motion.

Aubert was one of the first investigators to give us some measurements of thresholds for object motion. For a long line target in a structural field, he reported a threshold of 1 to 2 minutes of arc per second when the target itself was fixated. With a virtually unstructured field, the values given were ten times as great. Later investigators verified Aubert's results.

The threshold for movement perceived at 9 degrees from the fixation point was about 18 minutes of arc per second. Threshold differences in rate of movement for certain targets near the fixation point turned out to be about 1 to 2 minutes per second. Graham, Baker, Hecht, and Lloyd (92) obtained a value of 30 seconds of arc per second for the threshold difference in the rate of slow-moving targets, and a value of about 100 seconds for fast-moving targets. Brown (36) studied the relation of phenomenal (perceived) movement to rate of physical displacement in a field by using an endless broad belt upon which various sized, shaped, and spaced targets were placed, from experiment to experiment. Actually, Brown used two such setups, one as a standard and the other as a comparison field. The observer could shift his gaze from one to the other. Naturally, they were placed so that they would not both be visible at the same time.

Brown found the following: as the physical velocity of a moving square target is increased from 0 to 200 cm. per second, several kinds of thresholds can be obtained, including (1) just perceptible movement; (2) a kind of reversed movement, which is produced when one target moves out of the field as the succeeding target moves in; (3) velocity at which the targets become a gray band instead of being distinct individuals. For the threshold of the first type, he found angular velocities from 2 to 6 minutes of arc per second. The length and width of the field were apparently contributing factors in giving these values. For the reversed movement (threshold 2), values from 3 to 9 degrees per second were found. The factors producing variation here were field dimensions, target sizes, and distances between them on the moving belt. Threshold 3 was obtained at values from 12 to 32 degrees per second.

Apparent Movement

Apparent movement is the phenomenal movement produced without target displacement. Physical factors such as intensity, position, and timing substitute for the usual displacement. The understanding of how these factors operate as substitutes is the main task of studying apparent movement. In the discussion of real movement earlier in this chapter, it was shown that to produce the visual experience of movement, some kind of spatial change in the retinal image had to be produced *in* time. That is, a temporal sequence of events had to occur on the retina, a spatial receptor surface. Before we go into detail as to how intensity, position, and timing of stimulation can substitute for the traverse of an image across the retina, we shall list the forms of apparent movement.

Gamma movement is the perceived radial movement outward from the fixation point when the level of illumination is suddenly raised, and the movement in the opposite direction when the illumination is suddenly lowered. Raising and lowering of illumination may take on various forms. For example, illumination can be raised from zero value to some finite value, or it can be changed from some material amount to some greater or lesser amount. Furthermore, the whole field may be involved homogeneously in the raising and lowering of illumination, or the specified change may involve only a restricted portion, which we ordinarily call a restricted *target*. That is, gamma movement can be produced either by varying the level of the whole field or by varying some part of it only. More details will be given regarding conditions for gamma movement and the characteristics of gamma movement itself in a later section (pages 264–268).

BETA MOVEMENT. This is the perception of lateral movement of a single object from one place to another position not greatly distant when two stationary targets are presented in succession. Beta movement is exemplified in motion pictures, in electric crossing signals for railroads, and in theater marquees. The production of beta movement is dependent upon a crucial combination of circumstances. These factors are primarily the proper distance between targets (measured in units of visual angle), the proper time interval between the presentations of the targets, and the proper target intensities. Some study has been made of these three general factors. Kortë (147), one of the investigators, formulated a loose set of "laws," known since as Kortë's laws. They state that once optimal (satisfactory or convincing) movement is set up, it may be maintained, even if one of the three above-stated conditions is altered, *if* some compensatory alteration is made in the values of one or both of the other two conditions. These alterations are as follows:

If distance between targets is increased, the time interval between presentations should be increased $(d \sim t)$ in order to maintain good movement. If distance is increased good movement may be maintained by increasing the intensity of the targets $(d \sim I)$. If intensity is increased, the time between presentations should be decreased $\left(I \sim \dfrac{1}{t} \right)$. It is as though a space-intensity combination of brain activity had to be of a certain pattern for apparent movement to be seen. The pattern can best be held nearly constant in form by the kinds of manipulations just specified.

DELTA MOVEMENT. Delta movement is akin to beta movement, except in addition to being a movement in the direction of the sequence in the presentation of two targets, it is finally a backward movement in the reverse direction. Delta movement is produced only when the second target is considerably more intense than the first.

ALPHA MOVEMENT. This is the apparent movement produced by presenting two parts of a geometrical "illusion" in sequence. One of the most frequently used examples of this is the presentation, one at a time, of the two parts of the Müller-Lyer figure. This sort of target is presented in Fig. 11.4. In part A of this figure, the whole Müller-Lyer figure is shown.

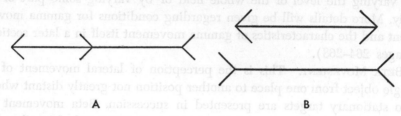

A   B

FIG. 11.4. The Müller-Lyer figure used in two parts in rapid succession to illustrate conditions for producing the alpha form of apparent movement.

Its right and left portions will be seen as two lines that are unequal in length. Actually, they are metrically equal. When the two parts are presented separately in time and the positions indicated in B, the horizontal-line portion of the two targets will lengthen or contract depending upon which is presented first. The wings on the lines, of course, "flop" back and forth from one position to the other as the one target follows the other.

The forms of movement thus far mentioned all occur in the frontal plane, being either horizontal or vertical. There is also a form of movement that leaves the frontal plane. This is exemplified in the way the wings in the Müller-Lyer figure behave as they change their lateral positions. They pivot as they change from the one lateral position to the opposite, and swing out toward the observer. This behavior may be called *pivotal movement*, for it does not remain in the frontal plane.

GAMMA MOVEMENT. Gamma movement, in many respects, can be taken as an example of all apparent movement. At least, it can be used to examine the necessary retinal conditions for movement experience. Let us, therefore, see what happens on the retina when a restricted portion of the visual field is raised. Fig. 11.5 is a diagram that shows the pattern of light across the retina when a target of restricted angular subtense is projected on it. The rectangle represents the distribution of the radiation on the retina were there to be no entoptic stray light, and were there to be a mathematically sharp image of the target. In contrast to this, the target is the source of radiation outside the image as well as in it. This was discussed in Chapter 6.

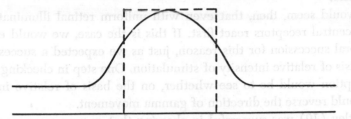

FIG. 11.5. The pattern of distribution of photic radiation across the retina is tapered and widespread (dark curve) rather than abrupt and restricted (broken-line figure).

It can be said, then, that the intensity of the illumination of the retina is tapered from the center of the image to a considerable distance outward, and then rather uniformly distributed from there out to the boundaries of the retina. When the target is presented, the center of the image receives the most radiation. It is a general principle in neurophysiology that tissue responds in terms of strength of the impingement upon it. The more energetic the impingement, the quicker (sooner) the measurable response begins. Tissue less strongly impinged upon responds, but only after a greater interval. This interval is called the latent period. So it may be said that the stronger the stimulation, the shorter the latency. As this rule applies here, it could mean that the part of the eye on which the image is projected responds first. Other parts would respond also, but only after greater and greater delay depending upon the distance from the stimulated area. This would mean that the receptors under the image would respond before those radial to it. The response of the eye would be in the form of a spatial sequence, the center of the retina first, and then the portions radial to it. Such a sequence would be expected to give rise to the experience of movement. Within limits, such a succession of activity being carried across the retina is quite like the succession produced by the traverse of an image of a moving target.

Although the description just given applies to the use of a restricted target, succession in activity in adjacent receptors in the retina can be produced by a uniform retinal illumination. That such a field can produce gamma movement is to be interpreted as meaning that the actual receptors do not all fire off equally rapidly. That is, the rods and cones possibly do not possess the same latency or the central and peripheral parts of the retina may vary in latency on account of the way the elements are connected neurally. We know that the neural hookup in the retina for the more peripheral receptors is different than for the more nearly foveal receptors.

It would seem, then, that even with uniform retinal illumination the more central receptors react first. If this is the case, we would expect a temporal succession for this reason, just as we expected a succession on the basis of relative intensity of stimulation. One step in checking on this assumption would be to see whether, on the basis of relative intensity, one could reverse the direction of gamma movement.

Bartley (10) was successful in showing that gamma movement could be reversed in direction. His target covered a large portion of the visual field. It was a large opal-glass disk, over which a number of layers of tissue paper were laid. All layers covered the center of the disk, whereas fewer and fewer layers were involved farther and farther out. When the disk was illuminated from behind, less radiation passed through central sections than through the peripheral ones. The retina, therefore, received more radiation toward its periphery than on portions toward the center. With the sudden onset of such a pattern of illumination, gamma movement was produced, but it originated at the periphery and moved toward the center of the visual field rather than in the usual way—outward from the center. Of course, at the termination of the stimulus, the movement spread radially outward—the direction opposite to the usual one.

Bartley, in another investigation, used disk targets of varying degrees of angular subtense to check upon the then fairly common idea that gamma movement was simply a perceptual aspect of the "emergence figure upon ground." Many experimenters of the day had been using targets of small subtense, and it had been found that the edge of the object did expand radially as the object emerged into view. It was taken from this that gamma movement of the object border was a function of its emergence. Bartley found that when targets of larger angular subtense were used, the gamma movement occurred within the object and the border did not expand radially as it emerged. (See Fig. 11.6.) He drew the conclusion that gamma movement was not a secondary function of the emergence of figure upon ground, but rather of the spatio-temporal distribution of stimulation of the receptor population. Once the images of target borders were a certain distance out toward the periphery of the retina, the intensity and sensitivity tapers were largely absent and movement was trivial or absent.

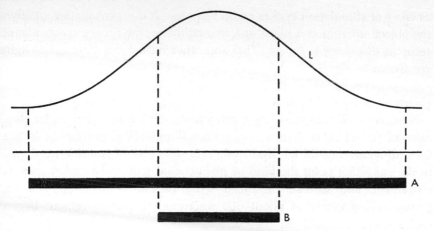

FIG. 11.6. Spatial relation of possible gradient of sensitivity across the retina to targets of various angular subtenses such as those of A and B. Those portions of the gradient, L, that are steep function toward producing gamma movement. If the retinal image lies within this gradient, apparent movement will occur both within and outside of the seen figure. If the border of the image lies radially to the steep gradient, the movement will lie well within the seen figure.

One of the arguments of the proponents of a psychological or central theory of the origin of gamma movement was that retinal factors were secondary because gamma movement could be produced just as well by a "black" target on a "light" ground as by a "light" target on a "dark" ground. The argument here is that by using a "black" target, no intensity or a negligible one was being employed in the target, and that the rules applying to intensive targets did not hold.

One can show that the rule of physiology used to explain movement by reason of differences in latency dependent upon relative amounts of stimulation holds as well for "dark" as for "light" targets. A withdrawal of radiation in the region of its projection on the retina is greater than for other regions. This withdrawal evokes an off-response in the retina, just

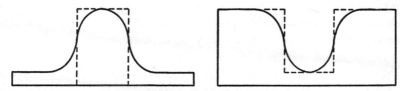

FIG. 11.7. Diagrams to show that the illumination of the retina is gradientwise regardless of whether the target is intensely and the background weakly luminous.

as onset of stimulation evokes an on-response. It does not matter whether the object emerges as a black one or a light one; the proper succession of receptor discharge is set up. This and other retinal distributions of light are shown in Fig. 11.7.

Movement in Third Dimension

Newman (*197*), in studying gamma movement, found that under slow rates of reduction or increase of retinal illumination, movement in the third dimension could be produced. This slow rate of transition reduced to the vanishing point the kind of phenomenal movement called gamma movement, and instead produced what he called depth movement. Gamma disappeared at about 300 msec. and depth movement began with 200 msec. transitions.

More recently, Bartley and Miller (*15*), using a Harvard tachistoscope, studied depth movement by varying other factors. They called this movement *adab* movement, since *ad* and *ab* are prefixes meaning toward and away from.

A target of a given size was replaced by another one within .01 sec. delay. In some experiments the second target was less intense but of the same size as the first, and in other experiments the second target was the same intensity but smaller in size. The timing arrangement permitted only the variation of the duration of the second target. At its termination the first target was re-presented. This arrangement involved a number of limitations, but a number of findings were made. They were complex. All that is to be said here is that one can produce depth movement by use of the two factors just mentioned.

TACTUAL MOVEMENT

Our consideration of visual movement involved not only a discussion of real movement but apparent movement. We are now ready to deal with apparent tactual movement, to which we shall largely confine ourselves.

Whereas there is no doubt that the visual modality provides for both apparent and real movement by way of its own mechanisms, there is some doubt about certain features of tactual apparent movement. It is with this matter that we shall mainly deal in this section.

It is a common observation as well as a deduction from special experimental conditions that movement is a visual phenomenon. One can see things move, and in order that this may occur, physical displacement need not occur.

Tactile stimuli may traverse the skin surface and be felt as something moving. Of this there is no doubt. The experiences of tactile movement aroused by successions of stationary stimuli have also been reported.

Burtt (49), in 1917, reported on results which he labeled tactual illusions of movement. This was not long after the work of Wertheimer (258) on visual apparent movement became well known. Following the lead of early workers, who manipulated the stimulus conditions in a fairly lawful manner, Burtt manipulated the same essential conditions in the study of movement experiences elicited by stationary tactual stimuli. The factors manipulated were temporal intervals between contacts with the skin, exposure times (i.e., durations of contact), and the spatial separations between contacts. The temporal intervals he used were 15, 21, and 40 msec. The durations of contact were multiples of the interval times.

He found that, in general, the greater the distance between contacts, the greater the time interval needed to produce apparent movement. He found also that the greater the intensity of contacts, the less the time needed to obtain or maintain movement. He also found that the greater the distance between contacts, the greater their intensities needed to be for movement. Furthermore, when the intensity of the second contact was made greater than that of the first, movement in the reverse direction was sometimes produced.

Another set of generalizations regarding his findings was made in the following fashion. Shortening the exposure time (duration) gives the impression of simultaneity or fusion of the two contacts, other things being equal. On the other hand, increasing the exposure time tends to produce the experience of movement. Still greater durations of contact tend to give the impression of discrete succession. Obviously, these manipulations work in the ways specified only up to a certain point.

Hulin (123), about ten years after Burtt, made his report on apparent movement. He varied the separations of his two stimuli from simultaneity up to 300 msec. between the ending of the first contact and the beginning of the second. The spatial separations varied from 5 mm. to 150 mm. In the many thousands of trials used, about 30 percent yielded some form of apparent movement. The forms of movement were classified into full, end, inner, and bow movement. These, taken together, were called optimal movement. In general, the most cases of movement were obtained when the two stimuli overlapped by about 75 msec. Full movement showed a decided peak with an overlap of 75 msec. The other types varied somewhat indefinitely. Hulin was unable to verify Korte's (147) law for the relation between space and time.

Hulin deduced that there were four principal factors at work to produce the experience reported. They were pressure irradiation, perseveration and associated factors, visual imagery, and kinesthesis. He pointed out that Wundt, many decades earlier, had said that the idea of locality on the skin stemmed usually from visual associations. This is to say, he attributed great potency to visual imagery in producing tactual space effects. Another earlier investigator asserted that persons with good visual imagery did better in tactual localization than those with poor visual imagery.

There is probably nothing about the strictly quantitative features of the results obtained by these and other investigators that can be used to distinguish whether the movement experience is actually tactual or a product of visual imagery. Various qualitative features of the reports that testify to visual imagery are our best evidences.

One of the kinds of movement reported upon was bow movement. This is the experience of movement from one place on the skin to another; but instead of the path of the movement being confined to the skin or body, it bows into the air above the skin surface. When this happens we must deduce that the movement elicited is visual. Visual imagery is the vehicle for movement in space apart from the body. Not only do we deduce this, but many astute observers who have undergone these experiences have come to the sure realization that what they were reporting upon in bow movement was visualized movement elicited by tactual stimulation. They tended to call it "illusory." Bow movement from tactual stimulation seems to be another case of associative imagery, which we have already described in other connections.

To say that bow movement as elicited tactually is a product of associative imagery, a product of the activity of the visual modality, is not to deny that tactual apparent movement can be produced. Your author has produced both sorts of end results—movement via visual imagery and pure tactual movement—from stationary tactual stimulation. Whereas the end result of one movement is highly spatial and suggestive of visual experience, the other is more restricted, definitely bodily localized, and possesses a more concrete tactual feeling. It is more as if something actually is dragged across the skin. Thus it is a decidedly sequential contact experience. It has a strong quality of contact and friction, whereas some observers realize for themselves that the bow experience is more nearly something seen rather than felt.

We must beware of which of the two experiences is being produced when we use tactual stimulation. The two forms bear upon what we have already said about the tactual modality not being outwardly spatial, and about true externalized spatial qualities arising only through the operation of the visual modality. The distinction seems to be borne out in the results we have been discussing. They point toward the conclusion that that which is really tactual is body-confined, and that not all experiences elicited by tactual stimuli need be tactual. Some of them may be so intimately connected with the tactual that many persons are unaware of what they are.

AUDITORY MOVEMENT

In the preceding section, the question of whether the experience of movement elicited by stationary tactual stimuli is actually tactual or not was given consideration. We have the same sort of question to ask in regard to the movement experiences produced by stationary auditory stimuli. Naturally, it is taken for granted that acoustic sources undergoing physical displacement in space produce genuine auditory movement experiences. We need to consider what happens when using stationary stimuli.

Phenomenal Spacing of Sound Sources

The phenomenal distance between two sounds has been studied. In an unilluminated room, two vertical-line (visual) targets separated by 4 cm. were presented successively by a known time interval. At the same time, two acoustic sources separated by a distance of from 20 to 40 cm. were presented successively with the two visual targets. Subjects were asked to locate the visual and auditory objects under various conditions. Phenomenal movement was found for both the sights and sounds, but their temporal relations were not certain. When partial movement was produced, sound moved over a wider spatial range than did the lines. Sound was heard in the third dimension, whereas the lines adhered to a plane. When the time intervals were made so small that the stimuli produced perceptive simultaneity, a single sound was heard in the median plane, but two lines appeared side by side. Reduction in phenomenal interval was out of proportion to the reduction of stimulus intervals and stimulus durations. The judgment of the spatial intervals between two sound sources depended more upon the intervals between the visual targets than upon the intervals of the sound sources themselves.

While this study did not give us a great deal about phenomenal movement produced by acoustic sources, it did indicate that localization of acoustic sources depended more upon visual stimulus factors than upon the acoustic. This is suggestive support for the supposition that the auditory mechanism is not a primary space-structuring mechanism.

Apparent Movement

Mathieson (177) studied phenomenal movement produced by acoustic stimulation. The acoustic sources produced clicks whose intervals were controlled. She also controlled illumination as well as space intervals between acoustic sources. The object of the investigation was to determine the compulsory conditions for auditory movement experience after the manner involved in visual experiments.

No compulsory conditions were found. With the conditions used, movement experiences were obtained in only 4 percent of the 6000 trials involved. Experiences called movement experiences included all those cases in which some sort of "filling in" took place between the first and second experiences produced by the pair of stimuli. The movement experiences were accomplished by visualization, according to Mathieson. The range of intervals within which movements were found did not tally closely with phenomenal reduction of distance. Conditions of dichotic hearing seemed the most favorable for filling in, or movement.

TABLE 2. Duration of Stimulation and Interval Between Exposures

A	B	C	D	E	F	G
190	33	190	18	200	60%	20%
190	33	190	27	200	40%	0%
76	10	76	18	200	75%	0%
76	10	76	27	200	100%	0%
76	8	76	18	200	50%	0%

NOTE: A equals duration of first sound source; B, time interval between; C, duration of second source; D, space interval between; E, distance to sound source; F, normal movement; and G, reverse movement.

The failure to obtain good movement would seem to be due to the use of click-producing stimuli rather than some less abrupt and quickly terminating sound sources.

Burtt (48) studied what he called auditory illusions of movement. He found a rather definite relation between the duration of stimulation and the interval between exposures needed for the movement experience. If the intensity of the second stimulus was greater than that of the first, the apparent movement was often experienced in the reverse direction. The longer the exposure, the shorter the optimal interval for producing movement. A second acoustic source may produce an abruption or added impulse before the first is completed, and the continuity of the two produces the experience of movement. A sample set of results is shown in Table 2.

CONCLUSIONS

It would seem that the production of movement experiences in either the tactual or the auditory realm is fairly difficult with stationary stimuli. The conditions are quite crucial, and in certain investigations the experimenters have not seemed to hit upon the most favorable conditions.

Additional factors in the determination of whether movement is reported in experiments involving stationary stimuli are the bias and training of the subjects, and the understandings of the experimenters. While these factors do not pertain alone to the study of apparent tactual and auditory movement, they certainly enter in quite crucially here.

If tactual and auditory movement experiences are considered to be *illusions*, by either the subjects or experimenters or both, a kind of bias toward dealing with them or reporting upon them will exist. To be reported upon, an experience of any sort must be clear and emphatic if it is a sort that contradicts "common sense," or the understandings of the subjects. Little can be done directly about biases. It is not good for the experimenter to explain and describe certain kinds of experiences to his subjects. He may bias them in directions opposite to those he suspects they will have of their own.

It seems fortunate that much of the work that was done on tactually and acoustically induced apparent movement was done during the period in psychology when imagery was a kind of phenomenon that was given some attention. It enabled the investigators to distinguish between associative imagery and experiences pertaining to the modality in which the sense-organ stimulation took place.

It seems plausible to conclude that many of the movement experiences induced by stationary tactual stimulation were actually visual experiences, i.e., results mediated by visual imagery. Some, of course, were true tactual experiences, and we believe they can be differentiated qualitatively from the former kind.

In audition, the movement experiences seem to be mediated by visual imagery. This is particularly true with stationary stimuli. But it also seems to be true when physical displacement of the acoustic source is involved. That is, hearing is spatial only by reason of visuo-imaginal participation which forms the matrix within which sound is heard.

Much more work needs to be done to check on this viewpoint so that what seems to be so plausible to some and so unintelligible to others may be rejected or established.

Chapter 12

THE BASIC FEATURES OF HEARING

In this chapter it is our aim to relate the fundamental characteristics of what we hear to the environmental conditions that produce them. In the preceding chapter on movement, auditory movement, as produced by stationary stimuli, was dealt with. Hearing, as it relates to space perception, was also dealt with. Now we are ready to deal with the fundamentals of acoustic stimulation and the auditory variables that are related to it.

THE ACOUSTIC STIMULUS

The ear is affected by a kind of mechanical force transmitted by the air. This energy is in the form of vibrations ranging from very low frequencies, let us say about 20 per second, to possible 20,000 per second. We shall begin with two amazing facts. One is the tininess of the amount of energy that will affect the ear, and the other is the great range of energy that the ear will accept without damage.

Auditory sensitivity is so keen that, at its best, the human can almost hear the random variations produced when individual molecules strike the eardrum. The movement of the eardrum needed to set up activity for hearing is less than a billionth part of an inch. At the other extreme, the ear can withstand pressure variations ten million times as great. Outside the body, no single recording system such as a voltmeter is able to cover such a range without auxiliary equipment, which, in effect, turns the meter into several meters, one for each lesser range.

As we implied, the stimulus for sound is a rapid fluctuation of pressure, causing the eardrum to vibrate. In dealing with these pressure waves, we classify them in several ways. First, some acoustic sources vibrate in a simple manner, setting up a single wave frequency. Other sources produce several wave frequencies. Such sources may be classified into two groups: those that produce frequencies related to each other by simple numbers, such as 1, 2, 3, 4, etc., and those that produce a random grouping of frequencies not related in this way, but by very complex relationships. Such sources produce a kind of random set of wave frequencies.

The acoustic sources producing single frequencies are called *tonal.* The sources that produce groups of waves that relate to each other according to simple whole numbers are also called tonal. Other acoustic sources are *atonal* or noise-producing sources. (See Fig. 12.1.) The waves

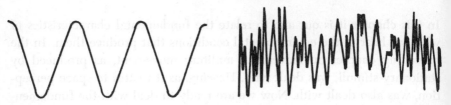

FIG. 12.1. Diagrams showing the regular pattern of a simple tonal acoustic stimulus and the erratic pattern of frequency of an atonal stimulus.

of the tonal sources are of two classes. The lowest frequency is the *fundamental,* and the others are *overtones.*

It will be fairly obvious that there are several primary variables involved—the wave frequency, the wave amplitude, and the degree of simplicity or complexity of the wave pattern. Insofar as a single frequency dominates, the result is a perceptual quality called pitch. The amplitude of the waves, insofar as the waves do not cancel, provides loudness. The complexity of the wave pattern provides for distinctions between tones, noises, and numbers of separate tones heard at once. Tonal sources can be distinguished from each other in terms of the number and relative strengths of the overtones. That is, a violin can, of course, be distinguished from a French horn or an oboe or a piano. This is on the basis of *timbre.* This assertion has been checked on many times by way of demonstrating that the sounds of various musical instruments can be synthetically produced by combining various wave frequencies of various amplitudes. This was first done in the days of the nineteenth-century experimentalists, who, as their first step, analyzed the sound sources by means of resonators. Nowadays we have electronic organs, the tones of which are all produced by electric oscillations that activate speakers (diaphragms) electromagnetically. Various frequencies can be blended to simulate well-known musical instruments besides the organ tones themselves.

THE DECIBEL

For the measurement of the energy of the acoustic stimulus, there is a very convenient and appropriate unit called the decibel. In biological work, it has scarcely been used at all except for quantification of the auditory stimulus, although it is applicable for other measurements, such as for the photic stimulus.

The decibel is a unit that is proportional to the general magnitude dealt with. This is a characteristic that is quite appropriate, since sensory reactions are themselves proportional to the energy levels involved. (See pages 107–108.) A decibel is specified as

$$db = 10 \, \frac{\log E_2}{\log E_1}$$

when E_1 is the threshold energy for activating the hearing modality, and E_2 is the energy in use at the time. Both of these measures are in absolute energy units. The use of the decibel provides for plotting, on the same graph, amounts of energy near threshold and huge amounts near the upper end of the usable range. The number of decibels generally considered to lie within the full range of stimuli for hearing is 120. At this upper limit, there are such acoustic sources as airplane motors and thunder. The acoustic energies generated in a boiler shop are about 100 decibels. Those of a busy street in traffic are about 70 decibels. Conversation is rated at 60, the typical office 40, and a whisper is probably 15 decibels. These figures sound very unrealistic, for in hearing them one tries to relate them in a simple fashion to the loudnesses of the various situations specified. The decibel does not refer at all to loudness, but rather to the energy involved in the pressure vibrations set up.

THE SONE

In order to have a unit that pertains to loudness, Stevens (239) used the ratio scale in obtaining the relation between experienced loudness of a tone and the energy that produced it. He had his subjects adjust a tonal source so that they would hear a tone one-half as loud as the standard tone. By using standard stimuli of various energy contents, the whole decibel scale was explored. To begin with, however, a unit of loudness had to be chosen. It was recognized that all sources of the same energy content do not sound equally loud. Sources emitting higher frequencies sound louder for the same energy involvement. Therefore, a frequency had to be selected for use as a standard. The frequency chosen was 1000 cycles per second. With this, a given energy content had also to be chosen. It was decided that a source with an energy of 40 decibels would be appropriate; that is, it would be a conveniently sized unit. Thus a *sone* is a unit of loudness and is the loudness of a tone produced by a source of 1000 cycles per second and an energy content of 40 decibels. The sone is simply the loudness heard under such conditions. Two sones will be the loudness of a sound twice as loud as one sone. By use of the fractionation method, the subject, bit by bit, built a loudness scale in which the numbers involved have the very same properties as those in our cardinal number scale in arithmetic. The curves in Fig. 12.2 show

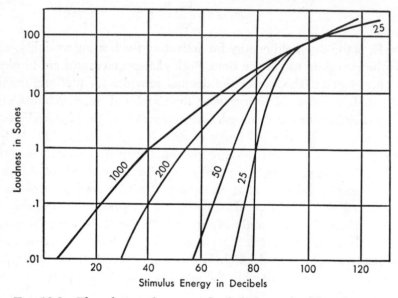

FIG. 12.2. The relation of sones to decibels for each of four frequencies (S. S. Stevens and H. Davis, *Hearing: Its Psychology and Physiology*, John Wiley & Sons, Inc., 1938, Fig. 43).

the relation of sones to decibels. It will be seen that in the graph sones are plotted in logarithmic terms. Decibels are already logarithmic units.

The family of sone curves, one curve for a given frequency, shows that when the stimulus has a low energy content, loudness varies most with energy. In the region of 100 decibels, a great shift in decibels varies loudness but little. The curves for the various frequencies tend to converge as loudness increases. It turns out that a loudness of 100 sones is produced by an energy of little more than 100 decibels for most of the frequencies shown.

A SCALE FOR PITCH IN MELS

In essence the same procedure was used by Stevens, Volkmann, and Newman (243) to construct a scale for pitch. Figure 12.3 shows a

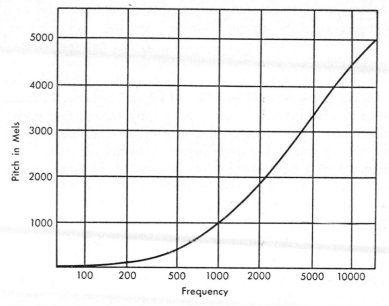

Fig. 12.3. The relation between frequency and pitch, in mels (S. S. Stevens, J. Volkmann, and E. B. Newman, A scale for the measurement of the psychological magnitude pitch, *J. Acoust. Soc. Am.* [1937], 8:185–190).

curve relating pitch and frequency. It will be noted that except for tones produced by sources having frequencies less than 1000 cycles per second, the relation of pitch to frequency is almost linear. The unit of pitch used by the investigators just mentioned was the *mel.* It is so defined that the pitch heard is 1000 mels when the energy level is 60 decibels and the frequency is 1000 cycles per second. In other words a source had to be chosen that was considerable above the one that would produce the pitch unit of the convenient size. A 1000-cycle source was chosen. The pitch heard could not be called 1 mel, for that would reduce the whole frequency scale to producing a range of only 5 mels. So the 1000-cycle tone was called 1000 mels, and the scale was worked out for sources both lower and higher in frequency, using the 1000 cycles as a standard.

COMBINATION TONES AND BEATS

Combination tones are formed by two frequencies being presented simultaneously. Not only are the tones arising from each of the single sources heard but also the tone that would be produced by a frequency that is the sum of the two frequencies actually generated as stimuli and the tone expected from a frequency that is the difference between the two frequencies of the stimuli. These two extra tones are called *summation tones* and *difference tones* respectively. Not only may there be a first-order difference tone and summation tone but there may also be second-, third-, and possibly fourth-order tones. It is doubtful, however, whether most persons could hear the second- and higher-order tones.

When two frequencies do not differ greatly enough to generate difference tones, a third phenomenon may occur. The difference in frequency may generate a low frequency variation called a *beat*. It is a low-frequency waxing and waning of the loudness of the tones. One knows by the number of these waxing and wanings what the frequency difference is between two stimuli producing closely similar tones.

CONSONANCE AND DISSONANCE

There is one major factor in hearing that is not generally treated as a quantitative matter, but is nevertheless an indubitable aspect of tones. It is the factor of consonance and its opposite, dissonance. When two frequencies are generated at the same time, the listener will hear either a pleasing or a displeasing sound. Some tones are heard as fusing and blending well. Others are described as jarring, rasping, or clashing. Perhaps this qualitative effect is nothing that can be considered stable and similar among all people. Sounds have meaning and can take on new meanings, and it is possible that what is called consonance and dissonance may have some basis in the listener's system of meanings and habits. In our society, the frequencies that have long been considered consonant are those having a ratio of 2:1 (the octave), 3:2 (the major fifth), 4:3 (the fourth), 5:3 (the major sixth), 5:4 (the major third), 6:5 (the minor third), and 8:5 (the minor sixth). The first three are better than the last four. It is with reference to goodness among these ratios that listeners differ even while calling them all consonant.

Examples of frequency ratios that are called dissonant are the following: 16:5 (the major second), 9:8 (the major seventh), and so on. Among the theories accounting for consonance and dissonance has been that of Helmholtz. It has to do with overtones causing beats. It has been found that dissonance does not disappear when pure tones are used. This has been used as an argument against Helmholtz' theory. It has been pointed out, however, that the tissues of the ear may be made to vibrate with harmonics even when the acoustic source lacks them. Hence harmonics in the ear itself may be produced and may support Helmholtz' idea.

MASKING

If two acoustic energies of different frequency and different intensity impinge on one ear, the weaker energy may not be effective at all. This is called *masking*. The weaker source may, of course, be made to be heard by intensifying it. Masking is measured by determining the amount by which the threshold of one acoustic source is raised by the presence of another. The masking effect extends over considerable ranges of difference in frequency, but is greatest for tones of nearly similar frequencies. One frequency will mask a higher frequency more easily than one of a lower frequency.

PITCHES OF COMPLEX SOUNDS

When a complex tone is produced by frequencies differing by a constant value, let us say of 100 cycles or more, the pitch is not that expected from a frequency represented by the mean of the frequencies acting, but rather the pitch produced by a source whose frequency is equal to the constant difference between the frequencies. Let us say that the component frequencies of the complex acoustic source are 800, 900, 1000, and 1100 cycles. Such a source produces a perceived tone expected from a stimulus of 100 cycles. By the same principle, a complex source composed of frequencies of 500, 700, and 900 cycles produces a pitch expected from a source with a frequency of 200 cycles. Furthermore, if to a complex acoustic source composed of frequencies of 400, 600, 800, and 1000 cycles the additional frequencies 500, 700, and 900 are added, the pitch seems to drop a whole octave, namely, from a pitch produced by 200 cycles to one produced by 100 cycles.

This principle was reported many years ago by Fletcher (77) at the Bell Telephone Laboratories. In addition to these findings, certain very unexpected results in connection with filtering out certain frequencies of a complex sound source were obtained. The common understanding with regard to the pitch produced by a complex source is that the pitch depends upon the frequency of the fundamental component. The fundamental component is the component with the lowest frequency. The other frequencies, being all higher, are called the overtones, and are expected to affect timbre, but not pitch.

Let us say that the complex source with which we are dealing contains a fundamental of 300. The first overtone will be a frequency of 600; the second overtone will be a frequency of 900. Thus it is that there is a common frequency *difference* between the component tones, and the sound produced will be a tone that is expected from a frequency of 300 cycles. This allows us to eliminate the fundamental, just so long as the remaining components still possess the constant frequency difference. All that this means is that usually, in order to get a set of frequencies differing by a constant frequency value, a wave of this very frequency is one of the components produced by the source. The physical characteristics of the acoustic source are such as to vibrate at a given rate, and at any one of several higher rates that are multiples of the lowest rate, the fundamental. If certain overtones are somehow left out, or greatly reduced, we may expect a rather indefinite tonal effect.

RELATING PITCH TO DURATION

The remarks already made regarding sound sources being tonal in their effects apply to stimuli of one second or more in duration. When the source lasts for less than one second, the phenomenal (perceptual) effect is a click rather than a tone. One might suspect that a click would have no pitch, but this is not strictly the case. Some clicks sound higher than others. The ear acts as an analyzer, even for short acoustic stimuli; thus some clicks sound sharp and others sound dull and lower in pitch. Stevens and Davis (*241*) have discussed how this analysis takes place. Figures 12.4 indicates the relations Ekdahl and Stevens found between duration of a tonal source and the pitch.

Bürck, Kotowski, and Lichte (*47*) studied the relation between the minimum duration of a sound stimulus and its frequency in order for the listener to experience a definite pitch. A source with a frequency of 50 cycles per second must last for 60 msec., whereas a source with a frequency of 1000 cycles need last only a little longer than 10 msec. Obviously, the latter source will involve twelve pressure waves in that

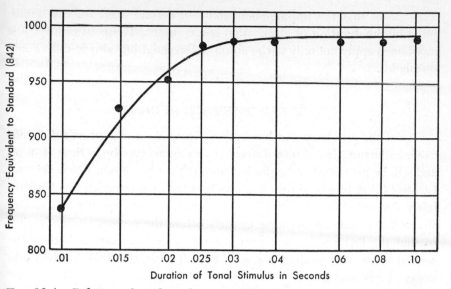

Fig. 12.4. Relation of pitch to duration (Ekdahl and Stevens, cited in S. S. Stevens and H. Davis, *Hearing: Its Psychology and Physiology*, John Wiley & Sons, Inc., 1938, Fig. 36).

time, whereas the first source would produce about three waves in 60 msec.

RELATING LOUDNESS TO DURATION

Just as in the case of experience of pitch, the experience of loudness depends upon the duration of the acoustic stimulus. When it is very short, the loudness is at its minimum. As duration increases, the loudness grows, finally reaching a maximum. With further increase of duration, the loudness diminishes to a stable value. This is reminiscent of the brightness produced by a photic stimulus, and therefore helps to unify our understanding of the way the organism operates. According to Békésy (20), acoustic stimuli lasting less than one-half second are heard as less loud than those that are longer.

One hypothesis covering the relation between loudness and duration, stated by Licklider (163), is the *diverted input hypothesis*. According to it, a constant portion of the acoustic input (power) is diverted from the excitation process and therefore is not integrated in producing the sensory end result. The threshold function can be stated by the following:

$$(I - I_0)\, t = \text{constant}$$

This means that the impingement minus a certain fixed fraction multiplied by the duration of application is a constant. The relationships just mentioned apply not only to the absolute threshold but also to differential thresholds.

THRESHOLD DIFFERENCES IN ONSET

One of the problems that has both a theoretical and a practical significance is the question of how different two sources may be in time of onset and still be perceived as beginning simultaneously. Bürck, Kotowski, and Lichte (47) determined this. It seems that the time intervals involved are fairly similar to the time needed to recognize the tonal quality of a sound. If the first source begins long enough before the second source begins, so that the first produces a sound whose tone is recognized, then the second source will produce a second tone. That is, there will be two successive tones heard.

THE VOLUME OF TONES

Certain writers have referred to a characteristic of tones called volume. Low tones of an organ, for example, sound bigger and more space-occupying than the squeak of a mouse. Even when two sounds are equated for loudness, the difference called volume persists.

Volume is a word that is also used in another way, and therefore we do not want to get the two meanings confused. Radio sets have volume controls, and when volume is dealt with in this way, it is intensity that is being manipulated. As far as the listener is concerned, of course, it is loudness that is consequently varied.

The property of volume as bigness has been studied by several workers. In the first place, volume was studied as a function of stimulus frequency. Later it was studied as a function of stimulus intensity. The thinking behind these attempts was as follows. If the difference limens for volume are different than those for pitch and loudness, volume is a different attribute of tones than either of the other two. In other words, if its threshold is different, it follows different laws; and if so, it is a unique attribute. The results of various workers have not agreed in testing the threshold. Despite this, there seems to be evidence from listeners that there is such an attribute as volume, and that it is distinct from the other two attributes.

Stevens (236) finally established that volume is a tonal attribute. In his investigation, the observer was given stimuli of unlike frequency producing alternately different tones of different pitch. He varied the intensity of one stimulus until it matched the other in the volume it produced. This procedure established the fact that the two tones could be made equal in volume while being experientially different in pitch and loudness. To produce the equality in volume, the source for the higher tone had to be made more intense than the one for the lower tone. It can therefore be said that volume increases with intensity and with frequency. Or to put the matter totally in perceptual terms, volume rises with loudness and with pitch. Figure 12.5 shows such relationships. The

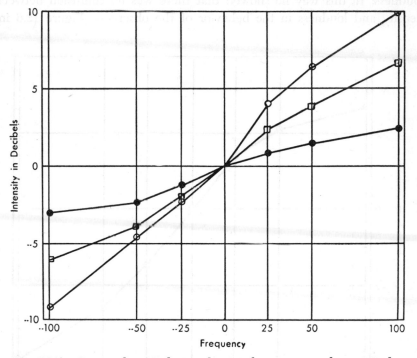

FIG. 12.5. Curves showing how volume is kept constant by manipulation of intensity and frequency. Each curve is for a constant volume (S. S. Stevens, The role and intensity of tones, *Am. J. Psychol.* [1934], *46*:397–408, Fig. 1).

graphs are so constructed that as the intensity and the frequency of certain sources are varied above and below a given common reference point, shown at the center of the diagram, the equal-volume conditions vary as represented by the curves. Stepping up frequency of a source requires that its intensity be stepped up also if equality of volume is to be maintained between the two resulting tones. The slopes of the three curves, each curve representing a fixed intensity, show that the relation just mentioned is more marked for lower intensities than for higher.

TONAL DENSITY

Observers have declared that some tones sound denser, tighter, or harder than others. This led Stevens (237) to study this fourth possible attribute of tones. To do this, he obtained the differences of two stimulus values that would result in tones that were equal in density but not in loudness. In this way he showed that there was no confusion between density and loudness in the behavior of the observers. Figure 12.6 in-

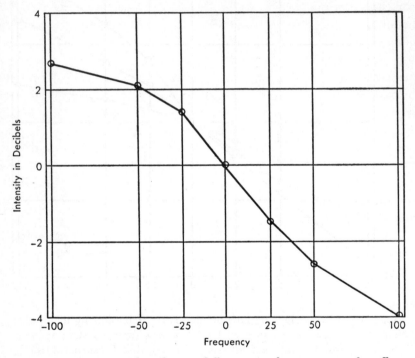

Fig. 12.6. Curve to show how a difference in frequency can be offset by a difference in intensity to keep density constant (S. S. Stevens, Tonal density, *J. Exper. Psychol.* [1934], *17*:585–592, Fig. I).

dicates the relation between density and frequency and loudness. Comparison between this set of relations and the behavior of volume is possible by turning back to Fig. 12.5. The two functions run in opposite directions.

BRIGHTNESS OF TONES

A fifth term has often been used by observers to describe the quality of the tones they hear. This term is *brightness*. Again several investigators addressed themselves to the task of finding what operations had to be performed to manipulate the quality which the observers alleged.

There is no doubt but that many observers find the terms bright and dull to be quite aptly descriptive of the tones they hear. Some investigators have identified, or at least closely associated, brightness with pitch. The ability to do this has led, of course, to the assumption that the two characteristics form a single operational dimension. Abraham (*1*) thought he had demonstrated that pitch and brightness were actually independent. He based this upon the demonstration that with a Seebeck siren tones differing in brightness could be produced by the same frequency. Boring and Stevens (*32*) examined the claim and found that the difference between Abraham's tones was produced by a difference in the proportion of some of the higher overtones present. The observers also called the louder of the tones the brighter. Brightness was thus found to be a function of the combined operation of the dominant wave components of a sound source and its intensity. This does not make brightness a myth; but since density seems to be a similar function of frequency and intensity, brightness and density may be two words for the same experience.

Observers can equate two pure (produced by a single frequency) tones in brightness, but they are unable to do so once brightness is declared to be something different than what they were calling density. There just do not seem to be two distinguishable characteristics amenable to this treatment. It will be remembered that brightness is a term that is mostly used in vision rather than in hearing. It is possible that, since the term is used in two modalities, one might construct an experiment to equate tones and brightness qualities in vision. That would be to ask whether a given tone is as bright as a given surface, and to deal with brightness in terms of the fractionation procedure. If a tone is capable of being judged as bright as a given visual presentation, can it be judged half as bright or twice as bright? The attempt to do this might add to our understanding of tonal experience. In a subsequent chapter, a similar procedure is described. It was utilized in making some comparisons between certain very unlike qualities: saltiness, sourness, bitterness, and sweetness. (See page 346.)

HEARING LOSS

Some hearing loss is such that the impaired ear provides for hearing less well at all acoustic-energy levels. In another form of hearing loss, hearing is as good as normal for acoustic energies well above threshold. The third type of hearing loss is the case in which hearing improves relatively as intensities are increased, but never reaches normal. This, of course, is a case intermediate between the other two types. In the first type of hearing loss, it may be assumed that the effects are reduced somewhere in the auditory pathway before reaching the cerebral cortex. This type of hearing loss is the common result with defects in the middle ear.

The second type of hearing defect is as if there was the same absolute loss in terms of sones for all intensities. This would be expected to occur if there was a deficiency in the total number of neural elements involved. We might call this a case of "nerve deafness." In dealing with this sort of deficiency we could subtract a given constant amount of "loudness." Thus, as intensity is increased and the relation between loudness in sones and the decibels of energy in the stimulus shifts, such deaf persons could "catch up" with the normal individual. Refer to Fig. 12.2, which gives the relation of sones to decibels.

THE AUDIOGRAM

The measurement of the thresholds for hearing at a series of representative frequencies is called audiometry. This is generally done by use of an instrument designed especially for the purpose. Such instruments are electronic devices consisting in audio-frequency oscillators constructed to generate eight or more fixed frequencies. These relate to each other as octaves, from, let us say, 64 cycles to 8192 cycles. This instrument is calibrated in "sensation units." For these the decibel scale is used, its zero point being the average threshold for the normal ear. The intensity in decibels that the energy at the given frequency must be stepped up above zero is stated as the hearing loss for that frequency. When all the frequencies have been tested, a profile or audiogram is constructed. Figure 12.7 shows the essential nature of an audiogram. The dotted line

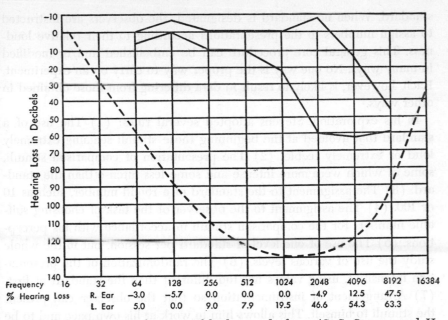

Frequency	16	32	64	128	256	512	1024	2048	4096	8192	16384
% Hearing Loss R. Ear		-3.0	-5.7	0.0	0.0	0.0	-4.9	12.5	47.5		
L. Ear		5.0	0.0	9.0	7.9	19.5	46.6	54.3	63.3		

FIG. 12.7. Audiogram of a case of high-tone deafness (S. S. Stevens and H. Davis, *Hearing: Its Psychology and Physiology*, John Wiley & Sons, Inc., 1938, Fig. 20).

is a curve showing the losses defining the "total loss of serviceable hearing." Some large-scale studies have shown that in males age has no impairing effects for frequencies below 1000 cycles, but that considerable losses do occur at high frequencies, that is, 4096 and 8192 cycles. The average loss there was about 31 decibels. Females manifest material loss for low frequencies but less for higher frequencies. Curious as it may seem, the sex differences are marked. One feature of this is that men show more frequent partial loss for high frequencies than do women.

FURTHER WORK IN LOUDNESS SCALING

Stevens (240) has continued his exploration of the perception of loudness beyond the initial development of the sone scale. This he has done in two general ways. One has been by using a standard that is presented only once per session, and with which a number of stimuli are compared by memory. The other has been by giving a group of stimuli without any one designated as a standard. When a standard is used, it is preassigned an arbitrary value such as 10 or 100, and all other presentations are evaluated in accordance with their perceived relation in loudness to the standard. When no standard is designated, the observers are instructed to assign numbers to the presentations according to their relative loudness. This general core procedure can be embellished and/or modified in many ways. No one way is the proper way to carry on an experiment. Each, however, is likely to result in data differing from those obtained in other ways.

In his exploration, Stevens adopted several rules: (1) The use of a standard that avoided at the beginning those stimuli seeming extremely loud or extremely feeble. (2) The presentation of comparison stimuli, some of which were more intense and some less intense than the standard. (3) The assignment to the standard of a round number, such as 10 or 100. (4) The assignment to the observer of the task of choosing suitable numbers for the comparison stimuli in accordance with his perceptions. (5) The use of one level of standard per session, but in the whole study the use of various levels. (6) The randomization of the presentation intensities, using values not too different than the standard at first. (7) Arrangement of instrumentation so that the observer can present the stimuli to himself. This allows him to work at his own pace and to be maximally attentive when stimuli are presented. (8) The making of experimental sessions quite brief. He favored ten-minute sessions. (9) The use of a large enough group of observers to establish a median.

It should be obvious that the two methods used are in part old and in part new. The use of a standard is conventional, but its use on only one trial per session is new. The omission of a standard introduces what has long been called the method of *absolute judgment,* or of *single stimuli.* This method has previously been used to show that the results are a product of the distribution of values in the presentation series; that is, physical values of the stimuli, the number of times each stimulus is repeatedly presented, and the order of presenting the stimuli. These questions are among those involved in Stevens' work.

The first factor to be mentioned is the question of whether the range of intensities included in the observer's task influences the results. You see, if intensities many decibels above or below the standard are presented, they would tend to call for high-ratio comparisons. This is like asking whether an observer can specify that a presentation is 200 times as loud as the standard, as in comparison to asking whether he can say that it is five times as loud. The early investigators felt that no such comparisons could reliably be made. Multiplying and fractionating, or designating equal sense distances, were not reliable enough to gain recognition. The development of the sone scale was the first demonstration that fractionation was reliable. Now we have the present question of range.

Stevens found that the extension of the range from 70 to 90 decibels yielded, in general, the same results, except at the very ends of the range. The loudness of intense impingements was "underestimated" somewhat, and the loudness of the weak ones was "overestimated."

The effect of presenting the standard only once per session was also studied. It was clear that an observer could operate on the basis of only one presentation of the standard, and even without any standard at all. But it was necessary to know what influences might be at work under the several conditions. For example, observers reported that when the 70-decibel standard was given at the end of a session, it sounded weaker than it was remembered to sound at the beginning of the session. On the other hand, the opposite was true for a 120-decibel presentation.

Stevens also compared his results in the present "estimation" series with those in the fractionation experiments. He obtained practically the same results in both. He also considered the classical question of whether the nature of the population of variable stimuli is a large factor in determining the individual's reports. Classically, the stimulus series had always been found to be influential. Stevens' conclusion was that the chosen stimuli can be made to play a biasing role, or that they can be so selected as not to do so. He did not find that spacing the comparison stimuli made a great deal of difference upon the outcome, when the observer was never given more than two trials with any single stimulus in a single session.

Stevens also considered what he called restraint. He compared his own experiments with those of two other studies. In one, all numbers were preassigned. In the other, all numbers between 0 and 20 were to be used. We can conclude by presenting Fig. 12.8, the net outcome obtained by Stevens in using the assignment method. It seems to be a refinement over the sone scale shown in Fig. 12.2.

If the observer is told that the upper limit of the scale is a certain number, the average value given to the more intense presentations will tend to be too low. The observer can make errors in only one direction. The same is true in reverse if the lower limit of the scale is preassigned a number. The net result will be a curve with a less-steep slope than otherwise. This was Stevens' argument for leaving his observers free to do all the assigning of number values to the stimuli. Stevens' observers claimed more difficulty with the fractionation method than with the assignment method. He also noted the introspective protocols given by the observers. Considerable visual imagery was reported. Often the observers reported "seeing a scale" to which they assigned the presentations.

Some of the early workers declared that the assignment of numbers

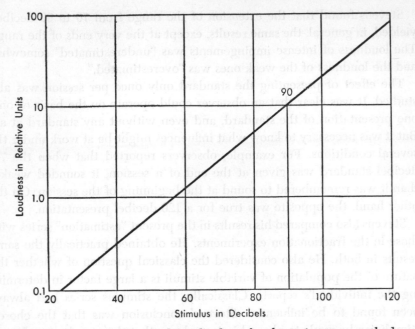

FIG. 12.8. Results from judging loudness by the assignment method.
For a 1000-cycle stimulus of 90 decibels, the number 10 was assigned
by the experimenter. The values were assigned to all the subsequent
stimuli by the observers. Each increase of 10 decibels in the stimulus
doubles loudness (modified from S. S. Stevens, The measurement of
loudness, *J. Acoust. Soc. Am.* [1955], 27:815–829, Fig. 4).

to stimulus presentations was a perceptual process. Ebbinghaus declared
that this was not the natural way for subjects to behave, and that for
them to react in this way was to involve a judgmental process. Although
we believe that perception can be pretty directly tapped by the scaling
methods, the experiments can be primarily those of judgment, that is,
ones in which the observers very definitely delay their responses, and
can include a weighing process beyond that involved in direct experience.

BINAURAL INTENSITY

One of the factors in aiding the individual to localize sound—that is,
to experience the direction from which the acoustic stimulus originated—
is the difference in the intensities of the impingements upon the two
ears. In general, the sound seems to come from a direction toward the
side the more intensely stimulated. This relationship has been studied by
various investigators, among them Stewart and Hovda (244), who used

two tuning forks in tandem. The stimuli were led to the two ears by tubes of equal diameter and length. The one fork was placed about 1 cm. from the end of one tube. The distance of the other from the second tube was varied from 0.20 cm. to 2.20 cm.

An intensity ratio of 10 to 1 was needed to shift the apparent direction of the sound source 45 degrees. This intensity ratio is much greater than the one resulting from an acoustic source placed at 45 degrees from the median plane. This would suggest that intensity is not alone in accounting for the normal accuracy in experiencing the direction of sound sources.

BINAURAL PHASE DIFFERENCE

Acoustic stimuli originating from a common source to one side or the other of the median plane do not reach the two ears at the same time, and when they do reach the two ears they are slightly out of phase. The higher the frequency, the less time involved in the various phases of a given wave. Very high frequencies might well be expected to provide no basis for utilizing phase difference.

Recent investigations have shown that binaural phase difference plays a role, but that it is effective only with pure tonal sources of 1500 cycles per second and below. As was implied, phase difference is reducible to time difference. This was taken advantage of in experiments of Wallach, Newman, and Rosenzweig (253), in which two click-producing sources, one for one ear and the other for the other ear, were used. Time differences of as little as 30 to 40 microseconds led to above chance numbers of reports to one side or another. When the time difference in the click sources was increased to 2 or 3 milliseconds, sound was heard as a double click. With still longer separations, the clicks were heard as fully separate and in widely separate locations.

Reverberation poses certain applications of the principles involved in binaural phase differences. It seems, however, that with click-producing sources, the first stimuli to arrive have precedence over the later ones in determining localization.

INTERMITTENT ACOUSTIC STIMULATION

It will be recalled that in Chapter 6 (pages 120–124) the results of using intermittent photic stimulation were described. It has been shown that intermittent acoustic stimulation can be used in a somewhat similar manner. Miller and Taylor (*183*) demonstrated this for two subjects.

One of the measures used in photic stimulation was critical flicker frequency, the rate at which a repetitive brief photic pulse just produces the experience of continuous uniform light. Sometimes restricted portions of the spectrum were used in this manner, but more often a stimulus producing the experience of whiteness or its approximation was used.

The stimulus used in the intermittent acoustic presentation was also productive of "whiteness," or noise. This is to say that a source providing a heterogeneous complex of frequencies was employed. In the conventional vernacular, this stimulus is known as white noise. Actually, if one is to use the metaphorical term, white, then all noise is to some degree white, for noise is the result as the stimulus departs from tonality.

Although both photic and acoustic energies can be presented intermittently in systematic fashion and produce stable, repeatable results in perception, there are some differences in the conditions to be pointed out.

The auditory mechanism is sensitive in higher frequencies of intermittence than the visual mechanism. Critical flicker frequency probably never exceeds 60 cycles per second, although recently there have been reports that send the value away above this. In contrast to this, auditory flutter may still exist up to 1000 cycles per second. Another difference lies in the fact that the threshold for the disappearance of auditory flutter is not so stable as for the disappearance of visual flicker. It is said that some intermittent acoustic stimuli may be productive of fused or unfused sound almost at the will of the observer. This makes it a serious problem to establish suitable criteria for the study of the flutter disappearance threshold (a.f.f., auditory flutter fusion).

The crucial shift in the perception produced by intermittent stimulation takes place between what Miller and Taylor call stages 3 and 4. It is a shift from a perceived quality different from continuous noise to a quality not different from continuous noise. This seems to call for an experimental procedure in which pairs of stimuli are presented, one intermittent, the other continuous. The subject is instructed to indicate by calling out "different" for any pair in which the sounds are not perceived as identical.

In addition to intermittence rate, there are other important variables for producing a.f.f. One is the fraction of the cycle occupied by the stimulus. In photic stimulation this was conventionally called l.d.r. (light-dark ratio). Another factor is the energy in the stimulus. Still additional ones are the distribution of the energy within the group of frequencies used, and the rise-and-fall times of the stimulus envelope.

Symmes, Chapman, and Halstead (246) studied a.f.f. for three stimulus intensities as the fraction of the cycle occupied by the stimulus was varied against frequency. The bursts used were 1.5 sec. long; the intrapair interval was 1 sec., and the interpair interval was 2 sec. The descending method of limits was used. Figure 12.9 shows the results for a

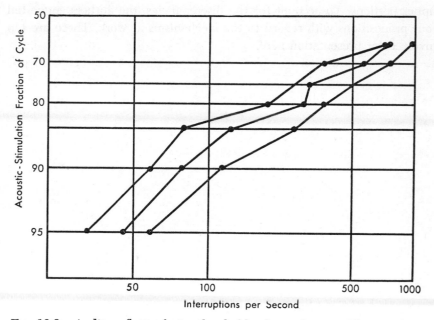

FIG. 12.9. Auditory-flutter-fusion thresholds of one observer. The top curve is for 45 decibels; the middle curve, 60 decibels; and the bottom, 80 decibels (D. Symmes, L. F. Chapman, and W. C. Halstead, Fusion of intermittent white mice, J. Acoust. Soc. Am. [1955], 27:471).

single observer. It will be noted that the lower portions of the three curves manifest a slope of about 45 degrees, which is to be expected if the duration of the off interval in the cycle is the determining factor in the fusion function. The upper portions of the curves manifest slopes whose steepness is less than 45 degrees. This was believed to represent a change in the listener's acuity. From the information they had, the workers were able to formulate an equation for the flutter-fusion function. It is as follows:

$$f = \frac{I \times c}{\Delta I \times T} \times 1000$$

where f is the repetition rate at fusion threshold; I, the intensity of the stimulus in decibels above threshold; ΔI, the intensity j.n.d. (just noticeable difference) for noise in decibels; T, the duration of the experienced decay to threshold in milliseconds; and c, 1.0 minus the fraction of the cycle occupied by the stimulus.

The use of the above equation provided adequate predictions for values for the lower parts of the curves in Fig. 12.9, but not for the upper portions. To account for the discrepancies, the authors suggested four propositions with regard to the mechanisms at work. These are too involved for presentation here.

Chapter 13

COMPLEX FEATURES OF HEARING

In the preceding chapter, the various sensory qualities of sounds were discussed. The chapter constituted a brief analysis of the relations between acoustic stimuli and the experiential qualities they elicit. Such an analysis is but the first step in dealing with the organism's employment of the auditory modality in its moment-to-moment activity.

The topics to be dealt with in this chapter include those of externalization of sound; auditory localization; the relation of reverberation to perceived distance; false localization; "facial vision" in the blind and blindfolded; the matching of auditory and visual perspective in the reproduction of situations, as in the case of talking movies; and sounds as abstract symbols.

EXTERNALIZATION OF SOUNDS

It will be recalled that in Chapter 10 the way that the auditory mechanism might function to provide the apprehension and appreciation of space (externality) was discussed. It was emphasized that the auditory mechanism did not include those facilities that would enable it to take a role in initiating the perception of space as a domain.

One of the investigations that bears on this point and at the same time is appropriate to mention here is the study of the localization of tones produced by earphones. In it, it was found that the resulting tones were localized within or near to the head. This is different from the localization that results when the same tones are produced in the more usual way, that is, by sources at some distance from the ears. In the one case, the subject cannot manipulate his geometrical relationships to the source; whereas in the other, he can. This difference may be one of the possible factors in producing the perceptual difference in the two cases.

Our chief interest in the fact that sounds produced by external sources may seem to originate *within* the body rather than outside of it lies in its demonstration that all sounds do not have to pertain to *externality* even in the sighted.

Those who know most about blindness assert that acoustic stimuli are not intrinsically interpreted as being localized *externally* by the congenitally blind. The present example with the headphones helps to make this assertion seem more plausible.

In vision, movement of the perceiver and change of optical information from space as a domain go hand in hand in a very direct manner. Persons with hearing but not vision have much less opportunity to relate their sensory experiences to externality. The main thing that the person without vision can do is to move his head or whole body so as to manipulate intensity and phase relations of sound waves. This is a gross affair compared to the achievements possible with vision. When the described motor manipulations are to be made in relation to hearing, the results would be related to the body as a domain rather than to externality. We would assume that the congenitally blind are not able to get away from the body as a reference. In fact, it would seem that the burden of proof would rest on those who assume that the congenitally blind do experience externality. For a review of this matter see Chapter 10.

AUDITORY LOCALIZATION

Vertical Localization

The location of sounds in the vertical dimension is very poor in the sighted person when the head and the sound source do not move. The listener must move his head in order to do much at all toward detecting the angle of elevation of the source.

Wallach (252) found that if he rotated the head and sound source together in the horizontal plane, the sound seemed to come from above. He called attention to the fact that the only sound sources for which horizontal head rotations usually produce no change in binaural phase and intensity relations are those directly above, and possibly directly below, the listener. Thus we can suspect that the location of sound is keyed to these two factors for hearing, no matter how curious the results in special experimental situations turn out to be. If this is so, deprivation of opportunity to learn may preclude the development of even some of the most fundamental features of human apprehension, that is, of the experience of an external space domain.

Localization in General

Newman (198) well summarizes the nature of sound localization as far as its accuracy is concerned. He points out the characteristics as follows: (1) The subject will almost never confuse an acoustic source on the right with one on the left. (2) He may occasionally report hearing a sound behind him when its source is in front or overhead. He may hear a sound as located to the right and in front of him when its source is to the right and behind him. (3) In general, the sort of confusion that may take place when the source is off to one side of the median plane is describable by means of a cone whose appex lies at the center of the head. This is shown in Fig. 13.1. Any position on the cone may be confused with any other position on it. Points on the cone's surface, of course, represent both a set of directions and a set of distances, although what we are mainly dealing with here is a set of directions. Hence, the opposite

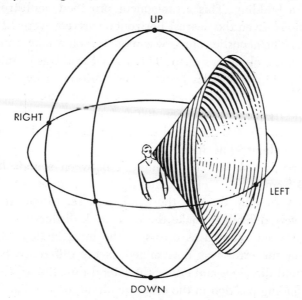

Fig. 13.1. *Cone of confusion in auditory localization.* The volume bounded by the cone represents the area within which two acoustic sources may be confused (E. B. Newman, "Hearing," in E. G. Boring, H. Langfeld, and H. P. Weld (eds.), *Foundations of Psychology,* John Wiley & Sons, Inc., 1948, p. 337).

sides of the cone represent the extreme amounts of discrepancy in direction between acoustic source and the sound heard. Lesser discrepancies are represented by various points within the cone at constant distances from the ear. The cone is the best descriptive device to picture range and combination of positions of two acoustic sources that would tend to be confused with each other; that is, those that would seem to be identical.

Localization in the Open Air

Most of the work done on hearing, whether on localization or on any other aspect, has been conducted in the laboratory, that is, indoors. Nowadays, we have two alternatives to using ordinary rooms with their reverberations that possibly distort results. There are "soundproof" (that is, acoustic energy absorbing) rooms, and there are possibilities of using open-air situations.

Stevens and Newman (242) chose the latter to study auditory localization. They set up a tall swivel chair on top of a nine-foot ventilator on the roof of a building. This arrangement provided unobstructed space in all directions. Even the nearest horizontal surfaces were 12 feet below the observer. The acoustic source was mounted on a long arm connected to the base of the observer's chair. This 12-foot arm was counterbalanced and could be shifted noiselessly from one position to another around a complete circle. The stimuli were those producing tones, a hiss, and a click. For the frequencies between 400 and 4000 cycles, the energy level was 60 decibels. For those beyond this range in either direction, the energy level was about 30 decibels.

The observer's task was to distinguish between sounds heard from behind and from in front of the lateral plane. The lateral plane is the vertical plane running through the head from ear to ear. It was found that it was very difficult to make the front-back distinction, and so such reversals were not counted as errors in the investigation at hand. The magnitude of the error was determined as the difference between the reported sound direction and either the lateral direction of the source or the corresponding position in the other quadrant, depending upon which was the smaller. For example, if the source was 10 degrees to the right of the straight-ahead position (degrees = 0), he would be considered correct if he reported it 170 degrees (counting clockwise).

Fig. 13.2 indicates the mean of the errors made by two trained observers. The errors made for the sources of low frequency were quite similar, but in the range of 500 to 3000 cycles they became progressively

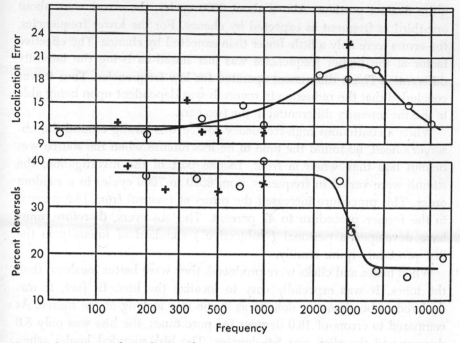

FIG. 13.2.   Upper plot indicates the average of errors in degrees (two observers) in localizing an acoustic source at various frequencies. The lower plot shows the percentage of confusions between front and rear quadrants (S. S. Stevens and E. B. Newman, The localization of actual sources of sound, *Am. J. Psychol.* [1936], 48.297–306, Figs. 2, 4).

greater. Above about 4000 cycles there is an improvement again, so that at 10,000 cycles the localization is about as accurate as at 1000 cycles.

The error maximum that peaked at about 3000 cycles was explained as follows. Low errors at low frequencies were to be expected because of the phase differences in the acoustic waves for the two ears. Phase differences reach their maximum effectiveness at a little over 1500 cycles. The effectiveness of intensity differences reaching the two ears from a source off to one side increases with frequency. Such an intensity differential sets in below 1000 cycles, and increases rapidly above 3000 cycles. This would suggest, then, that at 3000 cycles errors should be at a maximum in magnitude because phase difference is too slight at the point to help much as a factor, and differential intensity as a factor for localization has not yet become great enough to help much.

Fig. 13.2 also shows the reversals that were made in the investigation on localization. The frequency range was found to be divided into two quite distinct portions. Above about 3000 cycles, the errors were about one-third as frequent as expected by chance. For the lower frequencies, the errors were only a little fewer than expected by chance. The effective factor at the higher frequencies was just stated as being the intensity differential. Phase differences operated for low frequencies. Thus it was concluded that the reduction in reversals was dependent upon being able to use the intensity differential in the two ears.

When a continuous high-frequency source was swung around the observer's head, he found the tone to be less intense when the source was behind him than when in front. In one part of the investigation, the stimuli were varied in frequency from 3000 to 7000 cycles in a random order. This procedure increased the errors of reversal from 18.6 percent in the former procedure to 47 percent. The observers, therefore, must have developed a personal ("subjective") standard of intensity in the first procedure quite readily.

When hisses and clicks were produced, they were better localized than the tones. It was especially easy to localize the hiss. In fact, it was declared to be almost as definite as if one was looking at the source. As compared to errors of 16.0 degrees for pure tones, the hiss was only 5.6 degrees and the click was 8.0 degrees. The hiss sounded louder when the source was in front of the observer. It also sounded like *shh;* whereas when the source was behind the observer, it sounded like *sss.* Strangely enough, the intensive and qualitative differences did not rise to awareness in the main part of the investigation. This is a nice example of how certain factors may be operative below clear awareness, but nevertheless be considerable in effect.

Stereophonic Localization

With the existence of two ears and the instrumental facilities of leading into them various acoustic stimuli independently, there are tremendous possibilities for manipulation of stimulus conditions. A number of effects quite bizarre to the normal listener have been produced. To say the least, the discrepancies between what is heard and what exists in a spatial way in the external environment can be overwhelming.

The problem consists in manipulating (1) the positions of the sound sources, (2) in reproducing the acoustic wave patterns set up at various positions with reference to the sound sources, and (3) in leading separate end results to the two ears independently.

For example, a dummy listener can be set up with a microphone at each ear. The wave fronts reaching the two ears will be different for a single acoustic source located asymmetrically to them. If what reaches each ear is recorded on a separate tape or separately on a single tape, the result can be played back to a listener. The listener will wear earphones and the two different sound tracks will feed their outputs into the two ears separately. The simplest result would be that the listener would hear a sound coming from off to one side. If two separate sources were recorded in the first place, he would hear two sources located at different points. If the source moved, he would hear it as very definitely moving. The source could have been produced by an object moving toward the dummy. In that case, the listener will hear the object coming toward him, and will make the appropriate movements to get out of its way. If the original source is rotated around the dummy's head, the listener will hear sound being moved around his own head.

Nowadays, we have stereophonic recordings of musical compositions. These are double-track tape recordings of musical compositions, picked up from two different positions. The wave fronts picked up from one position are played to one ear, and those picked up at the second location are played to the other ear. The net result is that the listener hears the music as pervading space all about him. Instead of the music being heard as coming from some single direction—that is, from in front of him—he hears it as being everywhere. It fills space. He is within it.

This effect is the nearest thing in audition to what space (externality) is to the person visually. And it ought to be, for what was done was to lead effects from two widely separated positions in space to the two ears (and separately), rather than to have something come from one restricted direction in space, as is the usual case. We pointed out earlier that, through optical means, many points in space were represented on the retina from instant to instant. If vision was to be utilized by only looking through a narrow tube with one eye, no real notion of space, such as we now know it, would develop. The use of vision in this restricted perceived fashion would be somewhat analogous to the way hearing by its very nature is found to be used.

With the stereophonic conditions of hearing, sound takes on its maximal spatial properties for the sighted individual. What the effects are in the case of the congenitally blind has either not yet been tried or not reported in the literature. To test the blind with stereophonic instrumentation would be extremely interesting and possibly very informative.

With stereophonic conditions, one does not seem able to escape the sound he hears. He is within the sound field and is unable to move in any direction to get away from it, or to lessen its intensity, or otherwise to avoid or diminish its intrusion upon him. In this way, it is like visual space. It becomes not only sound but an extensional domain, a kind of medium within which the listener exists.

We need not possess a stereophonic setup to experience a moderate amount of this. Much of our auditory experience occurs indoors or in other partially confined spaces rather than in the broad out-of-doors where there are no buildings, hills, or other objects to confine the sound waves and to reverberate them. Therefore, although we are not producing separate acoustic wave patterns for the two ears that arrive from different locations, we are receiving, with the two ears, very complex wave fronts produced by reverberation.

To make this clear, refer to Fig. 13.3. The diagram indicates that although there is only one original acoustic source—that is, S—the waves

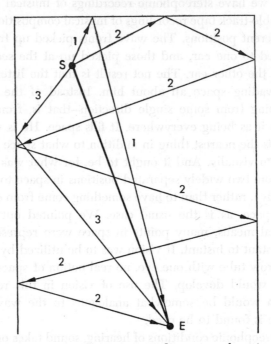

FIG. 13.3. A diagram to indicate reverberation from walls of a room in addition to the energy reaching the ear directly. S is the acoustic source, and E is the ear. Each wave front is numbered.

strike the walls at various places and are reflected off, and thus the listener, L, receives acoustic energies from a host of different directions. This adds to the "noisiness" or obtrusiveness of the sound, although the total energy reaching the ears is not any greater or as great as though he was nearer to the source out in the open. Out in the open, there would be a whole set of directions from which the acoustic waves would not be reaching the listener, owing to absence of reverberation. Sound would not seem to him to be coming from all around him, and thus would be unobtrusive. It would be as if he could escape the sound if he cared to do so.

REVERBERATION AND DISTANCE

There is a relation between the perceived distance of a sound source and the reverberation component in comparison to the energy that reaches the ear directly from the source. The diagram in Fig. 13.3 would tend to suggest that if a second source was placed closer to the listener than the first source, the major portion of the energy reaching the ear would reach it directly. Only a small amount of the energy would reach the ear after being reflected back and forth between the walls. This difference would be represented, then, in the character of the wave fronts reaching the ear. Since these relations between reverberation and distance from the ear is a lawful one, it can be learned. Thus part of the basis for hearing a tone as originated far away is to be attributed to its reverberation characteristic rather than wholly to its reduced energy content. Another potential spatial characteristic of sound, that is, its distance, is therefore based upon complexity of wave fronts.

FALSE LOCALIZATION

A conclusion easily arrived at is that the localization of sound sources is very poor. Whereas the usual technique of determining human capacity or sensitivity is to set up simplified experimental situations and determine thresholds, one may, on the other hand, examine what happens in unsimplified or everyday situations. It is several of these unsimplified situations which we wish to describe here. They are meant to illustrate the basis for concluding that sound fails to have strongly compelling spatial qualities or that perceived localization is always primarily dependent upon acoustic factors. Sighted persons may, at times, tend to localize sounds, and to become disturbed when no satisfactory localization can be made. The congenitally blind may not be impelled in a similar way. It is our supposition that if the localization of sound is poor in the sighted, it need not exist at all as a medium for experiencing externality in the congenitally blind.

A type of complex situation worth considering is one we could call ventriloquistic. Ventriloquism is the art of producing sounds that are falsely localized. By false localization is meant hearing a sound as originating from one direction and distance quite different from those of the actual source. It is not our purpose to present an exposition on ventriloquism. Instead, it is to use this type of situation to show that the localization of sound is quite poor. The illustrations should indicate that there need be nothing very compelling about a set of sound waves to make the perceiver detect the correct direction and distance of their origin.

In the more usual ventriloquistic situation, the ventriloquist (operator) employs a puppet with which to converse. The puppet is constructed with movable jaws, manipulated by the operator. The perceiver experiences listening to two people carry on a conversation. The words of the puppet are as perceptually realistic as those of the operator. Naturally, the puppet is in a different direction from the listener, so that the effect can be described as a false localization of sound when the puppet is perceived to speak.

In other situations, sounds of the human voice are made to seem to originate at considerable distances from the actual speaker. To do this, the operator must change his voice as ordinarily heard, so as to seem like a voice coming from a distance. This is sometimes spoken of as "throwing" the voice. Instead, it is the changing of the acoustic output as just described and providing a number of visual and other stimulus conditions consistent with the acoustic stimulus produced.

We might generalize offhand as to what is necessary for the success of ventriloquism. The conditions would seem to be the following: (1) The production of acoustic stimuli at one location, and of a character to be heard as coming from another. This often is accomplished by using two voices from one speaker. One is the natural voice, and the other is a differently sounding one and is not accompanied by any visual evidences that the real speaker is producing the sound. (2) The production of visual influences that are more potent in localizing the perceived origins of the sound than are the characteristics of the wave fronts as they reach the ear. This is accomplished most easily by use of a puppet which is visually perceived as a different person. One need not manipulate the distance characteristics of acoustic wave fronts as much as the visual characteristics of the situation.

In all cases there must be something definite to be seen at some location or other, so that a localization can be made. The seen object could be a distant puppet, or it could be a wall, just beyond which the sound could seem to originate.

False localization need not involve voices. In fact, it may well involve other familiar sound sources with regard to which the listener may be expected to react in characteristic ways.

On one occasion, the author pulled alongside the curb in an old model-T Ford to wait for a friend. It was in the days when not all streets were noisy, and the one in question was quiet. All that could be heard when he had settled down to wait was a recurrent click at the rate of one every two seconds. The clicks were pronounced enough to attract attention and elicit his curiosity. The source of the clicks was quite indefinite except that it seemed to be in the car someplace. When he looked toward the hood, the clicks seemed to be coming from under it. When he looked down at the floorboards, the clicks came from under them. In general, the clicks sounded like the cooling off of some heavy metal object. He thought the clicks could represent the cooling of the hot engine, but still he was not satisfied that such was the case. He got out of the car and looked up under the running board toward the engine and transmission. When he did so, the origin of the clicks was still elusive, but was perceived as being in the car someplace. He had no doubt but that the sound was produced by the car itself. Since he failed to localize the specific origin of the clicks, he finally gave up. When he climbed back into the car, the clicks still persisted. He shifted, however, to observing a couple of children swinging quietly in a porch swing. The houses were set up above the street beyond terraces that rose abruptly from the sidewalk, so that the children on the swing were not far away and were above eye level. They nevertheless were many times as far away from him as were various parts of the car. He finally noticed a synchrony between the clicks and the pendular motion of the porch swing, and readily deduced that the clicks were made by the friction of the suspension chains of the swing on the screw eyes that supported them. He had finally found the source of the sound. Nevertheless, it was still easy to hear each click originating below the floor boards of the car. He could thus still perceive the sound originating in an entirely different direction and at a very different distance than the true acoustic source.

The foregoing discussion would lead to the conclusion that sound localization is greatly influenced by seen objects rather than more especially by the quality of the sound waves themselves. The visual context is highly effective in the localization.

It is to be admitted that click-producing sources are among the least accurately localized sound producers and thus their effects are most easily influenced and manipulated. But the fact that localization of the click was not accomplished by anything the listener did in changing head position in getting out of the car, peering under it, and getting back in indicates how lacking in intrinsic spatiality is the process of hearing, at least on some occasions. Vision is never deficient in anything like the same way or to the same extent. Sound can seem to come from almost anywhere, and at times from nowhere in particular.

FACIAL VISION

Dallenbach, with colleagues Ammons, Cotyzin, Worchel, and Supa (6, 62, 276), studied what has been commonly called *facial vision.* They conducted a number of ingenius experiments indoors, and found that (1) audition is the necessary and sufficient condition for the blind's detection and avoidance of obstacles, (2) that pitch is the feature of audition that is involved, and (3) that frequencies of 10,000 cycles are necessary for the performance. From these factors it was deduced that anyone, whether blind or merely blindfolded, if he possessed normal hearing, should be able to learn to detect and avoid obstacles. This took much of the mystery out of "facial vision," such as expressed by some of the older students of the phenomenon. For example, Diderot had called facial vision an amazing ability possessed by only a few of the blind.

Ammons, Worchel, and Dallenbach (6) addressed themselves to the question of whether the extensive studies at Cornell on facial vision could be duplicated in outdoor studies under conditions more closely simulating those in which the blind perform in everyday life. A second question that was included had to do with finding out whether blindfolded sighted persons could learn the ability to perceive obstacles.

Their first experiment consisted in determining whether blindfolded subjects with normal or near-normal (group A) hearing could learn to perceive obstacles outdoors, and also whether this type of subject could learn even with his ears stopped (group B).

Both groups of subjects initially had trouble in staying without guidance on the sidewalk used. Collisions with obstacles were divided into three kinds: (1) collisions before reporting perception of an obstacle; (2) collisions made after having reported the perception of an obstacle, but before being finally sure; (3) collisions made during the time the subject was making final appraisal and was "inching up" to the obstacle.

The subjects of both the A and B groups were unable to learn as quickly as those in the indoor experiments and their ultimate perceptions were more variable. The perception of obstacles was influenced by wind, sun, and clouds. When walking into the wind, detection of an obstacle was based on the drop in pressure as the obstacle shielded the subject from it. When walking with the wind, obstacles were signaled by reflection of wind from them. Where there was no wind, of course, behavior based on such factors suffered.

When the sun was hot, the presence of obstacles was signaled by temperature changes. Sun shining on various material caused them to give off odors which were detected.

The net result of this experiment was to show that not only the blindfolded but the subjects with the additional deprivation of a certain amount of hearing could learn to detect obstacles out of doors by means undetermined.

The second and following experiments were made to determine the kinds of factors used by the subjects in detecting obstacles in the first experiment. The general conclusions derived from the whole group of experiments were as follows: (1) that blindfolded, and blindfolded and ear-stopped subjects could learn to detect obstacles; (2) that the behavior of the latter subjects differed from the behavior of the subjects blindfolded only; (3) that no single stimulus condition is necessary for obstacle detection. Audition is the principle basis for the detection, but is "necessary" only in the sense that it is the most reliable and universal of all the factors used. A number of corollaries to these three conclusions were also stated. The following are some examples. The "black curtain" or "dark shades" mentioned by some of the subjects upon approaching an obstacle were taken to be imaginal experiences evoked associatedly by auditory stimuli. The subjects who were helped or hindered by the experiments conducted at night fall into groups. Those subjects whose performances were bettered were those who were still able, when their ears were stopped, to use certain auditory cues and thus sought no others. The subjects whose performances were impaired sought other factors when, under the conditions of experimentation, the auditory factors were not usable on account of the ear blocks. The thermal and olfactory impingements served them well enough in the sunshine but failed them at night through their absence.

We can see, in the general type of performance just described, what many would call a form of space perception. For us it is another example of the sequential (bit-by-bit) sort of perception that enables persons to get about in space. Once an obstacle is detected, the next thing to do is to move alternately to the right or to the left so as to determine whether the signals from the obstacle diminish. This is involved as a feedback, and thus the skilled person can steer himself around the obstacle almost as if he "saw" it. Varying degrees of skill in this could be expected.

Facial vision, then, is another example of the piecemeal detection of the structure of space rather than the apprehension of space as a domain, i.e., true space perception. Naturally, facial vision could be expected to be more effective or differently effective in the adventitiously blinded than in the congenitally blind.

MATCHING AUDITORY AND VISUAL PERSPECTIVES

The other side of the story of sound localization lies in such findings as made by acoustic engineers in matching the picture strips and sound strips for sound movies. It is possible to mismatch these strips in such ways as to produce the perception of a person nearby talking, but having the sound appear to originate at some distant point. In one way this is an example of a ventriloquistic situation, such as we have already described. In another way it is an example showing that the quality of a sound and its perceived distance go hand in hand. If this interrelation was an extremely rigid and sensitive one, the argument for the relative spatial indeterminateness of sound would be negated.

The curious thing about mismatching sound and picture strips on a movie film is that little can be done to bring the phenomenal location of sounds any closer to the listener than the actual acoustic source that is generally placed right behind the projection screen. On the other hand, mismatchings that induce the hearing of the sounds as farther away than the visual source can manipulate phenomenal distance quite considerably.

It may be useful to the reader to know how the proper sound and picture strip matchings are made. By experimentation, the rules for this have been derived. The factors that go into the equation are the focal length of the camera lens, the relative distance of the microphone from the acoustic source to the camera, and the reverberatory properties of the walls of the room in which the movies are made. Cameras with long-focal-length lenses bring distance scenes up close. Microphones quite near the acoustic sources produce stimulus end results perceived as hearing nearby objects. If the walls of the room are highly reverberatory (live), the percentage of the distance from the acoustic source to the camera at which the microphone must be placed has to be reduced. This is to cut down the reverberatory component picked up by the microphone, even though the total energy content is increased. The total energy content is not as influential a stimulus factor for determining perceived distance as is the reverberatory content.

The relation between the three factors just mentioned is schematically pictured in Fig. 13.4. For its explanation, see the legend.

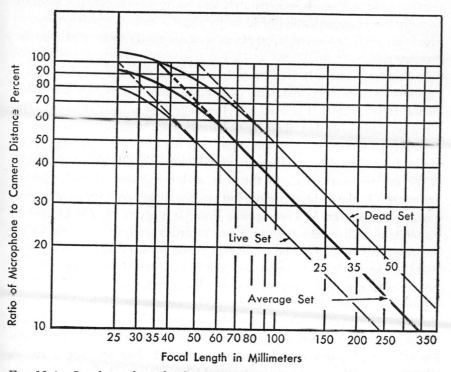

Focal Length in Millimeters

FIG. 13.4.   Graphs to show the distances from a photographed object (speaker, etc.) that a microphone should be placed, depending upon the focal length of the camera lens. The center curve is for a lens whose focal length is 35 mm. If the pickup is appropriate for this lens when the microphone is at camera distance, for lenses of other focal lengths the microphone must be placed at other distances from the sound source. If the focal length is greater than 35 mm., this distance is some percentage of the camera distance. The other curves are for sets (stages or scenes) where the sound absorption is either greater or less than average. For these, 25-mm. and 50-mm. lenses may be used instead of a 35 mm. as references (after J. P. Maxfield, Some physical factors affecting illusion in sound motion pictures, *J. Acoust. Soc. Am.* [1931], 3:69–80, Figs. 1, 4, 5).

SOUNDS AS SYMBOLS

Sounds do not as directly refer to objects as do visual experiences. Sounds often are of more significance to the human being as symbols than as indications of the existence and location of objects at the moment.

Sounds can be used independently of reference to the world that perception is relating the person to at the moment. That is, they can be used to convey ideas which may be independent of the present space field and temporal movement. This use is not nearly so common for most visual objects.[1] Although one may convey ideas by pantomime, it is not so often done, nor nearly so accurately and easily accomplished. Curiously enough, the communication of ideas by signs is called *sign language*. In broad principle, however, acoustic as well as photic sources of stimulation are signs.

In this connection, it is relevant to point out that the synesthete is a person who does use visual items as symbols, and in a manner somewhat similar to the way that sighted nonsynesthetes use sounds (words). The blind synesthete, as described by Cutsforth (*64*), uses visual experiences (imagery) induced by acoustic stimuli for his thinking processes. They are his language, although they are visual items other than written words.

We are not certain as to the role and conditions of operation of synesthesia in the sighted person, but we can make some suppositions regarding the matter. Let us suppose that for a given sighted individual visual items rather than auditory items (words) were the symbols for his language. He would thus be employing vision for his thinking in the way that the normal sighted person uses words (auditory items). The sighted person must use vision to get around in his world. He makes all kinds of visuomotor manipulations from moment to moment. If he had to use the visual modality for his thinking also, he would be forced into a double use of vision and into conflict. He could not well concurrently use vision for perceptual purposes relating to space and time and for purposes divorced from time and space. He would have to stop and close his eyes in order to think. Otherwise, what he would need to be "seeing" would not refer to what is taken to be out in front of him, and yet at the same time he would need to be referring quite directly to those very realities— the objects of space and their locations, sizes, and shapes. This is the very difficulty that is inherent in a small way when formalized movements such as those in ballet are to mean what they do not literally mean when functioning as direct perceptions of people moving about on a stage.

We can say then, in conclusion, that although it seems in keeping with observations to disclaim any initiating role for audition in the production

---

[1] The sounds meant here are sounds heard as words. Obviously, words are not exclusively auditory, for we have written as well as spoken language. Although this is the case, in verbal imagery it is the auditory use of words that is involved. Hence, it is perfectly legitimate to deal with words as sounds in such cases as we are dealing with here.

of perceptual externality, we can conceive for audition the prime role in dealing with abstract ideas. Hearing is greatly enough divorced from spatial realities, or dealing directly and inescapably with the space domain, that it can be used for abstract symbolism. Hearing is so space-free that it can play the role that it does. Hearing thus gives us a mechanism that at one and the same time involves sensory processes with their means of transfer (signaling) between persons, and a relatively space-free tool for abstract symbolism in the parties involved. Vision could not so well carry on this function.

Chapter 14

PERCEPTIONS BASED ON MUSCULAR MECHANISMS

It might be said that we live in our muscles. This is true with certain qualifications. We largely gauge body positions and limb movements and the like through sensory mechanisms in the muscles and tendons. We likewise perform most of our self-appraisals of body state through the way the muscles and joints feel. We may feel weak, limp, inert, achy, "tired," etc., owing to some conditions of muscle tension, or to tone or possible changed internal state of muscle cells. A great deal is yet to be explored and found out about muscle conditions and metabolic conditions by study of the sensory mechanisms in muscle. In fact, it will not be until we succeed in delineating the relations between muscle condition, muscle activity, and muscle sense-organ activity that we will understand the organism-as-a-person very well. The door is wide open for this vast territory of inquiry.

Our task in this chapter is one of reciting the few things that are known about muscle sense organs and muscle-mediated perceptions. To do so we must first examine the sense organs that lie in muscle and tendon tissues.

Muscles are of several kinds: the smooth muscles of the internal organs, including those of the blood vessels, heart muscle; and skeletal muscles. The kind that we mainly have reference to are the skeletal muscles. The sense organs that lie in these tissues give rise to afferent nerve impulse patterns we call *kinesthesis*. Elsewhere, we have noted that some authors suggest changes in tensional state of the circulatory vessels as activators for the temperature sense. Obviously, the tensional states of the muscles of the gastrointestinal tract give rise to both localized and diffuse experiences, some of which may be classed as pains and others as hunger, nausea, and so on. So far, these last experiences, though undoubtedly sensory, have not been given a great deal of study as such. Hunger has been related with appetite, and nausea simply with illness. We might call them *organic* perceptions. Various words have been used to label the senses of body reference and to distinguish them from senses referring to events in the outside world. Sense cells having to do with external events are called *exteroceptors,* and the remainder are *interoceptors.* The exteroceptors conventionally have included the senses of vision, hearing, smell, taste, and pain, although pain may originate from events within the body. Another term has been applied to certain senses. Kinesthesis and the vestibular sense have been called *proprioception,* since they have something to do with end results originated by the activity of the body itself.

KINESTHETIC SENSE RECEPTORS

There are four sets of sense receptors that belong in the kinesthetic category. Two of them are in muscle tissue, one in tendons, and the other in the fascia of muscles. Within recent years they have been given the simple designations of A_1, A_2, B, and C endings, respectively. The A_1 ending is also called the *flower-spray ending,* and is activated by passive stretch of the muscle, i.e., elongating tensions not originated by the attempt of muscle itself to shorten (contract). It appears that active muscular contractions terminate the impulses originating in the A_1 endings. About one-half of all of the fibers in muscle are associated with A_1 activity.

Another nerve ending named more or less in accord with its appearance is the *annulospiral ending.* It is the A_2 ending, and it also is sensitive to passive muscle stretch. Thus both the A_1 and A_2 endings are called *stretch afferents.* Type B endings are very specialized structures and are said to be activated either by an increase or decrease in tension at the junctures between muscles and tendons. No distinction between muscle contraction and passive muscle stretch is probably possible in this case. The B endings have higher thresholds than the A endings, but the impulse frequently set up in them manifests a lawful quantitative relation to tension. It is roughly proportional to the logarithm of the tension.

The C ending is likely the *Pacinian corpuscles* that are found in the fascia (sheaths) of the muscles and tendons. In general, it is thought that Pacinian corpuscles are organs of deep pressure wherever they are found, for they are found not only in muscles and tendons but also in subcutaneous tissue. The Pacinian corpuscle adapts fairly quickly to the initial activating agent and thus differs from other proprioceptor organs.

The fact that they adapt quickly and that they are activated by pressure is reminiscent of what was found to be the case with more superficial tactile (or pressure) perception. Nafe and Wagoner (195) attributed adaptation not to sense-organ failure but to termination of conditions that could be called stimulation.

As a final possible form of neural ending that may have something to do with signaling the state of muscle, there is the ubiquitous *free nerve ending*. Many of these endings may have something to do with pain, and with temperature in association with blood vessels. There is a plentiful supply of small endings distributed in muscle, ligament, tendon, fascia, and joint.

So far, we have said little or nothing about joints, but it has been found that the sensitivity provided at the joints is the major signaling device for limb position (posture) and movement. In fact, the appreciation of limb positions and movement may be destroyed, leaving muscles unaffected. The very opposite situation has been known to occur when the muscles and skin have been anesthetized. This has been accomplished with the sparing of the joints and the retention of appreciation of limb position.

All joints are not equally sensitive to movement. Goldscheider's study (88) indicated that the ankle was least sensitive and the shoulder most sensitive. In this study he attempted to measure minimum angular limb displacement (velocity constant) and at other times the minimal velocity that was discernible.

In a more recent study by Laidlaw and Hamilton (151), the results were in rough correspondence to those of Goldscheider. They found the hip to be more sensitive than the shoulder, and the main joint of the large toe (a joint not measured by Goldscheider) the most sensitive of all. In general, the articulations at the major joints seem to be more sensitive than the finger and toe joints.

Sensitivity of joints to movement and position is a puzzle. No sensory endings have been demonstrated within the surfaces of the joints. Therefore it is not known how it is that we can say the joints rather than muscles are the loci of movement and position discrimination. Jenkins (130) points out that Pacinian corpuscles are found in the tissues around the joints, and that if these are the joint receptors, then joint sensitivity is provided by subcutaneous pressure as it differs in keeping with limb position.

Pillsbury (210) in 1901 came to the conclusion that joint sensitivity was probably mediated by the sensitivity of the tendons that pass over the joint. Apparently, the motions of these tendons in their grooves rather than the rubbing of the surfaces of the joints together give rise to the experiences of movement.

Geldard (82) suggests that wherever the appreciation of movement and general position is based upon joint sensitivity, the appreciation of strain superimposed on the joint-sensitivity background is the role played by the sense organs in muscle.

THE WEBER FRACTION

Some of the earliest psychophysical experimentation was done in kinesthesis. It was in kinesthesis (weight lifting) that Weber did his work that led to *Weber's law*. Weber, too, pointed out that a smaller difference between two weights can be detected if they are lifted than when they are simply placed on the skin. This was to say that kinesthesis is more sensitive than touch in differentiating weights. Weber also concluded that the difference in two weights had to be at least .025 (1/40) of the value of the standard weight in order to be detected. This fraction was called the *Weber fraction* and the principle applies to discrimination in the other sensory modalities, although the size of the fraction varies from modality to modality. Some authors that followed Weber did not find the Weber fraction to hold true throughout the whole range of values they tested. Some authors found that the fraction decreases as the total weight of the standard is increased. This principle seems to apply to other features of kinesthesis, such as the force of movement.

Ladd and Woodworth (150) report a study of Biedermann and Lowit in which the fractions for lifted weights varied from 1/21 for weights of 250 grams, 1/114 for 2500 grams, and 1/99 for 2750 grams.

KINESTHESIS AND POSITIONING MOVEMENTS

Psychologists today are studying the ability of people to make certain kinds of movements. One of the main features of these movements is their accuracy. Whereas such studies may be thought of as solely studies of motor performance and not sensory performance, we see them in a different light. The very basis for being able to make movements according to some predetermined pattern is the feedback provided by the kinesthetic sense cells in the muscles and tendons. A description of the upper limits of performance is, in a way, a description of the characteristics of the kinesthetic control of movement.

Among the kinds of movements studied are blind-positioning movements, visual-positioning movements, continuous adjustive movements, and repetitive movements.

The blind-positioning movements are often divided into restricted-positioning movements and free-positioning movements. In the case of the former, it has been found that people overestimate short distances such as those between 1 and 4 inches, and underestimate movements between 4 and 15 inches. Positioning movements are more accurate away from the body than toward it. The smallest relative error and variability occur for distances within the range of 4 and 15 inches.

In general, the accuracy of free-positioning movements is somewhat better below the subject's shoulder than at the shoulder level, or above it. Upper portions of the target are undershot, and those at the lower portions are overshot. This estimation of positions as too high is not consistent, however.

To move between two predetermined end positions it takes about as long for a distance of 5 inches as for 15 inches. Rather than attaining speed in a constant time after starting, the subject simply moves faster for a longer distance. If the distance is short, the hand accelerates more slowly than if the distance is longer. Thus very little time is saved by shortening the movement distance. Apparently, the greater the distance, the faster the arm moves. Thus the movement is adjusted pretty well for the distance, all distances within certain limits requiring about the same time.

Two kinds of repetitive movements have been studied: tapping and cranking movements. Preferred tapping rates, or the comfortable rates for continued tapping, vary between 1.5 to 5 per second. It is not a very stable rate, and can be changed by any one of a number of conditions. The rate, however, over a range of 1 to about 40 mm., is not altered much by the amplitude. The highest tapping rate is achieved when most of the arm is employed. That is, only wrist motions will not yield as great a rate as the whole arm. The poorest tapping rate is achieved with fingers alone.

In cranking movements, the rate drops as radius is increased. When radius is increased from 2.4 to 24 cm., the rate is reduced to half. Thus, in cranking, the movement rate tends to compensate for distance. Factors that tend to reduce motor coördination or make the task more difficult tend to shift the best performance to greater radii.

These are a few of the findings regarding movements. It is possible that some day such kinds of data will be of service in better understanding the mechanism of stimulation of the kinesthetic receptors, and also the institution of the experience of movement.

MUSCULAR TENSION

A great deal of the study of kinesthesis is rather indirect. One of the more familiar forms of study is that of muscular tension. What is called tension has several aspects. Sometimes the tension that is spoken of is called personal tension, or nervous tension. To say the least, it is a kind of experience that has to do with one's own state and his relation to his surrounds, particularly with the task demands that he recognizes are being put upon him. What is sensory in this self-awareness has never been too well analyzed and comprehended. It can be said, however, that the major component is the skeletal muscle state. The sensory aspect of muscle condition is largely brought about by some degree or pattern of tension. Hence, for the study of kinesthesis, this tensional state and its relation to kinesthesis must be dealt with. Kinesthesis is not confined to regulating muscle movement and position and to the perception of such things, for example, as lifted weights and ones own body position.

Throughout the body, skeletal muscles are arranged in pairs and thus, when in sustained contraction, they act against each other, producing the state of tension. In movement, muscle pairs act in some degree of reciprocity. When one member of the pair contracts, the other relaxes and elongates. This opposition may manifest easygoing reciprocity or a tug of war. It may also involve many patterns of timing to produce the many forms of skeletal movement we know the human subject to be capable of.

The state of tonus may vary from a minimum during sleep to a maximum under high excitement when awake. Part of this may be spoken of as postural tonus necessary for the maintenance of upright or other position against gravity, and part of it may be excessive. When tension is too high, motor coördination is impaired. Awkwardness is the result.

The neck muscles are said to be crucial indicators of the general level of the individual's muscle tonus. The head is a fairly heavy structure, and is significantly involved in the balance of the body. This is based on the fact that the eyes, as distance or space receptors, and the vestibules, the organs of equilibrium, are located in the head. The muscles of the neck are governed in some respects by certain patterned innervations called neck reflexes, which have to do with head positions with reference to gravity and the body.

Central Effects of Muscular Tension

We have already spoken of the connection of muscular tension with experiential states, but nothing was said regarding cause and effect. We might ask here whether states of the central nervous system are reflected peripherally in muscular tension or just the reverse happens. Whichever way the tension is involved, kinesthesis is a part of the chain of events, and thus we are concerned with the matter in this chapter.

There are two general ways in which tension is alleged to be involved. The one is the case in which the central nervous system is the origin, as is the case in which an individual is involved in meeting a task demand. In doing something to meet the demand, only at times is he wholly effective. All activity is directed toward accomplishment. At other times, a part of the activity is expressed not in regulated and coördinated movement or in effective thought, but in the mere building up of static tension in skeletal muscle. This is to say that an individual's activity can be expressed in a set of effective movements, or it can be expressed in mere tension. The individual can "freeze at the controls," as well as perform as he should. Some degree of all activity directed toward meeting task demands ends up by being expressed in the tension form. *Irradiation* is one expression of this. Irradiation is the progressive involvement of more and more musculature during the performance of a prolonged task. This may happen, for example, in writing a long letter. The writer starts out by using only the restricted musculature that is needed to move a pen, but he ends up by using arm, neck, back, and so on.

On the other hand, muscle tonus and tension help sustain the excitation level of the cortex. Freeman (78) who has given a great deal of attention to muscle tension and motor activity, calls the peripheral input from the muscle a backlash and credits it with the task of maintaining alertness, etc. Here again, although we seem to be talking about motor activity, it is the kinesthetic sense mechanism that is involved. Kinesthesis, then, can be seen to play a role in personal alertness. This was also true for such modalities as vision and hearing.

Not only does muscular activity, including muscular tension, send a sustaining innervation into the central nervous system by way of kinesthetic channels but it also produces the feeling of effort. When a nonmuscular task is difficult, there is likely to be a greater fraction of the total activity spent in excess tension than when the task is easy. When there is little diversion into this ineffective sidetrack called tension, the task feels easy; and when tension is at its height, the task feels difficult. It must be remembered that not all tension is useless or inefficient. Some activity requires muscular action for lifting, pulling, pushing, and so forth. Here the tension is efficient and comes and goes with the specific moment-to-moment needs of the performance. Relaxation is a natural aftermath. But when tension builds only as a diversion, an expression of ineffectiveness, it remains and plays mainly the role of a central nervous excitant and a producer of the feeling of tension and jitteriness. Which is the cart and which is the horse may be a question, but it is likely that there is mutual sustenance between center and periphery in this state of affairs.

KINESTHESIS AND DISCOMFORT

What was said about the feeling of effort and kinesthesis may well be amplified here. Body discomfort is of two general sorts, namely, the feelings of tension and jitteriness, and those of lassitude, limpness, and weakness. Definite aches and pains are not included here, for it is supposed that nonkinesthetic sense channels, namely, those of the pain modality, are responsible for these. Neither tenseness nor limpness are disembodied affairs, but experiences of muscle state. Tenseness and jitteriness call for action. Feelings of lassitude and weakness call for release from demand. Discomfort continues so long as such muscles are being innervated. Whether feelings of weakness are produced by chemical states of muscles, or whether muscles in certain states behave mechanically (tensionwise) differently enough to affect kinesthetic sense organs differently, is not known. It is probably the latter. Under some systemic (metabolic) conditions, either the central nervous system innervates muscles differently or the muscles behave mechanically differently, but which is the case is not known. What is to be believed, however, is that in either case the nervous impulse patterns sent out by the kinesthetic sense cells are different than under normal conditions. This being the case, kinesthesis is responsible for more than appreciation of muscle position, movement, and tension. It is the mediator of general well-being or general discomfort and malaise.

KINESTHETIC ORIENTATION

It has been concluded from tests upon both humans and subhumans that during gravity-free periods of flight in aviation losses occur in visual and kinesthetic orientation. Visual-motor coördination is affected. Reid (216) reported a so-called illusion of movement complementary to the well-known visual horizontal-vertical illusion. Blindfolded subjects moved a stylus in a required direction and then attempted to simulate this movement, but in a direction at right angles to the first one. He found that the movement to right or left is "underestimated." Movements toward and outward from the body in the median plane are "overestimated." It is reported that the same overestimation and underestimation occur with reference to speed of movement. The author concluded that movement up and down (i.e., in a vertical plane) is equivalent to movement away from the body in a horizontal direction.

It was found that there was a significant positive correlation between judges' ratings on the wrestling ability of subjects and their "acuity of kinesthesis." Subjects were asked to maintain a uniform pressure against a moving object in a "dynamic situation." The more uniform the pressure, the more keen the so-called kinesthetic acuity. The results might be interpreted as suggesting an intimate interrelation between muscular skill and kinesthesis. In situations in which extensive muscle groups would be required to perform up to some measurable criterion, such as uniformity of position, or pressure, kinesthesis would certainly be dominantly involved. Both the ability to use muscle to the best advantage and to use kinesthetic information likewise would be expected. Unused muscle groups would not perform as smoothly, nor would the kinesthetic feedback from them be so helpful in performing to a criterion as would trained muscle groups.

Edgington (69, 70) studied the kinesthesis of motor performance. In one experiment he studied the influence of certain factors upon the ability of a subject to look where he is pointing, or to point where he is looking. In both cases, the pointing arm was shielded from view. He found the variability of localizing was greater when the subject looked where he pointed than when he pointed where he was looking. In turning their heads to look where they were pointing, the subjects did not turn far enough.

ORGANIC KINESTHESIS—HUNGER

Although the words hunger and hungry are very commonly used, the question of what constitutes hunger is not exactly what the man on the street may think it is. The words hunger and appetite are very closely related, and it is appropriate that we discuss this relation here.

The reason hunger is being discussed is that experimentation has shown that the stomach as a muscular organ manifests certain rhythmic contraction. The stomach is in some sort of rhythmic contraction during the digestion of a meal. It has also been found to manifest certain periodic contractions beginning a few hours after eating. These constitute the mechanical basis for hunger by way of kinesthesis. Whatever else hunger is, it is supposed to be a sensory experience. Among well-fed individuals, who are able to eat when they come to the table, it is not as certain that all of them experienced hunger just prior to mealtime. What various people call hunger must be quite unlike from person to person. For example, some people who have not eaten for four to six hours may begin to feel weak, even nauseated, or at least somewhat uncomfortable abdominally. In such a state they may "intellectually" rather than sensorially feel that food would relieve the discomfort. At least, after trying food on a few such occasions, they may have arrived at the supposition just stated. Other persons may be very reluctant to eat when they feel as we have described. It may be hard for them to think other than that their digestion is upset and that they had better partake only lightly of food. From such cases, it is easy to entertain the possibility that hunger may be defined both perceptually or purely physiologically. One may be in a state of "hunger" from the standpoint of stomach contractions and metabolic condition, but not from the standpoint of conscious personal realization.

TACTUAL-KINESTHETIC PERCEPTIONS OF STRAIGHTNESS

Before we leave this chapter on the role of kinesthesis in perceptual response, one or two other illustrative studies should be briefly mentioned. The first of these is a study by Hunter (124), who examined twenty blind and twenty sighted subjects. He had them explore target edges tactually. Both groups perceived as straight an edge which curved away from the subject. But the edge perceived as just barely curved was metrically more nearly straight for the blind than for the sighted. That is, for the blind the perceptually straight corresponded more closely to the geometrically straight than it did for the sighted. The blind, both as an overall group and individually, behaved more consistently than did the sighted. Hunter attributes this to a "more highly developed organization of the blinds' tactual-kinesthetic perception."

In line with what we have already said about visual imagery operating in conjunction with the other sense modalities when they are activated, we would suggest that the higher variability of the sighted might well be due to the inconsistent use of visual imagery.

The second study to which allusion was made is cited in the following section.

TOUCH AND KINESTHESIS IN SIZE PERCEPTION

Bartley (14) tested the hypothesis that visual imagery plays a role in the perception of size when the tactual and kinesthetic modalities are activated, as, for example, in the grasping of a target ("object") that is not seen. It is well known that it is very common for an individual to try to visualize ("see") the contacted target in order to perceive best what it is or what size and shape it is. The person is eager to know what it looks like.

Bartley used a number of different tests, including one in which his subjects ran their index fingers around the edge of the vertical face of a block. A standard, placed at a fixed distance from the blindfolded subject, was compared in this way with metrically equal, smaller, and larger blocks, at the same distance from the eye, and at positions nearer to and farther from the eye.

It was Bartley's supposition that if visual imagery played a predominant role, the distance from the eye at which the contact was made would affect perceived size. Perceived size should diminish with distance. This was thought to accord with the idea that the block would be visualized as smaller the farther away it was. Bartley, in this and in several other tests, received evidence in favor of the expectation. It is in line with this that we stated in the preceding section that we supposed the blind were more consistent and nearer to metric straightness than the sighted, because of the latter's use of visual imagery, and possibly in an inconsistent way from trial to trial.

It is to be kept in mind here that kinesthetic feedback occurs in reaching to contact the block. It is likely that a kinesthetic factor is involved in the operation of perceiving size. If so, it would oppose the visual-imagery factor. This is the hypothesis stated by Bartley, Clifford, and Calvin in a further study of the performance just discussed.

Chapter 15

THE VESTIBULAR SENSE

The vestibular sense is a mechanism whereby the organism relates itself to the gravitational field. In most cases it is assisted in this by one or more other sense modalities, namely, kinesthesis, vision, the tactile sense, and even audition. The sense organs for the vestibular mechanism are in the nonauditory part of the inner ear.

There are two major aspects of the organ's relation to gravity. One is change in the rate of motion. This is called acceleration. The other is static posture, in which relations to gravity are just as inescapable as they are in changes in rate of motion. The *semicircular canals* function so as to detect acceleration and the *otolith organ* detects head posture. These two kinds of information are relayed to the appropriate parts of the central nervous system, where necessary movements of muscles are brought about to maintain the needed static body posture, or to carry out motor performances without coming into conflict with gravitational demands.

Acceleration is of three general kinds. The first is *linear*, in which motion in a straight line is speeded up or slowed down. Slowing is called either deceleration or negative acceleration. The second kind of acceleration is change in direction of motion, and is called *radial* acceleration. This is the constant change in direction of motion as one is rotated about a point, as in centrifugal force, and we are all familiar with examples of its action, such as mud flying off a revolving wheel. *Angular* acceleration is the change in rate of a revolving object. Thus one undergoes angular acceleration as the merry-go-round slows down or speeds up. So long as the merry-go-round or centrifuge maintains a constant rate of motion, the person is subjected to angular velocity.

The centrifuge is a convenient device to provide body motion in experimental situations, and has formed a sort of standard reference for discussing gravitational effects.

Since the organism is constantly subjected to the compelling demands of the gravitational field regardless of whatever else he may be doing, vestibular functions, if they are to leave room for the organism to do other things, must be quite reflexive and automatic. Thus, in the vestibular sense, we have a sense modality that is quite different in many ways from the other sense modalities we possess. Much of its operation is not accompanied by the organism's self-awareness. We must avoid letting this lead us to the conclusion that vestibular activity is not a perceptual function. It has been pointed out elsewhere in this text that perception may be reflexive, just so long as it meets the criteria in the definition for perceptual activity; namely, that perception is an immediate discriminatory kind of response involving sense organs.

Consistent with the lack of any definite sense *experience* related to the function of the vestibule, it is not certain that there is a cortical projection area for the vestibule, as there is for the other sense modalities such as vision and hearing. One author, on the other hand, has presented data to indicate that there possibly is such an area.

While there have been differences of opinion as to whether there are unique sense experiences from rotation, movement, and position, Wendt (255) holds to the tentative belief that there are. Various experiences that might otherwise be thought of as kinesthetic, such as the experience of sinking slowly while under water and the awareness of the direction of gravity while under water, are examples Wendt uses to support his belief. The significance of Wendt's examples lies in the fact that the body, while under water, is pressed upon an equal amount from all directions. The findings of Griffith (97), who has seemed to hold a position opposite to Wendt, must be given some recognition. His study involved introspections under several well-controlled conditions before, during, and following rotation of subjects in a revolving chair. He stated that he found dizzinesses to consist of a large number of processes that included ocular kinesthesis, tensions in neck and arms, pressure in the abdomen from the viscera, pressure in the chest and head. In addition to these, certain vascular (blood vessel) processes were attributed to supply a diffuse background of effects that colored the whole experience in a characteristic way. That Griffith could make these conclusions stems first from the nature of his subject's reports, and second from the fact that under gravitational stress, such as induced in a revolving chair, body tissues are subjected to tensions that are neither tiny nor too usual.

Movement also can be experienced by moving the head while a visual target is stationary, or when the target moves across the visual field, or when the eyes are shut and the head is moved. Some of the experiences of movement, rotation, and posture are similar when the visual field is rotated or moved and when a sound source is revolved around the head. In the latter case the sound may be experienced as standing still and the individual himself as revolving. It is obvious, then, that the experiences of bodily movement basically are not dependent upon vestibular stimulation.

To say the least, if there are any unique vestibular experiences they are experiences of position, rotation, and rectilinear movement. It seems that the common element in perceptions of rotation at or near threshold is simply a vague "feeling" of rotation. Sometimes this has been described as a "swimming sensation." Griffith's study had to do with much more vigorous rotations, and there the experiences were complex and such as to lead to Griffith's description given above. The complex experience, however derived, was called dizziness. The same term is used when the visual field seems to whirl around the subject. A more technical term, vertigo, has come to be used nowadays. A word covering a more comprehensive variety of symptoms is motion sickness. Vertigo may be only a state of confusion or uneasiness with regard to spatial position, movement, and so on. It seems to have autonomic components and, of course, an unpleasant feeling tone. Vertigo does not always require body movements to elicit it. Witkin's (267, 268, 269) experiments with stationary subjects in a tilting room produced it. Hence it was produced without a kind of vestibular stimulation to account for it.

THE VESTIBULAR APPARATUS

The bony labyrinth of which the cochlea, the auditory mechanism, is a part contains two sorts of structures each containing the sense cells for the vestibular modality which we have been discussing. The semicircular canals, the more familiar structures, are three canals lying at right angles to each other. These form a sort of three-dimensional coördinate system so that acceleration in any of the three dimensions will affect one or the other of them. Within the canals is a fluid called endolymph that circulates in accordance with the direction and amount of acceleration. At the base of each canal is an enlargement called the ampulla. In it are the endings of the nonauditory part of the VIII cranial (auditory) nerve. Hairlike fibers of the nerve extend into a gelatinous mass that is disturbed by accelerations and set up impulses that are conducted up the nerve to the brain. Aside from the normal stimuli incident to acceleration, the ampulla with its hair cells is affected by thermal impingements. Let hot or cold water be put into the ear; the result will be a series of nystagmoid movements of the eye, and the perceptual end result will be dizziness. The water put into the ears possibly becomes effective by setting up convection currents in the endolymph. Two other forms of impingement will also induce vestibular responses: one is direct pressure, and the other is electricity.

Another portion of the vestibular structure is the utricle, which also contains sensitive hair cells. This portion constitutes what is sometimes called the otolith organ. The otolith organ is sensitive to static posture. It is thought by some to be slower in action than the semicircular canals. It is very difficult to isolate the actual functions of the canals and the otolith organ, for the various operations intended to produce stimulation not only may stimulate both of these organs but include muscular stresses and tensions that contribute to the overall sensory effect. For example, if one wishes to study the effect of posture, how should he do it? If he tilts the subject on a tilting board to which the subject is strapped, the whole set of mechanical pressures and pulls on body tissues is altered by each manipulation intended to affect the vestibular organs. This complicates the matter considerably. One of the best ways would be to put the subject in a tank of water, for when a subject is immersed in water the pressures on the body are equal in all directions. But this procedure is not so easy to put into practice, for one would have to fill the tank completely and put a lid on it so that tilting it would not churn the water. If the tank was not full, the water would be disturbed by the movements of the tank and the subject would be moved within the water. This, of course, would disturb the equality of pressure in various directions and violate the conditions for which the water support for the body was sought in the first place. We need not go further in this description to make clear how difficult it is to study vestibular function in the most precise way.

INVESTIGATIONS WITH THE HUMAN CENTRIFUGE

A number of studies have been made on human subjects by using a merry-go-round or centrifuge. Several large experimental centrifuges for this purpose exist in this country. These are very heavy and run with extreme smoothness. The accelerations and decelerations are smooth enough so as not to be detectable through the muscle and pressure senses as roughness or jarring.

A large part of the study of the vestibular sense is made up of obtaining thresholds. Thresholds for angular acceleration, for example, have been worked upon quite carefully. Such thresholds have been obtained with the body in various positions, that is, prone, upright, head down, and so on. Once it is found out just how sensitive vestibular and related mechanisms are, a beginning concept of perceptual response to gravity is possible. Another important kind of study is the ascertainment of the limits of tolerance for extreme accelerations. Part of the effects produced in such cases, of course, go far beyond effects on the vestibular mechanism to sheer mechanical effects on tissues and blood circulation.

Several centrifugal studies on vestibular function will serve to illustrate the sort of work that has been done in more recent years. The first of these is the study made by Graybiel, Kerr, and Bartley (96) on the thresholds for angular acceleration. To make this determination, a criterion of some sort or other had to be used. The "common-sense" criterion for a subject's sensitivity to speeding up or slowing down of a centrifuge while riding on it at or near its center would be the minimal feeling of being revolved very slowly. Various earlier investigators have used this direct experimental criterion. Graybiel and colleagues used a different one. They used what has been called the "oculogyral illusion." This so-called illusion must be explained before it can be understood how it was used.

Let us say a subject is revolved while in an upright position (a sitting position, for example). Let the axis of revolution be through the center of the body and head. If this is done in the dark, so that there will be no visual landmarks, the following effect can be produced.

If the platform on which the subject is revolved carries a tiny light source, which the subject fixates as best he can, this source will not only revolve with the subject but will be perceived to lie straight ahead, no matter at what speed the subject is revolved. But let the rate of body movement be suddenly changed and the light will appear to move to the right or to the left, depending upon whether the change has been one of speeding up the revolution or of slowing it down. This visual effect is called the oculogyral illusion. We prefer to call it simply the oculogyral effect.

The problem of Graybiel and colleagues was to determine how much the slowing down or speeding up of the rate of movement of the centrifuge had to be before the illuminated target they used appeared to move to the right or to the left. The authors controlled not only the rates of acceleration, positive and negative, but interposed uniform motion for necessary lengths of time between test periods for the canals to regain equilibrium. They controlled the lengths of test periods in order that they would be long enough to produce effects at minimal accelerations. The investigation disclosed that angular accelerations of .12°/sec² (degrees per second per second) were necessary to reach human threshold detection.

There is a phenomenon in connection with riding on centrifuges that is both significant and interesting. You will recall that when you rode on a merry-go-round you leaned "inward," that is, toward its center of rotation, once the merry-go-round got into motion. You gained the sensory impression that if you did not you would lose your balance and fall outward. Of course, the act of leaning inward was not a consciously calculated one; it was automatic ("reflexive").

If you were to be strapped into a chair fastened to the merry-go-round and facing the center of rotation, you would feel as though you were being tilted backward when the merry-go-round got into motion.

If the merry-go-round is in the dark and all that you can see is a light, the source of which is fastened at eye level to the axis of rotation, the light will appear to rise as the merry-go-round accelerates. To get a better understanding of this, consult Fig. 15.1. The forces acting on the subject are indicated by CF and G, and the visual target is indicated by L.

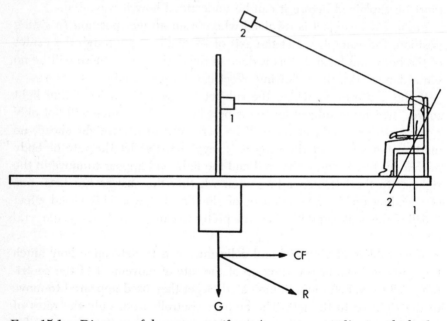

FIG. 15.1.   Diagram of human centrifuge (merry-go-round), in which the posture of the subject is held upright and he is given a visual target to fixate in darkness. Rotation produces centrifugal force, CF, active in a horizontal direction. This and gravity, G, form a resultant, R. Visual target is perceived to be in position 2 during rotation. Also, axis of body seems to be tilted to position 2 from 1.

Note that R is on a tilt from the perpendicular. It is this new direction of force that is the perceptual "straight down" direction. Hence, if this is straight down, then the subject himself must be tilted back of "straight down."

Consistent with the experience of being in a tilted-back position, the subject sees the light as above the old horizontal direction perceived to start with.

EXPERIMENTS WITH A WAVE MACHINE

The second type of study that you will be familiarized with is the use of the wave machine.

Motion that may be imparted to the body is of various sorts, such as the pitching, rolling, and yawing (sidewise movement) of vehicles. Among all the possible motions, the up-and-down or vertical motion is one of the more effective forms on the organism. Aside from revolving chairs and centrifuges and swings, up-and-down moving platforms resembling elevators have been used for experimental purposes.

An arrangement used for imparting various rates and amplitudes of vertical motion to experimental subjects was employed by Alexander and colleagues (2). The device resembled a common passenger elevator, and could be raised and lowered automatically by merely setting certain prearranged controls. It was called a *wave machine* because the motion was pretty much like an up-and-down wave motion. The investigation we are describing consisted in varying the amplitude of the vertical excursions from 4 to 10 feet (perhaps even more in certain experiments), and varying the rate of motion from 200 to 400 feet per minute. Variations were also made in the rate for reaching maximum motion. This is to say, the pattern of the wave was varied. Fig. 15.2 gives some indication of what certain of the wave characteristics were.

Healthy young subjects were used, and the criterion for the effectiveness of the wave motion was whether or not sickness was produced within a limited time by riding in the wave machine. No subject was used for more than one trial, hence numerous subjects were required. The relations of motion sickness to time of day, and to prior history of motion sickness of various sorts, in the respective subjects were also studied. Finally, the question of whether manifesting motion sickness in the wave machine bore any relation to performance deficits in subsequent military tasks was also studied.

The subjects were blindfolded during the ride and clothing was re-

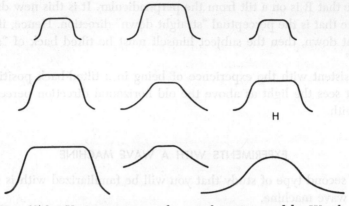

FIG. 15.2. Various patterns of vertical motion used by Wendt, *et al.*, to study motion sickness in a wave machine (by permission from *Beginning Experimental Psychology*, by S. H. Bartley, Fig. 68. Copyright, 1950, McGraw-Hill Book Company, Inc.).

duced to eliminate sweating, unless induced by motion effects. Some of the subjects examined became sick during the tests and some did not. The degrees of sickness produced were distinguished by the three categories: 0, 1, and 2. A value of 2 was assigned to those who vomited within the limited time allowed on the machine. Value 1 was given to those reporting definite nausea and/or manifesting profuse sweating. A value of 0 was given to all other subjects. Even those who received the assigned 0 were not necessarily entirely unaffected. Some of them reported some dizziness, headache, or slight nausea. Even some pallor, or a slight amount of sweating, showed up in some cases.

Not all of the wave patterns used were equally effective in producing sickness despite the fact that they all possessed the same energy content, and that at the midpoint of the excursions the velocity was the same, namely, 400 feet per minute. Fig. 15.2 shows that it was wave H that was most effective, even though it did not involve the most abrupt transitions from one rate to another throughout the excursion.

FEATURES OF MOTION SICKNESS

Motion sickness is made up of one or more of the following components: headache, cold "sweating," feelings of depression, dizziness, feelings of muscular weakness, experiences of malaise referable to various general parts of the body and head. The discomfort produced tends not to cease with the termination of body motion, but in some cases may last several days. It is reported that deaf persons who show no other signs of vestibular sensitivity do not become motion sick. Apparently, some separation of acceleration and deceleration of movement is highly effective in producing sickness. Short rapid phases of movement do not seem to be so effective. Such movements more nearly simulate ordinary head movements. Rotation in several planes at once or in sequence is most effective. Vertical motions, such as studied on the wave machine and occurring in rough plane travel or in ships or in the rear seats of automobiles, are among the most usual causes of motion sickness. It is believed that lateral motion is quite ineffectual in producing sickness.

Obviously, the general attitude of the subject is a large factor. Unfavorable past experiences or convincing descriptions of the effectiveness of certain motions tend to induce genuine uneasiness in subjects, and this can very easily be enhanced by the imaginative processes that accompany stimulation in present situations. One of the outstanding observations has to do with the slightness of the physical motions that may induce sickness in the passively moved subject, as in contrast to the many varied and energetic motions that do not so result when the subject is in active motion. It would seem that no movement self-carried out by the subject is taken to be at all threatening, whereas movements induced by vehicles, for example, do carry a potential threat to the subject. Habituation to motion may occur in many cases. The rough motion of high-speed passenger trains becomes an insignificant feature in the everyday experiences and economy of trainmen.

It should be obvious to the reader, once he grasps the details of the situations that produce motion sickness, that externally induced motion imparted to the human individual is a potential hazard that the organism through its evolution had to develop means to cope with. Motion had to be detected and adequate and appropriate kinds of adjustment had to be possible in response to such motion. Of all the forms of external impingement that the organism encounters, there is none more compelling than motion due to loss of support from beneath, or massive violent tossing, for example. Such forms of mechanical disturbance might mean violent death. The organism does not accept forms of impingement that resemble those just mentioned with comfort and passivity. Even lesser forms have their untoward experiential effects and seem to call for avoidance. Passive submission comes only after a learning period—a period that may have, as one of its aspects, familiarization wherein the given motions are discovered not to be harmful after all.

VISUAL VERSUS POSTURAL FACTORS IN PERCEIVING VERTICALITY, ETC.

It has long been supposed that when a subject is asked to adjust a visual target to the perceived vertical, the body factors (somesthetic[1] factors) will play the dominant role. If centrifugal force is combined with gravity, the subject would then use the somesthetic factors as determined by the resultant of the two forces just mentioned. Mach made this conclusion many years ago.

Koffka (144, 145) believed that when the visual and the somesthetic frames of reference were brought into conflict, subjects would use the visual in their perceptions. Wing and Passey (264) believe that Witkin and Asch's (267, 268) findings point toward a compromise between the two frames in the behavior of their subjects. Passey and Guedry's (206) subjects tended, under the conditions he used, to set the perceived visual vertical in line with the true, or gravitational, vertical in all cases.

Mann and colleagues (175, 176) have shown that when a subject is tilted away from the perpendicular and is not allowed to use vision, he will not readjust himself to the true vertical if he is held in the tilted position for a number of seconds. The error in readjustment is dependent both on the time in the tilted position and upon the angular value of the tilt. The amount of tilt that is most effective seems to be in the neighborhood of 35 degrees, and up to this point error increases with degree of tilt. Error increases with time in tilt up to about one minute.

Mann and Dauterive (176) found that the uncertainty of a subject in perceiving the true vertical in posture was greatest when he was tilted only a few degrees. This range on both sides of the vertical was called the "arc of uncertainty." The reduction of proprioceptive cues tends to increase the arc of uncertainty.

Many years ago, Aubert found that when a subject viewed an upright visual target with head tilted, the target seemed to be rotated away from the perpendicular in the direction opposite to head tilt. Müller refined the observation and reported that when the head is tilted only slightly, the apparent tilt of the visual target is in the same direction as the head tilt; but when the head tilt is great, the effect noted by Aubert occurs.

Mann and Berry (175) found that the mean error and variability in perceiving the visual horizontal are greater when the subject is in a tilted position than when he is vertical.

[1] Somesthesis is a term labeling the sensory effects that pertain to the body state, and thus it includes the cutaneous senses, the muscle sense, and the various experiences, such as dizziness, nausea, etc., that stem from senses just mentioned, with the possible addition of the vestibular sense.

Witkin and colleagues (268, 269) performed a number of experiments in which visual and postural factors were pitted against each other. One of the chief devices for making such studies was a tilting-room-tilting-chair combination. A small room, possibly about seven feet in each dimension, was fixed so as to be rotatable around a horizontal axis. The axis was through the center of the room and on the same axis the subject's chair was pivoted. This provided for lateral tilts of the subject to his left or his right as he sat facing the wall of the room, which could independently be tilted to the right or to the left. Thus, when the subject in his chair was tilted, posture with relation to gravity was manipulated. When the room was tilted, the subject's visual field was manipulated. At times the subject could be placed in the usual upright relation to the earth (gravity) and the visual field could be used as the variable. At other times, just the reverse could be done. The subject could be tilted and the visual field could be held in the usual relation to the gravitational field. At still other times both could be tilted. Such combinations of tilt could include tilts of both room and subject in the same direction, in either equal or unequal amounts, or tilts in the opposite direction, in either equal or unequal amounts.

Witkin and colleagues used both male and female subjects and found that they behaved differently. The results depicting these differences are given in Chapter 18. They are placed there owing to the suspicion that these differences may have come about through social development.

The results that are relevant here pertain to the relative weights of the visual and postural factors. One might suppose that even in the dark, where there are nothing but postural stimuli (those involving kinesthesis, vestibular activity, touch, and pressure) involved, the subject would be certain that he is tipped when he is actually placed a number of degrees from the vertical. This is not always the case, as was indicated by the facts already mentioned in this chapter. When a subject is confined in a chair whose arm and shoulder supports are adjusted snugly against him and he is tilted, the tactual and pressure experiences may mean simply pressure as applied laterally (horizontally) to him, rather than being perceived as indications of pressure due to tilt. Actually, such pressure resembles those induced by being squeezed against other persons in a crowd, and in line with this these experiences evoke social connotations. In fact they may have curious, affective flavors.

The room in the Witkin experiments provides, of course, an all-encompassing visual field. Visually, the upright of the room is the convincing upright of the earth. If a plumb line is suspended from the ceiling of the room, it naturally conflicts with the expected positions that a plumb line should assume when the room is tilted. The visual appearance of the plumb line becomes different. What we mean is this: whereas a plumb line *looks* as though it hangs by its own weight, it does not look that way when the room is tilted. It looks rigid; that is, it looks as though it must be rigid in order to deviate from what is perceived to be the vertical. This appearance is, of course, an immediately and directly perceived one. Incidentally, this example is one of the many kinds that indicate the close parallelism between perception and what would be expected to occur through "reasoning." Both processes seem to follow the same logic, the same self-consistency.

Chapter 16

TASTE AND SMELL PERCEPTIONS

Taste and smell are two of the so-called lower senses. This may be because the mechanisms for these senses are not so elaborate as those for vision and hearing, and the consequent perceptions are not reducible to quantification in as highly particularized ways.

Our interest in taste and smell is not confined to what can be said about mechanisms, but rather extends to the roles these senses play in the economy of the organism-as-a-person.

The taste (gustatory) sense and the smell (olfactory) sense are chemical senses and in the evolution of man have played the role of relating him to the chemical aspects of his environment. They relate to the selecting of food and the avoidance of harmful substances. In today's world they still play that role, but to a relatively lesser degree. This is in part due to the development of "higher" modes of living, and in part to the fact that man has come to the point of erecting a whole new universe of new chemical substances, regarding which taste is no clue to their harmfulness or acceptability. Were the environment to have been perfectly stable for a great enough time, these two senses might have provided an adequate criterion for what to accept and to reject.

Be all this as it may, odors and tastes play very important roles in the everyday economy of man. They are criteria not only of acceptance and rejection in foods, but of other classes of stimuli. They are involved in the judgment of cleanliness of articles of use, of living places, and of people. To say that something stinks is to apply a strong and effective criterion for its avoidance. Odors possess very intimate characteristics that sights and sounds may lack. They have the quality of telling us something about hidden matters, something that sights and sounds do not reveal. Hence they provide experiences that are relied upon in ways that sights and sounds may not be.

Tastes and smells may have biological significance outside that of food getting and food enjoyment. They are agents of sexual attraction and repulsion. What is more, the sensory impressions provided by these modalities are very greatly subject to learning. What is now abhorrent may become attractive if involved in the proper conditioning process. To some, the emotional impact of the olfactory combination of perfume, cigarette smoke, and the smell of alcoholic liquor on the breath is considerable, and possesses a peculiar significance. Such a result, for example, must have developed through the conditioning process, since one could hardly assign the impact to original pleasure of the smelling of smoke, or alcohol breath, or even of perfume.

Odors are well remembered. Whereas one cannot be sure that a given color is identical to one he saw a few minutes ago in another context, one can feel sure that a present odor is the very same one that he often smelled in childhood. This surely is not dependent upon a possible limitation in the possible kinds and varieties of odors that can be smelled. The stability that is represented here may lie in the evolutionary priority of the sense, although we have no good way of testing such a notion.

TASTE

What is taste? What we are going to call taste proper, and what in common-sense terms is called taste, are not identical. The whole configuration of experiences that are localized in the mouth and attributed to what has been put into the mouth is called taste in everyday speech. The common man does not search for sense organs, or classify them once they are disclosed. He only relates some outward operation and an experience that seems to accrue from it. Being more analytical and more precise, scientists do search for sense receptors and they do try to relate the effective stimulus to the resulting experiences or other responses.

Taste then, according to the strict definition, is not the entire combination of experiences that ensues from placing something in the mouth. It is the group of experiences that ensue from something activating taste buds in the tongue and perhaps certain portions of the mouth wall. It is to be admitted that these are two very different sets of end results. Accordingly, we ought to have two terms to label them. First of all, some of the substances that are placed in the mouth as food are able to stimulate olfactory (smell) receptors in the nose. The perceiver is not generally able to distinguish what is exciting olfactory receptors along with taste receptors, and this has given rise to the common-sense failure to distinguish fully between taste and smell.

The sheer mechanical properties of food and other substances has something to do with the overall experience produced, and thus with what is ordinarily called taste. Soft materials taste differently than hard. Even the same kind of substance may taste differently in two different mechanical (textural) conditions.

The temperature of food has a great deal to do with its taste. Lukewarm and cold coffee are greatly different in the experiences they evoke than are warm and hot coffee. Most soft drinks (bottled beverages) are very different when warm than when cold. Some are scarcely acceptable when not iced.

A number of central nervous contributions enter into the sensory experience and acceptance of materials that are placed in the mouth. Whether the substance is considered clean or not makes a great difference. While, according to some points of view in psychology, this factor may be spoken of as affective or emotional, with the implication that this factor is an embellishment added on to perception, we find it hard in many cases to disentangle the factor from other inherent aspects of perception. Many factors that contribute to the gustatory (taste) end result are learned. It is characteristic for children to resist sampling new forms of food. They assert that they do not like the new substances that are offered. Once in a while, when the new substance is put into the mouth ("tasted"), it is found to be palatable and pleasurable, but more often the initial encounters are begun with an *a priori* aversion, and a learning process may ensue. The question is whether, as the food becomes acceptable, the taste of the food changes or the person changes so as to like what was first unliked. It is possible that both sorts of change occur. In some cases, it may be more of one kind of change than the other. We know of no careful, extended study on this point.

Resolving a Dilemma

It would be desirable if this discrepancy in what is called taste by the two outlooks given in the previous section could be resolved. It seems very artificial to confine taste to the experiences mediated by taste buds of the tongue. Yet it would be a great departure from the principles used to classify sense modalities if all the elements in the experience produced by putting something into the mouth were included. This is one case in which simply choosing an additional word so that every item has a label will not resolve the dilemma. It will not do simply to have one word for the experience mediated by taste buds and another for the overall experience from putting something into the mouth. These experiences both have enough in common to merit being kept together as belonging to a single category.

Another possible way of resolving the matter that presents itself is to revamp the whole logic and terminology of sensory classification. It will be recalled that certain criteria have long been used to determine which sense experiences are to be put into the same category and thus determine how many categories there are. Among the criteria used in order to set up a new sense modality were that (1) a unique set of experiences had to be established; (2) a separate set of sense organs had to be proven; (3) a unique kind of stimulus had to be found; and (4) a specific afferent sense pathway had to be shown. It is on the basis of these criteria that men now confine taste to the results mediated by taste buds. The other qualities of "taste" come not from the thus-defined taste modality, but from other modalities.

It would be possible to revamp this whole outlook and deal with experiences and other reactions as they seem to fall into broad functional classes. For example, one of the organism's functions is maintaining body equilibrium. In our present case, the function is that of appreciating what is put into the mouth for acceptance, rejection, and so on.

Possibly this broad functional classification of human interactions with the environment would run into various sorts of troubles no less perplexing than the problem we are speculating about resolving. Even the beginning student of psychology ought, nevertheless, to be aware of the problem we have posed, and of its difficulty and the possibility of resolving it by a radical remodeling of the classification system of all perceptual performance.

Taste Receptors

Taste receptors are located primarily on the tongue and consist in those giving rise to four perceptual qualities, namely, salt, sweet, bitter, and sour respectively. The areas of greatest sensibility are the tip, sides, and rear of the top surface of the tongue. The middle of the top surface is quite insensitive for taste production.

Fig. 16.1 represents a combination of the findings of Hänig and of Henning (116) with reference to where the four taste qualities are evoked on the tongue. The experience of saltiness is easily evoked all along the edge of the tongue from tip to base. Sourness is well evoked along the

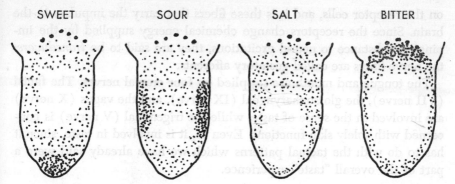

SWEET   SOUR   SALT   BITTER

Fig. 16.1.   A plot of the gustatory sensitivity of the tongue, using Hänig's and Henning's findings combined.

edge, but best along the side rather than at the tip. Bitter is elicitable at the tip, but much better as the base of the tongue is approached. Sweetness is best obtainable at the tip of the tongue, from which sensitivity tapers off along the sides and toward the base.

The receptor organs are called *taste buds.* They are made up of a group of cells, one to two dozen in a cluster. The sensitive cells are spindle-shaped, and are supplanted by co-lumnar cells around them. Each of the gustatory cells ends in a hair process that extends into a pore opening in which the hairs from the rest of the cells cluster. (See Fig. 16.2.) Taste buds are grouped in papillae, which are of four forms: *fungiform, foliate, circumvallate, filiform.* The circumvallate papillae are surrounded by a "moat," into which the taste pores, already mentioned, open. The papillae contain many buds, and the count remains about the same until late maturity, when the number reduces.

The gustatory receptors (cells in the taste bud) serve only the function of generating the impulse to be sent to the central nervous system. Nerve fibers arborize and terminate

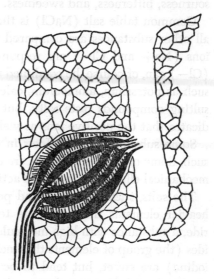

Fig. 16.2.   A taste bud. It is made up of two sorts of cells in a capsule: the sense cells, shown in black, and the supporting cells (striped). The sense cells terminate in hairs that project into a slotlike cavity or "moat."

on the receptor cells, and it is these fibers that carry the impulses to the brain. Since the receptors change chemical energy supplied by the impinging substance to neural excitations, they are said to be *transducers;* the nerve fibers are called gustatory afferents.

The tongue and mouth are supplied by four cranial nerves. The facial (VII nerve), the glossopharyngeal (IX nerve), and the vagus (X nerve) are involved in the sense of taste, while the trigeminal (V nerve) is concerned with solely skin functions. Even so, it is involved in taste, since it has to do with the tactual patterns which we have already said were a part of the overall "taste" experience.

Taste Stimuli

In order to be tasted, a substance must usually be soluble in water. Regardless of the physical state of the substance to begin with, if it dissolves to some extent in saliva, it is effective. The effectiveness of the impinging substances depends on several factors, such as the degree of solubility, concentration, ability to ionize, temperature, and chemical composition. From all the variables we know, there are only four elemental taste effects, if we keep to the activation of taste buds. These effects are saltiness, sourness, bitterness, and sweetness.

Common table salt (NaCl) is the standard stimulus for saltiness, and all other substances are compared with it for that quality. Both of the ions (Na+ and Cl−) are responsible for saltiness. The chloride ion (Cl−) can, of course, be combined with other elements and positive ions, such as potassium, ammonium, calcium, lithuim, and zinc. All of the resulting compounds taste salty, but not qualitatively the same. This indicates that the positive ions as well as the chloride ion must be factors.

Some substances have effects in addition to stimulating taste buds as such. Some of these substances are astringents and thus produce peculiar mechanical effects on tissue and activate the cutaneous sense.

The salts, such as sodium and potassium, are molecularly light. With heavier elements the salty taste tends to shift to bitter. Cesium chloride, a substance with high molecular weight, is sweet. Not all heavy halides (the group of elements that includes chlorine, fluorine, bromine, and iodine) are sweet, but tend to be bitter. Hence what we know about chemicals and the tastes they produce does not form perfectly simple relationships.

Sourness is a result of ionization, too. The substances that produce the sour taste are those providing acid dissociation and the liberation of hydrogen ions. The common inorganic acids, such as sulphuric acid, hydrochloric acid, and nitric acid, are similar in taste when matched in concentration. Organic acids do not resemble each other completely in their sour taste, and thus it is deduced that the concentration of the hydrogen ion is not exclusively responsible for their tastes. Perhaps such chemical compounds affect more than a single sort of taste receptor, and in that way bring about a taste complex.

The stimuli for bitter and sweet do not seem usually to be ionic. Among the most common bitter-taste producers are the alkaloids, such as nicotine, strychnine, quinine, and brucine. These seem to be effective in molecular rather than ionic form. The commonest ionic solutions that do give rise to bitterness are magnesium, iron, silver, and iodine.

The sweetest-tasting substances are the complex molecules of the sugars, and similar compounds used as sugar substitutes, such as saccharine. Some substances are supposed to be thousands of times as effective as ordinary cane sugar, but people's reactions to these substances are not as constant and predictable as they are to cane sugar.

There is a close connection between bitter and sweet, as evidenced by the result of slight changes in chemical composition that are needed to shift the sensory effect from sweetness to bitterness.

Some chemicals injected into the body via the blood stream give rise to taste. One of these is nicotinic acid supplied intravenously. The physician can pretty well predict the number of seconds from the instant of injection, let us say, in the wrist, until the patient will experience a tingle and a metallic taste at the tip of the tongue. Taste can be aroused also by electrical stimulation supplied the tongue. If the current flows in one direction, the taste is sour; if the current is reversed, a very different taste results. Geldard (82) describes it as soapy and somewhat burning. The frequency of alternating current manipulates taste. With low frequencies, sourness is elicited; with high frequencies, the taste tends to be bitter.

The complex tastes of many substances can be duplicated by combinations of other substances that elicit the four elementary tastes. The salt-sour-bitter quality of potassium chloride, for instance, can be duplicated by a certain mixture of sodium chloride (table salt), tartaric acid, and quinine.

Pointlike stimulation of areas of the tongue indicates that sensitivity to stimuli producing the salty quality is greatest on the tip and sides, that sweet is easiest to evoke on the tip, and that bitter comes out best with the appropriate stimuli on the back of the tongue. It seems that in some of the various papillae there are combinations of the four elemental types of taste buds.

Individual nerve fibers have been found to supply more than one taste bud. Certain fibers have been isolated in the cat that respond to the application of only a single substance, for instance, an acid, whereas two other types of fiber were also found by Pfaffmann (209). One of these responded to acid and salt stimuli, and another responded to acid and quinine (bitter). He did not find any responsive to sugar.

Taste Thresholds

Not all individuals taste the same qualities from a substance put into the mouth. In general, there must be considerable likeness, but in some cases there is an unquestionable difference. First of all, some people are virtually "taste-blind" to such substances as phenylthiocarbimide, while others taste it as bitter. The insensitivity seems to be inherited. The differences in threshold for the tasting of other substances may be based upon differences in the acidity of the taster's saliva. It has been reported that during pregnancy certain taste thresholds are raised. This is often the case for sodium chloride and for acid-tasting substances.

Bornstein (33) found that, in general, the following substances in the following concentrations gave the results indicated. For sucrose, 4 grams of sucrose per 100 cc. of water were easily recognizable. Ten grams tended to taste quite strong, and 40 grams very strong. Table salt was easily perceived with 2.5 grams per 100 cc. And solutions of 7.5 grams were medium strong. Double this concentration was very strong. Quinine monohydrochloride was easily recognized as a bitter taste when only .075 gram was placed in 100 cc. of water. One-half gram was moderately strong, and twice that concentration was very strong. The sourness of citric acid was easily detected when 1 gram was placed in 100 cc. of water. Five times this concentration was medium strong, and double the strong concentration was very strong. These concentrations were used for testing patients for taste deficits.

As was earlier pointed out, temperature has considerable influence on taste end results. The best and most recent extensive work on the effect of temperature was performed by Hahn and Günther (101). With the device they used, the tongue area under investigation was brought to the temperature of the taste stimulus to be used and was maintained there.

Starting with a temperature of 17° C. (about 63° F.), raising the temperature of a weak solution of dulcin, a sweet-tasting substance, caused the threshold for it to drop until a temperature of about 34–35° C. was reached. At about 36 or 37° C. the threshold began to rise again. This means that the sweet taste could be detected more easily as the temperature rose from around 63° F. to 95° F., where threshold began to rise. Sodium chloride at about 63° F. had an initial lower threshold than the particular acid solution just mentioned, but the threshold was found to rise in a virtually linear fashion up to the limit of the range tested (42° C., or 107.6° F.). Hydrochloric acid remains about the same in taste-producing effect over the entire range tested.

Quinine sulphate, which at the lower end of the temperature range tested was the most effective of the solutions used, soon rose slowly in threshold, then more rapidly as temperature was raised, and ended at being about as effective as sodium chloride at the upper limit of the temperature range.

Pfaffmann (209) points out that such complex effects cannot be interpreted to be simple chemical reactions between substances and taste cells, for most chemical reactions are magnified as temperature rises. Some of the end results just given run in the very opposite direction. Of the four substances mentioned, dulcin alone behaved this way, and it did so only over part of the range.

We have already pointed out the taste effect of direct venous injections of nicotinic acid. This and other similar effects have been taken to indicate that blood composition is a factor in the production of taste. Such a belief has not been fully substantiated, although certain food preferences in animals, under certain conditions, bear on the matter. Adrenalectomized animals, rendered salt deficient by the operation, manifest definite preference for salty foods and water. On the contrary, sensitivity for sugar is reduced in states of hypoglycemia (sugar lack). In the same subjects, sensitivity to the other taste-producing substances is left unaffected.

The sense of taste adapts quite fully. In precise experiments on restricted portions of the tongue, adaptation has been studied by Dallenbach and colleagues. Adaptation is proportional to the strength of the solution used.

A large number of salty taste-producing substances were tested, and found not to interfere with each other in their adaptations. That is, adaptation to one substance of the group did not affect the sensitivity to the others. This poses the question of whether there is more than one type of salt receptor.

All acids were found to affect each other, that is, to cross-adapt. Certain sweet and bitter tastes cross-adapted, but others did not. A possible conclusion arising from the failure of cross-adaptation is that adaptation and stimulation are two separate processes. This was suggested on the assumption that there are not as many kinds of salt receptors as there are salt-producing stimuli that do not cross-adapt. In the experiment, there were 24 such substances. On the other hand, if stimulation and adaptation are two separate processes, one cannot deduce the nature of stimulation from adaptation findings.

Taste Scales

The understanding of a process is promoted by success in scaling the end result in relation to the quantitative features of the stimulus. Lewis (162) worked on the scaling of the elemental tastes of salt, sweet, sour, and bitter, somewhat in the manner of those who have scaled loudness and pitch of sounds in sones and mels respectively, and lifting weights in wegs. He found that the classical scale units (j.n.d.'s, just noticeable differences) differed in size in different portions of the stimulus scale.

Beebe-Center and Waddell (19) made cross-comparisons between salt and sweet, for example. This was possible because the subjects were able to select a solution of a salt stimulus that would be as salty as sucrose was sweet. The scales for all four elemental tastes were integrated. As a consequence, they defined the unit of taste as a *gust,* it being the taste strength of a 1 percent solution of sucrose. Gusts, then, applied not only to strength of sweetness but also to strengths of sourness, bitterness, and saltiness.

In Fig. 16.3, gusts (in logarithmic terms) are plotted against the concentration of the taste-producing solution (log grams per 100 cc. of water). It will be seen from this graph that the strength of taste production of quinine (bitter) is greater than the strength of tartaric acid (sour), and that the acid is stronger in taste than sodium chloride, the standard of saltiness. In turn, sodium chloride is stronger in taste production than sucrose, which is sweet-tasting. It will be noted that the sloping of the curves for each quality is nearly the same.

Beebe-Center (18) went farther and examined common food substances with the gust scale. The scale data were, of course, obtained by use of the fractionation method. There is some doubt as to the full validity of what was used as "half-value." There has also been some suggestion that adaptation might have distorted the results. Despite these criticisms the scale, as a standardization, has some value.

Other Psychophysical Studies of Taste

Although not much success has as yet attended efforts to relate taste qualities with chemical structure of substances, certain psychophysical investigations have been successful in scaling tastes such as sweetness. For

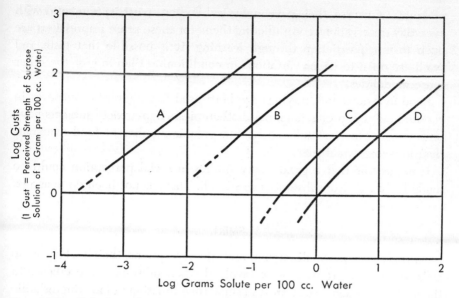

Log Grams Solute per 100 cc. Water

Fig. 16.3. Relation of gusts to concentration of solution. Curve A, quinine sulphate; B, tartaric acid; C, sodium chloride; D, sucrose (J. G. Beebe-Center and D. Waddell, A general psychological scale of taste, *J. Psychol.* [1948], *26*: 517–524, Fig. 3).

example, two sweet-tasting substances, sucrose and crystallose, were scaled in terms of concentrations of solutions needed to give a series of j.n.d.'s in sweetness between the two substances. It was found, in doing this, that equal numbers of steps above threshold were not equally sweet. For example, a concentration providing for six steps (j.n.d.'s) above threshold for sucrose required nine steps to match it in sweetness with the other substance. As concentrations of the two substances are made greater, the crystallose becomes relatively less effective than sucrose in producing sweetness when applied to the tongue. This is true also for certain other substances. Some substances increase slightly in relative sweetness as concentrations are increased. Investigations studying the possibility of scaling sweetness have indicated that j.n.d.'s for sweetness vary in their magnitude as concentration increases.

Foods, Personality, and Status

It also appears that tastes (odors as well) involve stronger effective aspects than perceptions in other modalities, excepting pain. The four taste qualities are not alike in the direction of their effects, as is indicated by strong bitterness being unpleasant and strong sweetness generally pleasant. Of course, their psychophysical findings must be tempered with everyday observations contradicting them, for these sense impressions are open to much variation through learning. It is possible that taste and smell are open to wider variations in conditioning than any of the other sense modalities.

Food aversions and cravings are both used for diagnostic purposes in certain modes of professional psychotherapies. High-anxiety subjects have been found experimentally to have a greater number of food aversions than low-anxiety subjects.

It is possible that a great many studies in social perception could be made by using taste substances as stimuli. This has not been done as yet.

SMELL

As was stated in the discussion on taste perceptions, the olfactory sense cells in the nose are very often involved when substances are taken into the mouth. The senses of taste and smell then function in indistinguishable combination in many everyday situations. To say the least, we often ascribe to the sense of taste the functions that belong, at least in part, to the sense of smell. In the foregoing sections, four fundamental taste qualities were dealt with. Substances evoking one of the four elemental taste qualities alone do not involve the sense of smell. But the situation is very different when common food substances are to be rightly identified and fully appreciated. The full flavor of butter, fruits, coffee, meats, and so on depend greatly on the sense of smell. It is startling to find that one cannot find taste differences between a piece of raw potato and a piece of apple when the nose is stoppered and the eyes are not used. The chief differences that may show up are mechanical, that is, dependent upon the hardness and textual qualities of the substances rather than differing in taste. Many other substances fail to produce their usual tastes, and instead provide only weak sweet, sour, or bitter tastes when the sense of smell is prevented from functioning. Such substances as peppermint, onions, cinnamon, all of which are thought to be quite strong in taste, elicit little taste when smell (olfaction) is precluded.

A good substance for gauging three major kinds of effect on oral and nasal tissue is ethyl alcohol. Three modalities can be tested with varying concentrations of this one substance. For example, smell can be evoked by concentrations 20,000 times weaker than needed to evoke taste. Concentrations three times as great as needed for taste produce a "cutaneous" burning effect.

Smell Receptors

The sense cells for smell are contained in two small patches of epithelium, the *olfactory epithelium* high up in the nasal passages. The cells are not in the main passageways for the air used in breathing. To reach them, the air must be deflected. In reaching the receptors, it is moistened and cleaned of dust.

The substance reaching the sense cells, obviously, must be airborne and in gaseous state. Not a great deal of the substance need reach the cells, as is illustrated by the fact that only four one-hundred millionths of a milligram of ethyl mercaptan in a liter of air is enough to evoke its perception. While this sounds like an extremely small amount, a single sniff of the air diluted as indicated will contain several million molecules. The olfactory epithelium is so inacessible that research is extremely difficult.

Classification of Olfactory Qualities

The elemental gustatory (taste) qualities are few and definite. The same has not been found true for smell qualities. Investigators have nevertheless attempted to discover natural classifications, which if found would provide a kind of rhyme and reason to a very complex situation. The oldest classification we know about was made in the middle of the eighteenth century by Linnaeus. In it there were seven categories: aromatic (carnation), fragrant (lily), ambrosial (musk), alliaceous (garlic), hircine (valerian), repulsive (certain beetles), and nauseous (carrion).

Just before the turn of the present century, Zwaardemaker (277) began his study of odors and continued it for thirty years. He expanded the classification just given. He added the categories of ethereal and empyreumatic. These came about as a result of the development of the then expanding organic chemistry with its many new substances. Zwaardemaker also divided the nine classes into a number of subclasses. A contemporary, Henning (116), during the later part of the Zwaardemaker period developed a very different classification in which there were only six categories, and these occupied the corners of a prism. They were fragrant, ethereal, resinous, spicy, putrid, and empyreumatic (burned smell). Henning's prism is illustrated in Fig. 16.4.

The findings that give rise to the Henning prism run somewhat as follows. A group of substances that seem somehow to belong together, according to smell, is examined carefully for the quality complex that each presents. As this is done, a sort of progression emerges. If one starts with sassafras, he may come next to nutmeg, then pepper, then cinnamon. There seems to be a progression in spiciness in the order mentioned. But as other substances of this general group are examined, a new quality emerges and the spiciness recedes. Speaking geometrically, it is as if a corner had been reached and turned. Cassia, cloves, bay, and thyme seem to represent a new progression. A corner is again reached; and since there are four of them, and the progression turns upon itself to make a closed cycle, the geometrical form taken to represent it is a square. It could be, instead, a rectangle or some other quadrilateral figure. When odors that do not seem to belong in the progression, or loop, are found, they must represent dimensions (progressions) running off at angles to the first one. Some odors studied did not belong in the surface just mentioned, so the geometrical figure had to be a three-dimensional one. Henning, as was said, ended up with a five-faced figure, a prism, on which he believed all odors would find a place along its edges. Pure odors lying between two other odors along an edge may resemble them, but cannot be synthesized by combining them. Experts as well as laymen have taken some cognizance of this fact.

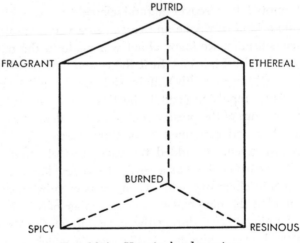

FIG. 16.4.   Henning's odor prism.

MacDonald (170) and Findley (73), independently, attempted systematic investigations to test a number of odors on the basis of Henning's prism. The stimuli they used for Henning's "primary" odors were (fragrant) oil of jasmine; (ethereal) citral and oil of lemon, respectively; (resinous) eucalyptol and turpentine, respectively; (spicy) anethole and cinnamon, respectively; (putrid) thiophenol and hydrogen sulphide, respectively; (burned) pyridine and oil of tar, respectively.

The procedure was to present one standard or primary substance to the observer, then one of the many secondary substances to be perceived, and then one of the other standard substances. The task of the observer was to tell which of the two standards the secondary or comparison substance smelled more like. Presumably, the report was to be based upon odor rather than intensity or some collateral quality such as coldness or bitiness. Each of the many comparison substances was compared to all six primary or standard substances during the overall procedure. It so happened that, even in this attempt to be systematic and orderly, the comparison odors were highly variable in their perceived similarities and tended to be like various standards in turn. This sort of result might be interpreted as requiring the placing of substances *within* the prism instead of only along the edges between the primaries at the corners. Henning, on the contrary, had insisted that the prism is empty and does not contain internal positions representing odor relations to each other. He declared that the prism was an odor prism and not a stimulus prism. Various odors do change—that is, any given substance is likely to be smelled differently from time to time—but this was not to lead to the use of the space within the prism for odor designations.

MacDonald (*170*) used only the four primaries contained in the FERS face of the prism. That is, he used only the fragrant, ethereal, resinous, and spicy-smelling primary stimuli. He used eleven stimuli, and asked his observers to place the separate odors where they seemed to belong in the square (face), or along its edges. The comparison stimuli used for this were those that supposedly had no resemblance to the P (putrid) or B (burned) odors. For some stimuli, the placement could be accomplished, but with difficulty. One of the curious results was that a given odor might seem to belong in the square but not well resemble all the corners. Some odors seemed to lie along the diagonals of the square. Nutmeg and geraniol lay along the ES diagonal, for example, while not always resembling E or S.

The logic of the prism would require that the middle of the ES diagonal would be also the middle of the FR diagonal. Anything at this point would be supposed to resemble F and R. It turns out, then, that the actual olfactory results do not fit the prism either as used by Henning or by MacDonald, who allowed the interior to be used if possible.

One modification of the prism would be to alter its faces from squares or rectangles to certain quadrilaterals, although this does not look too promising.

Substances may smell somewhat the way they taste, once the perceiver takes it that he is smelling instead of tasting. For example, substances may smell sweet, sour, and so on. Substances may smell prickly, warm, or cold. This is not surprising, because the nose is supplied not only with olfactory epithelium but also with the cutaneous senses of touch, pain, temperature (warmth and cold). The sharp, prickly, or biting odors obviously involve the sense of pain. Ammonia and chlorine would be substances to evoke pain, whereas menthol would stimulate cold receptors.

Woodworth and Schlossberg (274) say that the presence of non-olfactory sensations necessitates the revision of the classification of odor qualities, or at least experimental re-examination to factor out the non-olfactory components. The whole FERS face might coalesce into a single class, if pungency (pain sense), freshness (cold sense), and sweetness (taste) could be eliminated. The system of odor qualities might be simplified, or certain fundamental odors that fail to stand out when blended with non-olfactory components might be disclosed.

Herrmann (117), in trying to use Henning's prism, found that his observers balked. Some of them declared that the Henning choices as fundamentals were no more primary than certain other substances that could be given other labels. Among the items in this category were camphor and mint.

It still might be that a reworking of primaries would accomplish the end result expected of Henning's six groups. Actually, all faces would not need to be quadrilateral. Some might be three-sided, and some might be five-sided. It cannot be said that the idea of using a geometrical figure to represent systematic relations between odors (not stimuli) has been tried to the point of logical discard. The idea that all faces need not be of the same number of sides is borne out by the fact that at present some odors have been found not to belong at all to Henning's prism. This was the case in the work of Hazzard.

In Hazzard's study (106), various dimensions of olfactory experience, not commonly brought out, were examined. These were heaviness-lightness, looseness-tightness, smoothness-roughness, softness-hardness, dullness-sharpness, liveliness-inertness, thinness-thickness, brightness-dullness, surfaceness-deepness, and smallness-largeness.

It was found from Hazzard's observers that spicy odors tended to be sharp, lively, and bright. Putrid odors were dull and inert. Burned odors were hard, tight, and heavy. Fragrant odors were light, soft, and loose. Woodworth and Schlossberg suggest that the texture components reported for odors suggest the participation of the cutaneous sense in "smell."

Interaction of Olfactory Stimuli

It is very often said that one odor may mask another. If taken literally, the statement would assert that one sensory experience may mask another. It must be remembered that an experience that is masked is no experience at all. It is gratuitous to infer that the "masked experience" is one that exists but is simply covered up. Instead of implying that there are two experiences, one entirely covered up and the other not, the result in the case in question should be understood as being only one experience. All that should be meant is that two olfactory impingements, each of which produces an experience when operating alone, may, when operating concurrently, intract in such a way as to produce the experience expected of one of them alone. The illogic of common speech shows up in its most extreme form when masking is talked about with its usual connotations. In such cases, it is implied that something exists that at the same time does not exist. If there is any case in which this cannot be so, it is in sensory experience. Sensory experience is not a matter of imputation, inference, or conceptualization. An experience, to exist, must be an experience. That which is not being experienced does not exist.

When two olfactory stimuli are presented together in time, any one of six results may ensue. (1) The most frequent is the blending of the two odors, that is, the production of a single odor having some properties of both, and possibly some new characteristic. In what is called a blend, one may detect the resemblances to the separate odors produced by the same two stimuli, when they are presented independently in time. Substances that produce end results more nearly alike will produce the best blends, that is, those in which it is most difficult to isolate one or the other of the two components. It is possible that increasingly more precise experimentation will find this conclusion not strictly true in all respects. (2) When stimuli yielding very dissimilar odors are presented together, the two odors will both be produced, one and then the other being the center of attention. (3) When one odor is presented to one nostril (dichorhinic stimulation), the results are somewhat as in binocular rivalry. The two odors will be smelled in alternation. Whether this is a compelling result from some basic perceptual standpoint or merely a shift of attention is not certain. Some declare it is the latter, and should not be called rivalry. (4) It is also declared that two odors may be experienced simultaneously and yet separately. They may appear, according to Woodworth and Schlossberg (274), as a chord of musical tones, or as two separate but unrelated odors. Henning (116) declared that this last result is possible only with dichorhinic stimulation, whereas von Skramlik

(229) says that it can occur with the use of either the one or the two nostrils being involved. In fact, Skramlik says that all so-called dichorhinic effects can be obtained with a single nostril. (5) One odor may mask the other entirely, an effect that has already been discussed. (6) One odor may neutralize another. This, too, must be an effect taking place below the level of consciousness so that nothing appears in consciousness as an odor. There has not been complete agreement as to whether neutralization can occur, but the authorities who have declared it possible include those who have never been surpassed in carefulness.

COMMENTS

The literature in psychology that deals with the perceiving of odors and tastes seems to be lacking in the kind of experiments that characterize studies in vision, for example. In vision, not only are there many studies of sense-organ structure, neurophysiology of vision, and so on, but they also definitely relate the perceiver to his surrounds, and try to get at the purposiveness of the perceiver. Such studies attempt to relate purposiveness, set, motivation, and so forth to the nature of perceptual behavior. Up to now, the literature on taste and smell has largely been confined to the classification of simple tastes and simple smells. What is needed is a treatment of the role that tasting and smelling play in biological and personal economy.

Hazzard's study (106) comes closest to examining the role of olfaction in the economy of the individual. At least, it possesses possibilities in this direction. When it can be said that an odor is more than something sweet, or fragrant, but possesses qualities belonging to other sense modalities, one broadens the significance of the olfactory experience and shows how olfaction plays a broad role in the affairs of the individual.

Chapter 17

THE SENSES OF THE SKIN

The skin is the seat of three general forms of sensitivity. These are touch and pressure, temperature (cold and warm), and pain. Since it is the skin that forms the organism's largest sensitive surface, it is not surprising that it should contain the mechanisms of several sorts of sensitivity.

It was stated elsewhere that sense organs consist in two components, a nonneural as well as a neural portion. In line with this, the skin, exclusive of the neural elements embedded within it, constitutes one huge and continuous nonneural portion of a sense organ. The neural elements within the skin constitute the neural components of at least three types of sense organs: those for touch and pressure, those for temperature, and those for pain.

Geldard (82) points out that one of the most persistent problems in all sensory psychology is whether cold and warm experiences are manifestations of a single sense modality or should be considered as separate. Although it is obvious that the stimulus, namely, thermal activity, is a single dimension, it is not certain whether the mechanisms for the two experiences are two distinct mechanisms or parts of a single biological device. Two of the factors that tend to lead to the conclusion of separateness of modality are that the thresholds for warmth and cold are not similar and the skin spots for warmth and cold are different in distribution. The same spots are not the foci for the two experiences.

Such problems are not confined to the matter of warmth and cold, but are inherent in other sense modalities, vision, for example. We find different structures (receptors) for sensitivity to various parts of the spectrum. If we were to take the principle of "anatomical distinction" to its ultimate conclusion, we should not have a single sense of sight but a number of senses. If we ran dissimilarity of experience to its ultimate, we certainly would have separate senses for redness, blueness, yellowness, and so on. Geldard says that "despite the fact that the skin is, from the

355

evolutionary standpoint, the oldest of the sensitive tissues of the body, it has yielded up its secrets reluctantly."

The sense of "touch" or "feeling" was one of the five senses listed by Aristotle, and out of it all of the additional senses that have been added to the original five have emerged. Boring (29) listed the numerous sense qualities of feeling for which claim to independence has been made over the past several decades. These include contact, deep pressure, various forms of pain (prick pain, deep pain, quick pain), warmth, cold, heat, muscular pressure, tendinous strain, dizziness, sense of translation (vestibular sensation), hunger, appetite, thirst, nausea, sex, pulmonary sensation, cardiac sensation, and such others, for example, as itch, tickle, vibration, suffocation. It will be recalled that we earlier mentioned the criteria that have come to be adopted as the basis for isolating a sense modality. They were the existence of a unique sort of experience; a specific sort of stimulus, or at least the dependence upon a stimulus; and finally, a definite anatomical pathway and sense organ. If we scan this long but possibly partial list of the various modalities proposed, we can see first that all of the experiences are not related to a single form of stimulation, do not all involve the same sense organs, and are not similar in the experiences involved. Hence we have reason to subdivide the sense of feeling. By now there has come to be fair agreement that this classical category can be divided into the tactual sense, the pain sense, the temperature sense, and the vestibular and muscular senses. Skin, then, the original organ of touch or feeling, is the seat of three basic sense modalities: touch, pain, temperature. In stimulating one or more of these modalities, any one of four kinds of energy is effective: mechanical, thermal, electrical, and chemical.

THE STRUCTURE OF THE SKIN

The skin has more or less arbitrarily been divided into three layers: the *epidermis*, the *dermis* or corium, and the *subcutaneous tissue*. Each of these layers is far more complicated structurally than the average reader would suppose. Considerable could be said in the description of the layers. The only reason for our doing so would be to make concrete the statement that they are complex. The need for realizing that the tissues are complex rests upon the fact that tactile stimulation (primarily or usually mechanical) is a form of energy that distorts the shape of the tissue out of its usual resting form. Stimulation seems to come about by reason of the distortion. The more we could know about what mechanical

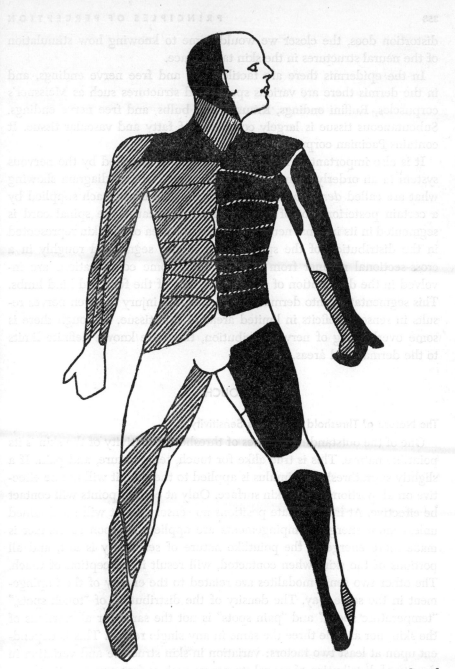

Fig. 17.1. Division of skin areas into dermatomes. These are named and numbered in accordance with nerve supply. Dermatomes overlap each other; hence the odd-numbered are shown on one side, and the even-numbered on the other. Labeling is omitted, however.

distortion does, the closer we would come to knowing how stimulation of the neural structures in the skin takes place.

In the epidermis there are tactile discs and free nerve endings, and in the dermis there are various specialized structures such as Meissner's corpuscles, Ruffini endings, Krause's end bulbs, and free nerve endings. Subcutaneous tissue is largely composed of fatty and vascular tissue. It contains Pacinian corpuscles.

It is also important to realize that the skin is supplied by the nervous system in an orderly segmented fashion. Fig. 17.1 is a diagram showing what are called *dermatomes*. These are the skin areas, each supplied by a certain posterior root of the spinal cord. Because the spinal cord is segmented in its internal neural structure, the area of the skin represented in the distribution of the spinal nerve is also segmented roughly in a cross-sectional manner from head to foot. Some complications are involved in the distribution of the innervations of the fore and hind limbs. This segmentation into dermatomes means that injury to given nerves results in sensory deficits in limited areas of skin tissue. Although there is some overlapping of nerve distribution, there are known definite limits to the dermatomal areas.

TOUCH

The Nature of Threshold Cutaneous Sensitivity

One of the outstanding features of threshold sensitivity of the skin is its pointlike nature. This is true alike for touch, temperature, and pain. If a slightly suprathreshold stimulus is applied to the skin, it will not be effective on all portions of the skin surface. Only at certain points will contact be effective. At intermediate positions no sensory result will be obtained unless more energetic impingements are applied. As soon as contact is made more energetic, the pointlike nature of sensitivity is lost, and all portions of the skin, when contacted, will result in perception of touch. The other two sense modalites are related to the energy of the impingement in the same way. The density of the distribution of "touch spots," "temperature spots," and "pain spots" is not the same for all portions of the skin, nor are the three the same in any single region. This is dependent upon at least two factors: variation in skin structure and variation in density of distribution of neural structures such as free nerve endings.

Although there seems at times to be some variation in the locale of these sensitive spots, their anatomical stability has been reported by various authorities. Dallenbach (*66*) has relocated certain pressure and cold spots after an interval of more than a decade. The pointlike nature of threshold sensitivity of the skin was discovered independently by three men at about the same time. They were Blix, in 1884, and Goldscheider and Donaldson, both in 1885. The method of von Frey, namely, the use of manually applied horsehair, long ruled as the technique for investigating tactile sensitivity. In more recent years several different investigators constructed electromechanical devices whereby tiny styli could be raised and lowered upon the skin with more or less uniform impact, and with precise timing. The instruments were called *kinohapts*. In this country, kinohapts have been used at Harvard, Cornell, the University of Kansas, Michigan State University, and the University of Chicago. Bishop (*24, 25, 26*), at Washington University Medical School, has used tiny electric sparks as cutaneous stimuli. This form of a stimulation avoids the production of momentary distortions of skin tissue. This mode of stimulation, being electrical, is able to elicit the complete gamut of basic skin perceptions: touch, pressure, pain, cold, and warmth.

Kinds of Tactile Experiences

The experience aroused by mechanical contact with the skin, usually called touch or pressure, is not always the same, and consequently a number of terms have arisen to label the variations. Among them, we have "contact," a lively and bright experience. "Deep pressure" is another, and it is dull and heavy. Some pressure experiences are pointlike, some dense, some diffuse, and some even granular. One of the differentiating features that stands out is the degree of superficiality vs. the degree of depth. Sometimes pressures are abrupt; others well up slowly. Apparently few, if any, cutaneous perception is simple in composition, so here we have some similarity to what was found for the experiences elicited nasally and orally. Pressure, then, seems to be patternwise, varying in timing, intensity, and spatial distribution. Aside from mere touch and contact, there are special experiences which we call tickle, itch, vibration, creep, and so on. Of course, impingements that are displaced along skin surfaces give rise to the experience of movement. Properly timed sequences of momentary stationary impingements also give rise to the experience of movement, called apparent movement.

For tactile experiences the most common stimulus is, of course, mechanical. Tiny masses (disks, styli, etc.) that are placed on the skin deform it to some extent or other. This deformation requires time. Gradients of skin deformation may be produced not only by applying the kind of impingement just mentioned, but may be produced, for example, by immersing one's finger in a vessel of quicksilver (mercury). Everywhere but at the juncture of the air and mercury the pressure on the finger will be equal. It is also there that the greatest changes in pressure occur as the finger is moved. The experience of contact will be felt at the air-mercury juncture, for it is there that the deformation gradient is located.

The most enlightening work in recent years on the fundamentals of the pressure or tactile sense was done by Nafe and Wagoner (195). They constructed a precision instrument whereby pressures could be manipulated, and whereby minute differences in the amount of deformation of the skin could be measured. Their stimuli consisted in a series of disks of various areas and of different masses. Their instrumentation measured and recorded the rate at which these disks sank into the skin by force of weight. Their subjects were instructed to indicate, by pressing a key, when they felt the pressure of the disk and when they did not feel it. It was found that so long as the disk's "rate of fall" into (depression of) the skin was above a certain value, the subject felt the disk's pressure. When this critical rate no longer was being reached, no experience of contact was produced. The common-sense viewpoint makes stimulation the mere contact of the disk with the skin. Nafe and Wagoner had to substitute for this the idea that stimulation consists in deforming the skin. Without the deformation process no stimulation occurs. They found that not only was the process of deformation necessary, but the process had to occur at or above a critical rate to constitute stimulation.

It is customary to speak of adaptation as the cessation or reduction of activity of a sensory mechanism, while supposed stimulation is held uniform. The final failure of the disk to be felt has long been considered tactual adaptation. Nafe and Wagoner had to attribute adaptation, not to sense-organ failure while stimulation was held constant, but rather to the termination of conditions which, in themselves, could be called stimulation. Hence, it could be said that what is ordinarily called tactile adaptation is not a sense-organ failure. One simply ceases to feel the disk when the process of stimulation ceases. On the other hand, if one must adhere to the older definition of adaptation, namely, that it is partial or total failure of the sense organ to be able to respond to stimulation, then our present tactile example is not adaptation. Nafe and Wagoner's concept of what is the stimulus, and why the disk finally ceases to be felt, is one that avoids the curious paradox of talking about a stimulus that does not stimulate. For that reason, among others, it seems to be a very fortunate way of envisaging the situation. Nafe and Wagoner's interpretation also coincides with the general notion we have expressed in several earlier places; namely, that sense organs are made up of two sorts of tissue: neural and nonneural. Adhering to this concept, it would be said that the skin that surrounds the free nerve endings, and other sensory endings, is a part of the tactual sense organ. Tactile stimulation consists, then, in doing something to the nonneural part of the tactual sense organ. According to this, the skin does not become exhausted by "stimulation" (the presence of the disk). We simply do not keep the disk moving and thus continually deforming the skin at a sufficient rate. When this is the case, we do not feel the disk.

Guilford and Lovewell (99) made a study on the tactile spots on the skin. It was based upon the fact that the more forcefully a stylus is applied to the skin, the more dense the distribution of the skin spots becomes. This relationship was implied in what was said earlier in this chapter.

Guilford and Lovewell's nine styli ranged from .01 to 1.60 gm. Each was applied to 200 equally distributed locations on a 1 sq. cm. area on the back of the hand. Fig. 17.2 gives the results. As pressure was increased, a greater and greater percentage of all the spots responded. The shape of the curve (sigmoid) represented the relation between impinge-

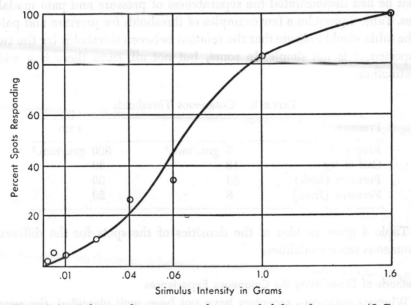

FIG. 17.2.   Relation of pressure on skin to probability of response (J. P. Guilford and E. M. Lovewell, Touch spots and the intensity of the stimulus, *J. Gen. Psychol.* [1936], *15*:149–159, Fig. 1).

ment intensity and density of spots. To some, this suggests that any unit area (spot) of the skin possesses some probability of responding to a given impingement of a given intensity.

Various calculations have been made concerning the minimal energy required for eliciting tactual experience. One author reported that 0.026 erg on the end of the thumb and 0.037 to 1.09 ergs on the tips of the fingers were threshold values. Putting threshold tactual values into comparison with visual and auditory thresholds, it may be said that one hundred million to ten billion times as much energy is required by touch as by the other two senses.

Von Frey reasoned that if there were two separate senses, touch (pressure) and pain, they ought to have separate thresholds. He believed that the threshold for the pressure experience should be lower than for pain. Accordingly, he carefully explored a restricted area of the skin on the subject's leg. In this area he found about 15 points, and they had a threshold of about 33 grams/mm². or less. He gradually raised the stimulus pressure and did not find any additional pressure spots. When a pressure of about 200 grams/mm². was reached, he began to elicit a pricking and painful experience. He also found that the distribution of the spots was different for the two experiences. From this he concluded that he had demonstrated the separateness of pressure and pain modalities. Table 3 provides a few examples of thresholds for pressure and pain. The table would indicate that the relation between thresholds for the two experiences is not simple. In some, but not all, cases there is a wide distinction.

TABLE 3.   Cutaneous Thresholds

Pressure		Pain
Fingertip	3 gm./mm.²	300 gm./mm.²
Calf of leg	16	30
Forearm (back)	33	30
Forearm (front)	8	20

Table 4 gives an idea of the densities of the spots for the different cutaneous sense modalities.

Methods of Dissociating the Cutaneous Experiences

Whereas cutaneous receptors have not been well identified, the separateness of the experiences and the pathways that subserve them have been dissociated in various ways. In fact, there are six ways by which the

TABLE 4. Spots per Unit Area (10 sq. cm.)

	Touch	Cold	Warm	Pain
Forehead	500	80	6	1840
Tip of nose	1000	130	10	440
Chest	290	90	3	1960
Volar forearm	150	60	4	2030

dissociation is brought about. (1) Local anesthesia. This is accomplished in several ways. Sometimes it is done by nerve block. To understand this sort of dissociation, as accomplished by Heinbecker Bishop and O'Leary (*111*), one must first be acquainted with their analysis of cutaneous modalities. They have disclosed, to their satisfaction, four forms of superficial cutaneous sensibility. They are touch, pricking touch, warmth, and cold. Pain is the experiential quality arising from suprathreshold stimulation of pathways of the pricking-touch modality. Perceptions of hot and burning arise from strong stimulation of warmth pathways. Deep cutaneous sensibility is made up of two modalities, pressure and pressure pain. Dissociation brought about by local anesthesia begins with effects upon the smallest nerve fibers and ends with the largest. The cutaneous sensibilities are obliterated in the following order: cold, warm, pain, and touch. Deep pain goes along with superficial pain, and deep pressure goes along with touch. Of course, upon the return of sensibility, as the anesthetic wears off, the reverse order is followed.

(2) The second form of dissociation is that involved in complete loss of sensibility through injury or through asphyxiation (mechanical pressure block). In asphyxia, the first experience obliterated is light pressure (touch). Thenceforth the order is somewhat opposite to that obtained by the use of anesthesia (cocaine and procaine block). (3) Dissociation is produced also by removing thin slices of skin. This layer-by-layer technique provides for certain sensibilities disappearing before others, touch being the first to go. (4) Reliably different chronaxies for warmth, cold, touch, and pain have been obtained. (5) Spinal anesthesia produces some dissociation of the cutaneous senses. Likewise, nicking the spinal cord (that is, severing certain portions of it) may stop pain and spare touch. (6) Various pathological conditions result in dissociation. One of the outstanding forms of pathology that achieves this is syringomyelia, a lesion that begins in the central gray matter of the spinal cord and moves toward the periphery. Pain is the first to disappear, while the other sensibilities are still intact. Warm and cold experiences go next, and

finally the sense of touch. This, of course, is because various sensory tracts are separate and one is reached by the disease before the others.

Tactual Localization

Our interest does not lie solely in where on the skin tactual impingements can be felt but also in where impingements that are made are perceptually localized. Do subjects feel the contacts to be made where they are made?

Renshaw and Wherry (218), among others, have addressed themselves to this problem. Renshaw (217) studied the ability of subjects to localize spots on the back of the nonpreferential hand and the flat surface of the volar forearm throughout a daily practice period ranging from 7 to 32 days, depending upon the subject. The subjects ranged from 8 to 65 years of age. Renshaw found rather large practice effects in both the young and old subjects. The children were not only more accurate than the adults but showed a more rapid reduction in magnitude of errors. During the first two days, the children localized the stimulus more accurately on the forearm than on the hand. The adults did just the opposite. Renshaw suggests that the poorer performance manifested by adults may be due to having handicapped the adults more than the children by the use of blindfolds in the experiment. The supposition here is that the adults' behavior is more dominantly visually controlled than that of the children. This idea was tested by using a different procedure than used in the foregoing experiment. Four subjects were chosen: two adults 28 and 58 years of age, and two boys 12 years of age. Two methods of reporting upon where the subjects had been contacted were used. One was the tactual-kinesthetic method of having the subjects quickly touch the spot felt to be the one. The other method was simply to look at the skin surface upon which a grid had been marked. In merely looking at the grid, the subjects were to answer as to which square in the grid had been contacted. Here we have a tactual-kinesthetic method and a visual method. The adults did better by the visual method, and the children did better by the other method. This was in the direction of a confirmation of Renshaw's idea that the dependence upon contact for tactual localization in children is substituted, as time goes on, by visual control of the performance. He suggests this substitution might occur near the age of puberty.

Renshaw, Wherry, and Newlin (219) studied tactual localization in congenitally blind children and adults in comparison with sighted young and old. They found the following: Blind adults are superior to blind children in tactual localization. Blind adults are likewise more accurate than sighted adults. Sighted children are superior to sighted adults. Sighted children are superior to blind children. Initial performance is better on forearm than hand for sighted children, but the opposite is true for all others. When the results of the blind are plotted agewise, the results of the adults are a projection of those of the children.

The inferiority of the sighted adults with reference to sighted children is thought to be due to the shift in the adults to dependence upon distance receptors in localization, that is, to vision.

Renshaw and Wherry (218) studied a group of subjects over an age range of 6 to 16 years to determine when ocular dominance in tactual localization sets in. They concluded that tactual-kinesthetic localization is superior to the visual from the eighth to the twelfth year. At this point, the difference vanishes. At puberty, there seems to be an increase in the accuracy for both methods. Between the thirteenth and fourteenth years, the visual method becomes superior. This superiority continues to become greater as age increases.

The authors point out that when the children use the visual method (their poorer method) and the adults use the tactual-kinesthetic method (their poorer method), there is no true difference between their results. This would nullify the Rivers-MacDougall law that states that sensory discrimination is inversely proportional to age and degree of civilization of a population.

The findings of Renshaw and colleagues bear on the findings of Bartley and colleagues obtained on children versus adults. In the study of the problem of whether children perceived block size in relation to distance from the eye, it was found that children did the same at all distances and made smaller or fewer errors than adults. Putting all the information available together, it would seem to indicate that the children did not use visual imagery, at least to the same extent as the adults, and that visual imagery was responsible for the size-distance effect found in adults.

The Tau Effect

The tactile sense may be used to demonstrate one of the most fundamental principles we have in the process of stimulation. This is that both time and place are involved in defining or specifying stimulation. Tactual impingement not only reaches the skin at some *place* but does so at some *time*. It makes a difference, then, both in terms of time and place, what the end result will be.

Helson and King (*115*) performed experiments some years ago upon a phenomenon called the *tau* effect. They called it this because they did not want its name confused with those of other phenomena. The tau effect was demonstrated by contacting the skin in three places in temporal succession. To make the following description more understandable, refer to Fig. 17.3. The points A, B, and C are the three points of contact

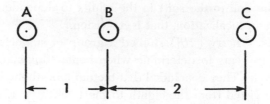

FIG. 17.3.   The arrangement of spots contacted on the skin to produce the tau effect.

on the skin. The distance on the skin from A to B marks off space interval 1, and the distance from B to C marks off space interval 2. The task of the subject, who was blindfolded, was to report upon which of the two intervals was the larger. Or he could just as well have been asked whether space interval 2 was larger or smaller than interval 1.

The authors used an instrument called a *kinohapt* (see Fig. 17.4) to make contact with the skin at A, B, and C. The results of their study will be given after we have made clear the possible manipulations in such an experience.

There are several possibilities with regard both to spacing and timing. A and C can be equidistant from B lying between them, or A can be nearer or farther away than C from B. The same possibilities hold true for the timing of the contacts. A, B, and C can be presented so that there is an equal interval between A and B, and B and C. Or else the first time interval can be made longer or shorter than the second. Of course, the timing and spacing can be related to each other in various ways.

For purposes of explanation, let us start with space intervals 1 and 2 equal, but with the time interval 1 longer than interval 2. The subject is likely to report that the space interval 1 is the longer. This effect can still be maintained when space interval 2 is made longer than 1. The procedure is to determine how much longer time interval 1 must be than time interval 2 to have the space intervals appear equal. As one makes

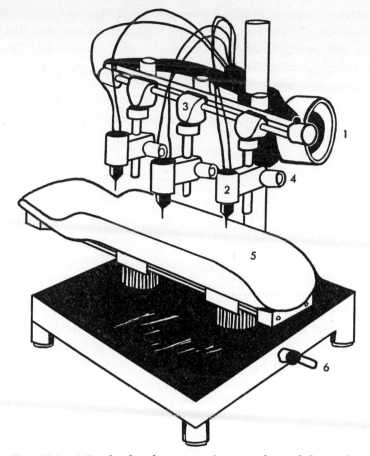

FIG. 17.4. A Bartley kinohapt—an electromechanical device for contacting the skin with tiny styli, with precise pressures and time relations. Item 1 is the knob for adjusting the whole carriage vertically; 2 is one of the solenoids activating a stylus; 3 is a solenoid carriage adjustable horizontally; 4 is a knob adjusting a single solenoid vertically; 5, the arm rest, adjustable in all directions; 6, the arm-rest lock.

the time intervals unequal, he must also make the space intervals unequal in the opposite direction.

We can now turn to some of the findings of Helson and King, which are summarized in Table 5. In it, the first column shows time interval 1 divided by time interval 2. In the third column, space interval 2 is divided by space interval 1.

In the second and fourth columns, the ratios of columns 1 and 3 are given. These are the ones found necessary by Helson and King to make space intervals 1 and 2 appear equal. This means that for the time intervals 500 and 200 msec. the space intervals were 30 and 50 mm., respectively. That is, while the time intervals were to each other as 2.5 to 1, the space intervals were not quite the actual reciprocal, but rather 1 to 1.67. To make the two spaces appear equal, it took time compensation. The time compensation in milliseconds was greater than would be expected in simple reciprocity.

TABLE 5.   Time and Space Intervals

t^1/t^2	Ratio	S_2/S_1	Ratio
500/200 msec.	2.5	50/30	1.67
500/250 msec.	2.0	45/30	1.50
500/300 msec.	1.67	40/30	1.33
500/350 msec.	1.43	35/30	1.20
500/400 msec.	1.25	30/30	1.00

According to the common outlook, the tau effect is a *time-space illusion*. But it is to be recognized that the results were perfectly according to law and depended upon the operation of time and space factors in neural activity.

To see how certain variations of the procedure work, we turn again to Helson and King. Instead of using contacts A, B, and C in a straight line, they were used as the corners of an equilateral triangle. With this new and very different arrangement, manipulation of the timing, as the contact sequence was followed through, changed the apparent shape of the triangle to one having unequal sides. Also, the authors contacted two points instead of three, but in the following order: A, B, A. When the timing was different in going from A to B than from B back to A, it did not seem that it was A that was being contacted upon return. By this result, it was shown that a given point on the skin does not possess, in itself, some unique property whereby it is localized. The point lies in a cutaneous field, controlled by both spatial and temporal factors. Helson and King's investigation was a demonstration of the fallacy of Lotze's theory of *local signs*, in which it was asserted that every point on the skin possesses its own unique and sufficient characteristics for being localized when stimulated.

We must remember that time and space are operants of two sorts for us. In the one case they are *concepts* that are applicable to operations performed or processes observed. In introducing the tau effect, we said that stimulation involves places on the skin and places in the nervous system at which processes take place. We said that the processes that occurred, occurred in time, and that the relative timing of several neural processes controlled the perceptual end result.

Space and time are to be looked upon, also, as something *perceived*. There are spatial and temporal features of perception. Helson and King's study involved space and time in both ways. Once we see how space and time are involved in neural processes, it is not so surprising to see them involved in perceptual response (experience).

Apparent Movement

It will be recalled from Chapter 11 that movement was sometimes produced by the use of stationary stimuli. Movement produced in that way was called apparent movement. Most of the study of apparent movement has been conducted in vision. Tactual stimuli produce the experience of movement also when properly timed and spaced. To produce this experience, it is only necessary to apply two styli to the skin in quick succession with, of course, the proper time interval between. The experience produced will be that of something being dragged across the skin. The distance involved in the dragging experience will, of course, depend upon time and intensity conditions of stimulation. This is a true tactual experience.

There is another kind of apparent movement produced by tactual stimuli that is not really tactual. It is called *bow movement*, and is the experience of an object beginning to move from one position on the skin to another; but instead of dragging across the skin, the "something" makes an arc or bow into the air and retouches the skin only at the end of its excursion. Obviously this experience is elicited by tactual stimuli and for that reason it is likely to be called a tactual experience. For further discussion of tactual apparent movement, see Chapter 11.

WARMTH AND COLDNESS

We come now to the second sense modality—temperature. The reservation should be held in mind, however, that temperature may involve two modalities, namely, those of warmth and cold. For simplicity's sake, we shall consider the temperature experiences as making up a single modality and proceed on that basis. Our first question then is, What are the stimulus conditions for eliciting the experiences of warmth and coldness?

Stimulus Conditions

Electrical as well as thermal impingements activate both "warm" and "cold" spots of the skin. Manipulation of thermal conditions, since they are the usual ones the individual encounters, will be the first to receive our attention. It was discovered before the turn of the century that thermal impingements, spoken of as warm stimuli, sometimes produce the experience of cold. This is, of course, an unexpected result and thus is paradoxical. The experience elicited in this way has been called *paradoxical cold*. Paradoxical cold is, of course, produced not by activating warm spots by "warm stimuli" but by activating cold spots by "warm stimuli." It was found that a decidedly high temperature of stylus was necessary to obtain this result. It required a temperature of 45° C. (113° F.). As contrasted to this, a stylus of 33° C. (91° F.) will usually be high enough to elicit warmth. To obtain paradoxical cold, the stylus must not be one contacting much surface, except under special circumstances. With extensive contact, warm spots are also activated and the experience of warmth is the net result. If, however, the skin is first well warmed up, let us say to 45° C., and then stimulation at 48° C. is applied, cold will be the first experience, with later a little bit of warmth showing up. The present explanation lies in the adaptation of warm spots to warm stimulation and the consequent unmasked activity of the cold spots.

What has already been said about the means whereby paradoxical cold is elicited is to be taken as a basis for saying that a moderately high thermal impingement tends to activate both warm and cold receptors. In fact, it is quite commonly stated that it is the arousal of both types of receptors that gives rise to the experience of heat (hotness).

Paradoxical warmth has been claimed by several workers; but whatever can be said about it, it is very much more difficult to achieve. One author believed that slight warmth could be elicited by contact of a stimulus about 0.1 to 1.5° C. below physiological zero. Another put the range at from 6 to 10° C. below physiological zero. No one has yet established just what the necessary and sufficient conditions are for the paradoxical experience, if it really can be produced.

It has already been implied by what has been said that the actual temperature of the skin has something to do with the thermal experience produced by contact of some specific impingement. This is definitely the case, and impinging styli that are exactly the same temperature as the skin do not elicit warmth or cold. The temperature of the skin is called *physiological zero*.

Alrutz, many years ago, scaled the experiences produced by contact styli above physiological zero, as follows:

At the first thermal threshold	Experience of slightest warmth
Above this threshold	Marked warmth
At paradoxical cold threshold	A kind of warmth called heat
Above this threshold	Heat resembling cold
At next higher (pain) threshold	Burning heat
Above this	Pain itself

Lowenstein and Dallenbach (*166*) studied these thresholds on 100 subjects at a room temperature of 20–25° C. (68–77° F.). In this investigation, the experience of heat was produced by styli at 40–46° C. (104–114.8° F.). The average was close to 43° C. (about 109° F.).

A unique way to produce the experience of heat is by the *synthetic method*. This method involves the use of a "heat grill." This consists of a set of small copper tubes in which alternate parallel tubes carry water at different temperatures. The one set of tubes taken by itself would be experienced as warm; the other would be cold. This arrangement tends first to produce an experience of cold, then of heat, and then a possible return of cold. To say the least, heat is produced by this method without the use of high-temperature stimuli.

Woodworth and Schlossberg (*274*) point out that the elicitation of paradoxical cold and synthetic heat are by no means the most frequent results when making thermal explorations of the skin. Only two of Jenkins' (*129*) subjects out of four reported paradoxical effects at all and then only 27 times out of 9000 observations. Geldard (*82*), on the other hand, states that paradoxical perceptions of cold are produced commonly enough in mapping warm spots.

The explanation for divergence in effects when several observers place their wrists upon a metal grid, in which alternate rods are of different temperatures of suitable values, has to do with the observer's set and with his quickness of responses. There are those who retract their hand quickly as though burned. There are others who are slower. They report heat. And there are still others who report warmth and cold. The time required for the experience to emerge is shorter for cold than for warmth, and warmth emerges before pain. For those observers set for heat and thus drawing their hand away quickly, all that would occur are the ordinary processes for cold and warmth, but heat would be reported. For those who keep their wrists on the grid a little longer, the distinctions between cold and warm would likely be experienced for what they are.

Theories of Temperature Sensitivity

Since we are not concerned as much with bodily mechanisms in this text as would be the case in texts in physiological psychology, or those solely on the senses, we shall not spend much effort on theories of temperature sensitivity. We are rather concerned with the personal behavior that stems from stimulation of sense organs.

The classical theory of temperature sensitivity rests mainly on the supposed correspondence between distribution of sensitivity and distribution of certain end organs. Attempts to correlate structure and function have not been very rewarding. At present we cannot say for sure which form of specialized ending subserves the function of the temperature experiences.

A much more recent theory of thermal sensitivity is that of Nafe (192). It can be called a neurovascular theory. He believes that the smooth-muscle walls of the blood vessels of the skin, arterioles, for example, are responsible for thermal experience. In their walls there are free nerve endings, button-formed endings, and terminal loops. It is supposed that contraction and relaxation of the vessel walls activate these endings in appropriate ways. The resulting neural activity is utilized by the central nervous system to provide the ultimate experiences of warmth and cold. This amounts to saying, then, that temperature perceptions are a form of kinesthetic or muscle-induced experiences. Nafe rests his case upon the reports of various investigators to the effect that smooth muscle is thermally sensitive, relaxing in certain upper-temperature ranges and contracting in ranges below them. Much of what is proposed in Nafe's neurovascular theory is quite convincing; nevertheless, his theory does not at once tell us why the distribution of the two kinds of temperature spots is different. The best we can say is that at present the understanding of the mechanisms responsible for temperature sensitivity leaves considerable to be desired. Geldard (82) leaves the way open for the possibility that nerve tissue is directly sensitive to thermal conditions, and therefore no specialized nerve endings may be needed for mediating temperature experiences.

Contact and Radiant Stimulation

So far, we have been reporting results from thermal stimulation through contact. Thermal effects can be transmitted to the skin not only by contact but by radiation. These two methods lead to different results. It seems that warmth cannot be experienced at all when restricted areas of radiant impingement are used. When skin areas of less than 700 sq.

mm. are radiated, pain is experienced when radiation is strong enough to elicit any experience. When contact styli are used, areas as small as a single sq. mm. or even less may be effective in eliciting warmth. Whether this distinction has some meaning in the economy of the organism is not known, although the question is a worth-while one to ask for those who are interested in perception.

In line with what was just said about large areas being required for the effectiveness of thermal radiators, it can be said that spatial summation is characteristic for this form of stimulation. The energy per unit of skin area needed to produce threshold results is much less for two regions than for one alone. Summation is marked enough to show up when these two areas are represented by the backs of the two hands. It is not equivalent for all portions of the skin. This is shown by the fact that two regions, if one is hand and the other is forehead, will not summate to the same extent as if the two regions are on the two hands, respectively.

Detection of Thermal Conditions in the Surrounds

One of the functions of the temperature sense is to "inform" the organism of the thermal nature of its surrounds. The surrounds are made up of three kinds of thermal conditions. One is the set of conditions that involve *radiation,* either to or from the organism. Sources of radiant energy, such as fires, lamps, stoves, the sun, radiate to the body. Other situations involve the very opposite by reason of the fact that the body is definitely higher in temperature than its surrounds. The second thermal condition or process is that of *convection,* and it is carried on by air currents. The organism is obviously sensitive to this form of thermal effect. The third process is that of *conduction,* and it is the transfer of heat by contact.

All three of these conditions are encountered by the organism in its moment-to-moment activities, and when near-equilibrium thermal conditions exist there is no conscious realization of temperature on the part of the organism. It is only as optimal or equilibrium conditions are departed from that awareness of warmth or cold arises.

The avoidance of thermal extremes through radiation convection and conduction cannot be well handled by reflex activity. There must be the participation of the cerebral cortex, for it is the cortex that is involved in direction of the overall purposive higher-order processes of the organism. Were reflex processes to handle all the avoidance processes, or the warmth- or cold-seeking processes of the organism, very curious behavior would be exhibited. The organism would be in conflict. The purposive activity would be working toward a certain end and would be "pulling" in one way, and the reflex activity would be manifested in another. This opposition does emerge in extreme cases even with body organization as it is. An individual may be dreaming or otherwise preoccupied and happen to touch something "hot." Reflex activity takes priority and a very simple but effective form of behavior momentarily takes over. The individual jerks his hand away from the hot region. This alleviates the trouble. Extreme thermal conditions no longer are acting on the hand; and unless burning has occurred, the cortically guided purposive processes are resumed. The action that occurred is called reflexive because it was definite, almost unvarying, very compelling, and occurred without prior awareness of the need for the act.

Less extreme conditions can be "tolerated" by the organism, and the awareness of need for responses to these conditions breaks in slowly and easily upon the individual, and he makes adjustments that are integrated with whatever else he is doing at the time. It is like being called to dinner. One responds when he finishes what he is doing at the instant, and in this way there is no manifestation of a sheer "automatic" form of relation between the call and the ensuing response.

Although, as it was previously pointed out, pointlike radiation to the skin is ineffective in producing perception of warmth, large skin areas are extremely sensitive to radiation. Certain authors reported that only a trivial radiation playing onto the forehead produced the experience of warmth. An increase in radiation intensity of only .0014 calorie per square centimeter per second, inducing a rise in skin temperature of only .003° C., was felt as warmth.

Solids with which the body comes in contact vary widely in their property of conducting heat. We experience the difference in the way common solids feel to the touch. A stone bench is colder in winter and hotter in summer than a wooden bench. This is because of a difference in thermal conductivity. Metals are among the coldest and hottest of objects. The conductivity of silver is about 18,000 times as great as the air. Cotton is about seven times as conductive and glass is about 44 times as conductive as air. Hence, the way these substances feel could be expected to be quite different in various circumstances.

Regulation of Body Temperature

The organism employs the temperature sense apparatus in the reflex regulation of internal processes involved in stable body-temperature maintenance. This activity is in general spoken of as homeostatic and reflexive.

It is easy for one to think of temperature regulation of the body as being solely a vegetative (vital) process carried on by reflex mechanisms and thus very different from perception. It may be recalled, however, that in an earlier chapter (page 25 f.) reflexes were classed as perceptual responses, if and when they involved the cerebral cortex and were immediate discriminatory responses to environmental conditions. Temperature regulation is an instant-to-instant response to environmental conditions and, at least at times, involves the cerebral cortex and is discriminatory. When so, it is a form of perceptual response.

The regulation of body temperature is better understood when the matter is thought of as a system of exchanges of heat back and forth between the body and its surrounds. In this there are four factors: metabolism that produces heat, evaporation that always transfers heat from the body, convection that either takes away from or gives heat to the body, and radiation that also may cause the body to lose or gain heat.

The human environment is divided functionally into three different temperature ranges. The upper range is called the range of *vasomotor and evaporative regulation*. This runs down to about 86° F. Below this, for a distance of about 4° F., there is a *neutral or transitional* zone. Below this transitional zone, the range is spoken of as the cold range, or the *zone of body cooling*. This zone begins at about 82° F. These values pertain to unclothed resting subjects and, of course, do not represent environmental temperatures applying when clothes are worn and active body movement is occurring.

In the range of vasomotor and evaporative regulation, the blood sent to the skin and superficial tissues increases with environmental temperature. Evaporation from the body also rises, but not in any simple or uniform fashion, with temperature. Skin temperature rises only a little. Body heat loss slowly increases. It turns out that even though a working equilibrium of body temperature is maintained under such environmental conditions, personal comfort diminishes.

In the neutral or transitional zone, heat loss is well adjusted for by shifts of blood to or from peripheral tissues by vasoconstriction and vasodilation. Personal comfort is at its maximum, and heat loss by the combination of the several means already listed is at its maximum. Perhaps it is some feature of this rate of heat loss that is effective in giving the maximum body comfort. This sort of perception would, in a large part, be mediated by the temperature sense organs.

In the cold range, some authorities say, no regulation of heat loss occurs. The body loses heat just as does any inanimate mass of substance. If one is cold under such circumstances, he must seek a new environment, put on more clothes, become more active physically, or do something that directly changes metabolic rate. Individuals vary greatly in their degree of comfort or discomfort under given low-temperature conditions.

Since humidity conditions of the atmosphere alter the rate of evaporation from the human body, humidity figures largely in human comfort and in the efficiency with which body temperature regulation is carried on.

One of the most recent investigations that seems to bear on the role that the temperature sense mechanism plays in body heat regulation is the following. Benjamin, Wagner, Ihrig, and Zeit (21) cooled a group of canine subjects from 100° F. to 80° in twenty minutes by leading the animals' blood from the carotid artery to an outside cooling system and back again. That is, the animals were made to circulate their own blood through an outside cooling system while they were in a room of normal temperature. This manner of cooling was accomplished without the usual unfavorable symptoms of cardiac fibrillation, shivering, and other shock manifestations. In some cases the temperature was reduced to the point of complete stoppage of the heart. The animals were rewarmed by using the outside system to rewarm the blood. When return from the low temperatures reached a certain point, heart activity returned. When the animals were warmed up to 90° F., they were able to go on from there. That is, they reached their original temperatures without further artificial warming.

The point we wish to make is this. Under ordinary cooling conditions, the cooling is done by putting the animal's body in a cool environment. That is, the body is made to cool from the surface inward. In the technique just described, the cooling was accomplished via the blood stream and was thus a uniform way of producing the temperature reduction.

It would seem that this second way of cooling in effect by-passed the temperature sense mechanism. That is, cooling was accomplished without activating this mechanism. If so, then the avoidance or omission of shivering and other systemic manifestations could be attributed to this avoidance. The facts suggest, then, that the temperature sense plays the initiating role in activating certain compensatory reactions to cooling. If cooling goes on in spite of the initial compensatory reactions, still more drastic reactions set in. If cooling by-passes the reaction-initiating system (the temperature sense), it can be accomplished without much, if any, harm to the organism. Obviously, unaided Nature could not work this way. Animals must, if they are to survive, "kick up a fuss" about being subjected to untoward situations. If, on the other hand, the same agency that subjects the organism to the otherwise unfavorable condition avoids activating the alarm mechanism and also takes care that the animal is restored to normal, then the whole procedure goes along reasonably well and in a manner very different than we should expect from our common-sense background.

Physical Conditions and Comfort

Winslow, Herrington, and Gagge (265) studied relations between physiological conditions, such as sweating, physical conditions (temperature and humidity), and the feeling of body comfort.[1]

The investigators used a five-point scale, varying from very unpleasant to very pleasant, by which the subjects indicated their feelings under various conditions imposed. It was found that as relative humidity increases, the environmental temperature at which distinct pleasantness is lost drops somewhat. The zone of perceptual indifference narrows as relative humidity becomes greater. For example, whereas with between 25 and 70 percent of moisture content on the skin the indifferent zone was exhibited by a temperature range between 104.5 and 92° F., with dry air. The range shifted and narrowed as humidity rose. When relative humidity rose to 50 percent, the indifferent range lay between 95 and 89.5° F.

A number of facts are known regarding the various environmental conditions for personal comfort, but we cannot give them here. A great many more facts need yet to be determined in this area, and the job is awaiting the investigators who are, among other things, well trained in dealing with human perception.

PAIN

Painful experiences are the third general kind that can be elicited by doing something to the skin. Naturally, the usual stimulus for touch is mechanical. The stimulus for warm and cold is thermal. The stimulus for pain may be thermal, or it may be mechanical. In the laboratory,

[1] Perhaps we should say personal comfort here; for although we "project" the comfort to the body, it is the organism-as-a-person that is or is not comfortable.

electrical stimuli are used for the most precise study of all the skin senses, for such stimuli can be graded and timed more exactly. Shorter durations of applications can also be achieved.

We find again that with threshold stimulation the skin is pointlike in nature for the pain experience. The reader must hold in mind the idea that cutaneous experiences which he is acquainted with are not summations of points, but rather effects brought about by more intense and more extended impingements. These set extensive cutaneous mechanisms into action. Laboratory experiments must of necessity be analytical, and to be so they must explore thresholds for tiny skin areas.

Bishop and colleagues (23, 24, 25, 26, 110, 111) have studied the relations between cutaneous sensations and precise stimulation more extensively than any other investigators. Hence in our discussion of the analysis of pain, we shall follow Bishop quite closely.

One of Bishop's investigations (24) disclosed what he called a "peripheral unit for pain." This unit can be conceived of as the tiny skin area served mainly by a certain branching nerve fiber. Anywhere within this skin area a weak stimulation will elicit a kind of sensation, depending upon actual intensity. The threshold will be lower in the center of the area than at the periphery. It must be cautioned, however, that the skin area does not correspond to any well-defined describable anatomical nerve-ending distribution to which a specific pain experience can be assigned. Peripheral units thus overlap each other, and it takes careful exploration to detect any behavior that would lead to the concept of the peripheral unit for pain.

The sensory experiences arising from the activation of a peripheral unit for pain vary in keeping with the nature of the stimulation applied. Bishop's stimulation consisted in trains of tiny electric shocks which he could vary in intensity and in rate of delivery to the skin. These factors determined various rates and durations of afferent neural discharge to the central nervous system. The perceptual experiences that resulted differed, accordingly, in both qualitative and quantitative properties.

At the lowest threshold, an "inconsequential" touch experience is elicited; at a little higher threshold, a pricking experience is elicited; and with certain specifications of stimulation, itch and/or pain ensues. The pricking experience does not become painful when stimulus intensity is raised. Pain is something distinct from prick. It is as if the central nervous system utilizes the stronger stimulation in a different way after a certain intensity level is once reached.

If two skin units are stimulated concurrently, or by alternate bursts of electric shocks, a two-point discrimination between them is possible. That is, the two separate loci, each being stimulated, do not summate into pain. Some adjacent points, when stimulated, result in a masking effect. That is, they neither summate nor are they recognized as two separate spots.

The electrical threshold for the prick endings we have been discussing is lower than for touch endings, and this precludes complicating the experiment by stimulation of the true tactile sense, at least at threshold. However, shocks strong enough to induce pain may elicit nonpainful touch. Touch is more sharply localized than pain. Even so, one might ask the question whether pain and touch are not unavoidably confusable. Bishop (23, 24, 25) points out that the two are distinguishable by differences in their temporal characteristics. Touch is "deadbeat." That is, a separate brief experience occurs to each shock. Prick and pain, in contrast, are persistent and rise gradually rather than abruptly to maximum. A ten-per-second rate of administration of shocks to a touch spot will not summate or induce a fused sensory end result. On the other hand, pain from such stimuli will rise to its maximum only after five or six shocks have been delivered. Pain also persists for almost a second following the cessation of stimulation. Thus shocks at a ten-per-second rate are, in a way, a single continuous stimulus rather than many separate ones. The maximally sensitive skin areas (skin spots) for pain and touch are generally not identical in location. If a maximally sensitive spot for pain is stimulated, touch will generally not be aroused by the range of stimulus intensities used.

From what has been said, then, it will be seen that pain spots are identifiable and the results of stimulating them are distinguishable from the results of using similar stimuli upon nearby skin areas identified as touch or temperature spots.

Experiential end results elicited by activation of the mechanisms giving pain are at their lowest thresholds not painful, but rather have a pricking quality by no means describable as pain. Pain is elicited only by more intense and/or longer trains of stimuli.

The analysis of pain mechanisms, pain qualities, or pain thresholds by this precise electrical method gives somewhat different impressions to the experimenter than he gets from mechanical or similar methods. In all cases, however, the investigator ends up with the conclusion that he is dealing with a different mechanism than is involved in producing tactile or thermal experiences.

Special Forms of Pain

The usual textbook presentation of pain ends when a good description of what has been found out by topical explorations of the skin has been given. We shall not stop there; we have something to say about pain in tissues other than the skin, and about pain in the economy of the human individual.

Much of the pain which the average individual suffers is localized *within* the body. It is this noncutaneous pain that possesses the greatest significance in the life and economy of the individual.

Looked at from one standpoint, the study of pain is just a considera- tion of one of the several forms of body sensitivity that have been in- vestigated in the laboratories of sensory physiology and psychology. Not too much is yet known about it except the kind of facts mentioned in the previous section. Looked at in another way, the subject of pain is one of the most important in all psychology, for it is through pain that most of the bodily derangements are expressed. It is in this form that such trou- bles are made known to the individual himself. It is through the nature and location of pains that much of medical diagnosis is made possible. Moreover, pain is in a way a personality expression. Some individuals experience pain for which medical men can find no bodily correlate. It behooves psychologists to give serious attention to the subject of pain.

Although the word *pain* is widely used, it is not a term that has as precise a meaning as could be desired. Accordingly, very subtle problems arise in its use in both scientific and professional circles. In the previous portion of the chapter, pain was dealt with as simply one of the several sense modalities we possess. Attention was given to the peripheral struc- tures that when activated give rise to afferent impulses sent to the central nervous system, and eventuate in peculiar unpleasant or even distressing experiences. There are specific pathways from the skin and other tissues up the spinal cord to the brain that carry the impulses about which we are talking. But this is not all. Activation of pain nerve endings does not always end in the same distressing experience. Modification of function in central nervous tissue alters the end result considerably, so that something that can be identified as pain is, rather, devoid of qualities usually attributed to pain. On the other hand, distress may be experienced that is out of proportion to what would be expected from the minute peripheral disturbance. In this connection, a distinction must be made between the peculiar and bizarre forms of pain originating from central nervous trauma and the exaggerations or distortions in pain originating from cortical functioning for which no lesions can be found. Such is the case in various individuals with distorted personalities, or in peculiar forms of stress.

To say the very least, these facts present a broad problem that needs careful consideration, and consistent effort must be made toward arriving at a logically acceptable formulation of all the interrelated end results which we have just briefly sketched.

Our first consideration is to be given to forms of pain for which something bodily can be and has been found to account for. So-called simple pain, that which arises from the activation of certain end organs in the skin, has already been discussed. The forms to be dealt with here are the special forms that are met with in everyday life and are much more impressive than the incidental pains experienced from day to day.

The four kinds of pain that are to constitute the topics for this section are *headache, spontaneous pain, referred pain,* and those that are spoken of as due to *neuritis.* In this latter class, it is possible to include neuralgia, although it, at times, seems to be partially a form of central pain.

Headache is, of course, intracranial pain. All that is to be said about it is based upon this distinction. Nevertheless, the origins of headaches are so complex and poorly understood that it is possible they possess something in common with other forms which we are in the process of distinguishing.

Spontaneous pain, sometimes called *central pain,* is to be distinguished from other forms by the fact that its origin does not seem to be the stimulation of sense organs. In fact, it is attributed to lesions in the central nervous system itself.

Referred pain is still another kind of phenomenon inasmuch as its origins generally do lie in the activation of peripheral tissue, though the localization of the experience is at some site removed from the point of stimulation.

Neuritis involves a form of pain originating, presumably, from an abnormal condition of the nerve sheath.

HEADACHE. One of the commonest and most distressing forms of pain is headache. Since headache is a form of human experience, it should be considered by psychologists. Headaches can be dealt with from the standpoint of what apparently causes them. They arise not only from malfunctioning body mechanisms but also from nondisease origins, such as personal conflict. This is tacitly recognized in the everyday use of the term "headache" as a symbol for nuisance and other forms of personal trouble.

Our first task is to discover the body mechanisms most immediately underlying headache. This is somewhat easier to do than to determine the many conditions which set into motion chains of events leading to the immediate conditions underlying this form of pain. One of the most direct attacks of the problem consists in determining what intracranial structures give rise to pain when they are disturbed in any way.

Penfield (208) has found that the dural sinuses[2] are particularly sensitive to pressure, traction, heat, and electrical stimulation. Disturbance of the middle meningeal artery and its dural branches likewise gives rise to pain. Cerebral vessels in general are insensitive except for an occasional vein near a dural sinus or low in a brain fissure. The skull and the brain are themselves insensitive to cutting and to electrical stimulation.

Regardless of the types of stimulation used, the only forms of experience that can be elicited from within the cranial cavity are pain or pressure. The individual usually calls his experience that of headache, pressing ("splitting") pain, or sharp pain. Pain elicited from adequate disturbance of the meningeal arteries is usually sharp and fairly restricted in locality. Pain elicited by action on the dural sinuses is generally referred to another part of the head.

Clark, Hough, and Wolff (60) produced headaches by the administration of histamine and measured both the cerebrospinal fluid pressure and the blood pressure within the cranium.

They concluded that the headache following the giving of histamine is produced by the difference in the behavior of the blood vessels inside the cranium and elsewhere in the body. Systemic (body) blood pressure is raised, but the cerebral blood vessels dilate and consequently are less able to absorb pressure changes of the arterial pulse. These mechanical changes are thus left to affect more intensely the sense organs in the vessel walls. The authors suggest that the same mechanism operates when various vasodilators, such as amyl nitrite, carbon monoxide, and foreign proteins, are taken into the body. Clark, Hough, and Wolff found that raising the arterial pressure or lowering the cerebrospinal pressure during headache intensified the pain. Likewise, raising the cerebrospinal pressure or lowering the arterial pressure decreased the pain. From this,

---

[2] The brain is covered by two connective tissue sheaths, the *dura mater,* generally called the dura, being one of them. Sinuses are pockets or cavities. Dural sinuses are pockets formed at the junctures between the medial and transverse partitions in the dura that we have just described. These sinuses are part of the venous circulation system and are thus filled with blood that ultimately empties into the internal jugular vein. The sinuses thus drain the blood from the brain. They represent portions of the dura that mechanically would likely to be most subject to stress, owing (1) to variations in blood pressure, and (2) to the fact that they lack the solid masses of brain tissue on both sides, as elsewhere along the dural partitions.

it would seem that those adjustments which returned the relationships between the pressures on the two sides of the arterial walls toward the normal balance reduced pain. This seems to be true regardless of whether or not the vessel walls are dilated.

CENTRAL OR SPONTANEOUS PAIN. In most cases, spontaneous pain has been attributed to lesions in the thalamus. Early in the century, Head and Holmes, two outstanding men in brain pathology, believed that the thalamus was responsible for the feeling tone that accompanies visceral and somatic sensation. This doctrine has since become quite widespread. However, more recently, other evidence has indicated that lesions in the spinal cord, cerebrum, medulla, or even in peripheral regions, as well as those in the thalamus, can cause spontaneous pain.

It has been reported that cranial nerve lesions produced "burning sensations" localized along the distributions of the nerve. Certain spinal-cord lesions were accompanied not only by central pain but also by vibratory sensations and distorted thermal sensations (cold being called hot).

In two cases, for example, in which no thalamic lesions were found, but in which there were lesions in the parietal cortex, central pain existed. This was associated with the impairment of deep pressure and tactile sensations. In most of the cases reported by these two authors, spontaneous pain was associated with lesions involving incomplete destruction of the spinothalamic tract.

It would seem, then, that lesions in a variety of locations might be expected to result in central pain. Further study may tend to show, however, that although central pain and distortions in sensation may result, lesions in the thalamus result in somewhat different effects than lesions elsewhere.

REFERRED PAIN. We have already seen that in the conditions producing headache the principle of *reference* (discrepancy between locus of stimulation and locus of sensation) is at work. When the dural sinuses were mechanically disturbed, the pain was felt not in the sinuses but elsewhere. Part of this apparent reference could possibly be brought about by mechanical effects being transmitted to tissue distant from the point of application. This is not, however, the general interpretation in these cases.

Referred pain, as commonly spoken of, has generally to do with pains felt in the body wall when the disturbance lies in the visceral organs. One of the most marked origins of this form of pain is the heart, as in the production of *angina pectoris*. In this affliction, the pains are not localized in the heart, but include these intermittent pains ranging from dull oppressive sensations to severe intolerable pain about the sternum, often radiating to arms, throat, and face. Many "heart pains," however, have no relation to the heart or its blood supply, but are common phenomena in high-strung, overworked individuals and may be related to the vague state called "nervous hyperirritability."

The neural pathways for referred pain have not as yet been delineated with satisfactory certainty. Among the routes suggested are:

1. Visceral and somatic impulses may lead into a common neuron in the spinal cord. The combined innervation would tend to make many subthreshold excitations from the body rise above threshold. When this occurs, the location to which the pain is referred is the skin and skeletal muscles, for example, rather than the viscera.

2. Visceral afferent impulses may set up "reflex" actions on blood vessels of muscles, skin, meninges, and so on, by causing release of chemical substances, or indirectly through vasomotor changes. The ultimate result would then be activity in somatic fibers leading to the cord, and sensations of disturbance in skin or muscle.

3. Visceral afferent impulses may conduct in the reverse direction (antidromically) along certain branches of their axons, either before or after they have entered the spinal cord. The antidromic impulses act on blood vessels, and affects such as suggested in paragraph 2 take place. The pain that results is, of course, referred to skin, skeletal muscles, etc., instead of visceral structures.

Whatever the exact mode of transmission of effects, referred pains are an indubitable phenomenon and must be taken into account in interpreting painful sensations.

NEURITIS. Neuritis in peripheral nerve trunks is of two sorts: inflammatory and degenerative. Whatever the disturbances are, nerve tissue is stimulated and the result is pain in the somatic members involved, particularly when there is muscle movement. Some physiologists suggest that since mechanical and vascular influences are involved in the former, and chemical and toxic in the latter, a closer study of disturbances of pain, tactile, and temperature modalities might help distinguish the type of neuritis existing in any case. The services of psychology might be of help in diagnosing such diseases. Physiologists point out, however, that most of the pains usually attributed to "neuritis" do not arise from changes in nerves but rather as referred pain from joints. Thus they may be arthritic rather than neuritic.

Conclusions

In most of the forms of pain just discussed, one or the other, or both, of two sources are involved: (1) the traumatic (chemicals and mechanical lesions), or (2) the visceral, which includes disturbed circulatory function, among others. In the cases in which the latter is true, it is easy to see how the individual's personal reactions to his environment may be involved as the initial origin of the trouble, particularly if such maladjustments have become habitualized. Such cases are frequently interpreted by the layman as the action of "mind over matter." We should, however, see them as forms of disorganization of the individual. The individual is not necessarily always to be divided into mind *and* matter, but seen as a functional unity. When such an organism is not coping appropriately with its environment, it, in the struggle, may be expressing the strain in patterns of bodily activity that have as their end results those we have just described.

Chapter 18

STUDIES IN SOCIAL PERCEPTION

Previous chapters have developed the position that perception is not a rigid, stimulus-bound, discriminatory response pertaining only to physical properties and unmodifiable through learning processes. Many examples of behavior could be used to reinforce the traditional view of the matter, but they would have to be arbitrarily selected for that purpose. Today we are able to produce as many examples of immediate discriminatory behavior that are tangibly modifiable as we are those that are not.

Social psychologists have in recent years become interested in what they call perception. The term social perception is now coming much into use. In using the term, some imply that it is a different kind of perception than that represented by size perception, though perception nonetheless. Others wish to demonstrate that social perception is different only in the sense that it applies to performances that we are in the habit of calling social.

If in insisting that perception is social we are only emphasizing that it is characterized by flexibility, we are not having to make a new point. It is just one species of perception with the properties already reviewed in the preceding chapters.

The connection between social processes and perception must, however, be made explicit and understandable. Some social psychologists have been at work on this task. At present there seem to be two sorts of social influence. First is the influence upon the subject's perception brought about rather directly by other people. This influence may be the kind operative through the presence of other people, the examples of other people, the wishes of other people, or the prestige of other people though not present. These influences are not always detectable for what they are. It requires considerable ingenuity to ferret them out and make sure they actually are involved in specific cases.

Possibly in this same category, or at least in one analogous to it, are the perceptual responses that are what they are by reason of specific personal need. These responses represent the subject's value system in ways not so clearly assignable to social influences as to his own personality.

The second sort of social response is one in which socially meaningful and socially originated properties are responded to. As an example, there is the immediate response that is guided by a social concept or ideal. In all such examples the perceptual property of the situation is socially describable. It is a property that evolves only in a social context. This differs from the first sort of social perception. In it, the perception may pertain to a "physical" property of a physical object, such as size or shape. Superficially there may be nothing social at all that one may easily be able to put his finger on in such a case. It is only if the investigator suspects a social influence and designs an experiment appropriate for checking on the matter that the social aspect of the perception emerges. For example, if it is found that one class of people sees certain objects as possessing one physical value and some other class of persons perceives it differently, then a social influence may possibly be discovered by making several more steps in the investigation.

A third aspect of that which can be considered social is the phenomenon of individual differences. Some individual differences in organisms are basically anatomical and are acquired not by reason of a social context, but others, evolve out of the very interaction between organisms. Some of human perception is what it is because of this sort of interaction. When individual differences are manifested in human behavior and are not assignable to structural causes, the problem arises of whether and to what extent the differences are assignable to social interaction.

A CAUTION

A very important caution to the reader is that the concepts involved in many studies of social perception are not strictly what they should be to investigate perception. No distinction is made between perception and processes that lie outside of perception. Experimental conditions are such as to allow the subjects freedom to report on judgment. Judgments, as we saw earlier, are not identical to perceptions; they are the culmination of a "problem-solving" task in which perceptions are only one of several ingredients. In many "perceptual" investigations, the reasoning processes of the individuals are allowed to creep in at will. This is to say that it is thinking rather than perceiving that is being studied. This makes the utilization of much material in the social realm difficult, if not entirely impossible, since discussion of perception cannot well proceed with two diverse definitions of it tacitly involved.

Our rigor in differentiating between perception, judgment, and other processes has determined the sorts of studies that have been omitted or included in this chapter.

CLASSES OF ASSUMPTIONS IN SOCIAL PERCEPTION

Allport (4) lists six propositions found in the study of social perception, particularly as pertaining to the directive-state theory. They are as follows: (1) that bodily need determines, within limits, *what* a subject will perceive; (2) that reward and punishment are also factors in determining *what* a subject will perceive, and that they greatly influence thresholds at which items will be recognized; (3) that values represented in the personality of the perceiver tend to determine thresholds of recognition; (4) that the size perceptions evoked by stimuli are in line with the social value connotations involved; (5) that the personality features of the perceiver predispose him to perceive in a manner consistent with such features; and (6) that overt recognition reactions to personally disturbing stimuli have a longer latency than do reactions to neutral material, that this material tends to be misperceived in radical ways, and that such material evokes autonomic reactions at thresholds below overt recognition thresholds.

It is not immediately obvious that these six categories are mutually exclusive. Some of them tend to sound as though they are simply different ways of saying the same thing. We shall not try to clarify the problem at this point, but rather attempt to follow the discussion of social perception as formulated by the workers in the field.

Bruner (41) and Postman put the determinants of perception into two distinct categories: the structural and the behavioral or motivational. It is with reference to interests in studying these categories that they divide the investigators, past and present, into "formalists" and "functionalists" respectively. The structural factors include the stimulus, the effects of the stimulus energy on sense organs, the afferent neural pathways, and the cortical projection areas of the sense modalities. These factors are looked upon as the innate, given, and relatively fixed determinants. They are, for the most part, the relatively unchangeable endowment of the perceiver. The behavioral determinants, in contrast, involve the "higher level" processes. They have to do with the functional relation of the parts of the nervous system already mentioned, with the central nervous system. The central nervous system underlies personality and social behavior. It performs a directive role in dealing with new sensory material. It is the nature of this assumed central directive process and its influence upon perception and judgment which many social psychologists have more or less recently turned to studying.

Bodily Needs

The following are a few representative studies made by social psychologists in which factors having to do with personality and the interplay of social influences tend to modify perception of geometrical targets, or targets seen as words. The first study to be described was conducted by Levine, Chein, and Murphy (161). They used as their target material eighty white cards with simple pictures seen through a ground-glass screen. The ground glass served to blur the pictures so as to make them very vague indeed. Forty of the cards contained black and gray pictures (achromatic series) and the other forty contained colored pictures (chromatic series). The cards included fifteen "meaningless" drawings, fifteen ambiguous drawings of food articles, and ten drawings of miscellaneous household articles. All of the drawings, when viewed behind the screen, were ambiguous but could be seen as food articles by the hungry.

During each session, twenty archromatic and twenty chromatic cards were presented in random order. Two sessions taken together were called a trial, since the second session used the cards not used in the first session. The same cards, of course, were presented to both experimental and control groups. For the control group, some sessions were 45 minutes after eating, some 1 hour, some 1½ hours, some 2 hours, and some 2½ hours. The experimental group, however, was deprived of food for 1, 3, 6, and 9 hours.

The authors found that autistic processes were definitely manifested under conditions of food deprivation in the experimental group. The subjects deprived for 3 hours showed more food responses than the 1½-hour subjects, and the 6-hour subjects showed more responses than the 3-hour subjects for the achromatic, but not for the chromatic, cards. For the chromatic cards, the number of food responses at 6 hours decreased from the number at 3 hours. For both kinds of cards, the food responses at 9 hours were fewer than they were at 6 hours. This is to say that the food responses first increased with both kinds of targets, and then decreased. The responses to chromatic cards decreased earlier than those to the achromatic.

The subjects in this investigation were not asked specifically to report on what they saw, but rather to put into words the associations evoked by the blurred patches they saw on the screen. It is not possible to tell how close these associations were to perceptions. They might have been actual perceptions or they might have been several steps removed from "immediate behavior." Assuming that the subjects were reporting upon sensory impressions (perceptions) and not secondarily evolved meaning, it can be concluded that the subjects' states had something to do with the characteristics of their perception.

Brozek, Guetzkow, and Baldwin (40) obtained opposing results in the responses of food-deprived subjects to ink blots. They found no preponderance of food-naming responses in such individuals. The apparent contradiction might rest on the very character of the ink blots, as in contrast to the blurred targets. The ink blots do not in any way predispose themselves to be seen as food articles. In the Levine, Chein, and Murphy experiment, other features of the investigation may have biased predisposition in the stimuli themselves toward being seen as food articles. There was no way for these authors to report to their readers just *how* ambiguous the targets were. It is possible that they could have been made more so, for all we know, and of course they could have been made less so.

We do not doubt but that under certain conditions those deprived of food are more likely to perceive ambiguous material as food objects; that is, that perception becomes quite autistic in such cases.

Reward and Punishment

The following investigation deals with the influence of rewards and punishment on perception. We have reference here to the study of Proshansky and Murphy (214) in which the perception of the lengths of lines and the magnitudes of weights were investigated. Rewards and punishment, in this case, were devices to impose values on certain stimulus presentations that they would not otherwise have. The experimenters imposed symbolic values or properties upon visual targets that under ordinary circumstances would not possess such properties.

The investigators used a pretraining sequence of two sessions per week for five weeks, during which several lines of different length were presented to their subjects. The same thing was done with weights which subjects lifted.

After the pretraining series was concluded, a second period, or training period, was begun. It lasted seven weeks, with two sessions per week.

In this part of the study, the subjects were instructed not to make any overt response. They were simply to observe. During this training period, a reward was given for each long line and heavy weight shown to the subjects. For each short line and light weight, the subjects were punished; i.e., previous rewards were taken away from them. For the stimuli of intermediate physical value, reward and punishment were interspersed an equal number of times at random.

A third period in the study consisted in the subjects again reporting their perceptions of length and weight, respectively, as the stimuli were presented. In this period, only the intermediate stimuli were presented. The object of the investigation was to see what influence the second period had upon the third.

For the control subjects, the first of the three periods was the same as for the experimental subjects. In the second, or training period, the control subjects were neither rewarded nor punished. They were simply presented with the lines and weights.

In the third period, the two groups, the control and the experimental, responded differently. The control group showed no significant differences in perception in this period from perception in the first period. The experimental group, on the contrary, did show significant shifts in perception in the direction of perceiving the lines and weights of intermediate magnitude as similar to those that were always rewarded in the second period.

Rock and Fleck (221) obtained negative results in using ambiguous figure-ground targets. Smith and Hochberg (230) and others have obtained positive results. The fact that anybody achieved positive results shows that they are possible. We need, however, to know why failures occurred in any case. Journal reports cannot always give us the material with which to resolve apparent contradictions.

There are many subtle features to experiments of this sort. The experimenters must keep the subjects from a kind of influence which we could say is not expressed in perception at all. If it became known that certain kinds of responses *ought* to be made, it might be possible to make them by using ordinary size discrimination. The results would not represent the intended function of size perception at all. The fact that some investigators did not get the shift in size reports in line with *intended* reward and punishment might mean that these were not *actual*. It could be possible that the subjects' behavior was an expression of the ability to do what would run the best chance of escaping punishment. The most important thing to discover is whether the actual size perception is changed without the subjects' awareness and that the behavior is not an indirect way of obtaining awards and escaping punishment. It does not seem as though this indirection could be in the Proshansky and Murphy study.

In all cases, the investigators have to be sure of what the experimental situation is to the perceiver and whether the results can be interpreted by the investigator in only one or in more than one way.

The Individual's Value System

Certain social psychologists maintain that the values of the individual tend to influence the duration thresholds at which materials related to these values are recognized.

Postman, Bruner, and McGinnies (211) gave the Allport-Vernon Study of Values to 25 subjects, obtaining their scores on the six value categories: religious, political, social, aesthetic, economic, and theoretical. The subjects were given 36 words by tachistoscope, with six words related to each of the categories just mentioned. The exposure times were at first very short and became increasingly longer until the words were correctly perceived. It was found that subjects responded correctly to shorter exposure of words which belonged to the high-value categories. This, of course, was in line with the investigators' expectations.

The authors analyzed the nature of the incorrect responses made by the subjects. These were grouped as follows: the response words representing the same value category as the stimulus words themselves were called "co-valuant responses"; the responses that represented an opposite meaning were called "contra-valuant responses"; certain other responses were called "nonsense responses." Stimulus words in categories of high value to the subjects evoked more co-valuant responses than stimulus words in less-value areas. Stimulus words in low-value areas evoked more contra-valuant responses and nonsense words.

The same kinds of results were obtained in a similar study by Vanderplas and Blake (248), in which the variable was the intensity of the sound of spoken words; consequently, the principle has, in a way, been demonstrated in hearing as well as in vision.

Perceived Magnitude and Value

The perceived size of an object is changed when size has some relevance to some need of the perceiver. The kind of evidence that is adduced for such a conclusion was first obtained by Bruner and Goodman (42) in the following experiment. They used 10-year-olds to report on perceived sizes of coins by use of a spot of light whose size could be altered to match that of the coins seen in a different part of the visual field. A knob varying the size of an iris diaphragm was the means of varying the light spot. The coins used were 1-, 5-, 10-, 25-, and 50-cent pieces. The perceived sizes of all the coins were enhanced. The magnitudes of the overestimation increased for successive coin denominations up to the 25-cent piece, and then dropped somewhat for the 50-cent piece. A control group was given cardboard disks to use as standards instead of the coins. With these, there was essentially no overestimation. The values clustered around true size for each coin. A further comparison was made by using two groups of subjects: one from "poor" homes, and the other from "rich" homes. The poor children "overestimated" the coins definitely more than did the rich children. When, on another occasion, the children were asked to imagine the sizes of coins, the poor children overestimated them. The exaggerations reported by the rich children occurred only for the half-dollar.

Carter and Schooler (57) redid the Bruner-Goodman study and failed to confirm the original findings except in the nonperceptual task of remembering coin sizes.

Ashley, Harper, and Runyan (7) also repeated Bruner and Goodman's experiment in perceiving the size of various coins. The authors put their subjects into different socioeconomic categories by hypnosis. Their subjects were adults, to some of whom they suggested while in the hypnotic states that they were "poor," and to others that they were "rich." While still in the hypnotic state, they were put through the process of reporting upon perceived coin sizes. The results confirmed the findings of Bruner and Goodman. As a control, the reports of the same subjects before hypnosis were used. The subjects saw the coins as substantially their normal sizes.

Not only were actual coins accentuated in size in the hypnotic series but also slugs, whose metals were variously described as lead, silver, white gold, and platinum. They were accentuated in keeping with the value of the metal suggested and the suggested economic status of the subjects. Even remembered sizes of coins bore relation to value.

It is extremely difficult to evaluate such experiments and their results, since we do not know what goes on in hypnosis. Were we to think of hypnotic subjects as merely in a peculiar state of pleasing the hypnotist, and thus being under his control, then the behavior that turned out to be in line with his knowledge and expectations could not be used to support the kind of hypothesis implied in the experiment.

Another investigation in which social context has determined the nature of resulting perception is the study of Bruner and Postman (44) that investigated the role of symbolism (value, again) in influencing visual perception of size. These authors used disk targets. One set bore a U.S. dollar mark, another set a swastika, and a third set a supposedly neutral symbol, namely, a square with its two diagonals marked across it. Each of these symbols were of equal size, and were contained within a circle. The targets themselves varied from three-quarters of an inch to a half-inch in diameter. The task of the subjects was to adjust the size of a circular disk of light seen elsewhere in the visual field until it appeared equal in size to the symbol-bearing disk.

It was supposed that the subjects were oriented differently toward the symbols—positively toward the dollar mark, and negatively toward the swastika. Ten subjects were presented the neutral and positive targets, and ten were presented the neutral and negative targets. Each subject made 48 trials, one-half with the neutral and one-half with the other targets.

The three symbols made differences in the perceived sizes of the disks. The disks with the dollar sign were perceived as largest, those with the swastika the next largest, and those with the square the smallest. This was true regardless of the various literal sizes of the disks.

If the patterns as symbols were to have made a difference in perceived disk size, one might have supposed that symbols toward which the subjects were negatively oriented might have been seen as smaller than disks bearing a neutral sign. This need not be the case, for any symbol toward which some distinct attitude is held might merely heighten perceived size. The most exacting critic might feel that there is a shadow of a doubt left in the experiment with reference to the sheer visual attributes of the three target configurations as *geometrical* forms. Both the dollar sign and the swastika are open forms, whereas a square with its diagonals is a closed form. What would have happened were the diagonals alone used for the neutral symbol? This might be submitted to test. On the other hand, we should not be so conventionally and rigidly oriented toward attributing vision to geometrical determinants alone as to refuse to believe that the symbolic character of a visual pattern has something to do with its perceived size.

Klein, Schlesinger, and Meister (140) performed their own version of the Bruner-Postman experiment on the perceived size of symbolic targets. Their results did not represent a single marked tendency for all subjects, but rather a set of consistent individual differences. It was interpreted that the size enhancement does not flow directly from some broad specified need, but rather in the way that the specific individual is organized to deal with his needs.

Lambert, Solomon, and Watson (152) set up a token-reward situation in which, by a conditioning process, poker chips that had no special value to begin with were used to obtain natural rewards. After the chips had come to function in the role of token rewards, their perceived size was retested and found to be greater than it was before the reward role was developed.

These experiments, although they do not rule out the possibility of geometrical designs having a spatial influence of their own on the perceived size of the disk targets upon which they are inscribed, do indicate that there is something that the individual perceiver contributes to his perceptions. This contribution shows up in perceived size, making it decidedly different than would be expected were perception stimulus-bound. The contribution, although we do not know the mechanisms underlying its expression, has enough connection with what is otherwise expressed as "personality," "personal needs," "personal values," to be attributed to these entities in certain specific situations. Of course, as a result, broad *generalizations* regarding perception are then made in such forms as "personal needs influence the sizes of perceived objects," for example. This does not mean that perception is fickle, and it does not mean that the ordinary psychophysical experiments on perceived size are to be discarded. The findings demonstrate that the differences obtained in the "social situations" and in conventional laboratory experimentation are the products of very different sets of conditions. Our understanding of perception ought to encompass both of these extremes of circumstance.

The use of the concept of need in explaining behavioral results is open to some criticism inasmuch as there are no criteria for determining what needs are and which ones are operating in a given subject in a given case. The concept of *need* is in as much need of verification as is the perceptual behavior under study. Without criteria for establishment of needs, anyone is at liberty to state a need at any time. The term ought to have more than a mere common-sense meaning. Even food deprivation is not always an ironclad need. Length of food since last food intake may, in a statistical way, seem to serve. But when results vary considerably, what is going to be the interpretation? We are not to be understood as denying that some concept of need might not be scientifically valid and useful, but it is certain that the term *need* cannot be made an explanation in an indiscriminate way. It can be said, in general, that the term has not been used carefully enough in many cases.

Personality Characteristics and Autisms

It is said that the personality features of an individual predispose him to apprehend objects and situations in ways relevant to these features.

Schafer and Murphy (222) made the following study to disclose the autistic nature of perception. For their purposes, they used an ambiguous figure-ground target in which human faces could be perceived. To form the targets, circles were bisected by an irregular line so devised that either the right- or left-hand portion taken alone could be seen as a face unambiguously. With the two portions of the circle taken together, the target as a whole was ambiguous. The right-hand portion could be seen as a face, and the left-hand as the ground field; or at other instants the left-hand position could be seen as figure—that is, as face—and the right-hand portion as ground field.

The investigation used two such ambiguous targets, in which, of course, a total of four faces was involved. The four face targets could be shown singly, and were first shown that way in random order. From the experimenters' point of view, the targets were two pairs of faces; but from the subjects' point of view, they were seen as four distinctly different faces. Each target presentation was made by a Whipple tachistoscope for an exposure of one-third second. The subjects were told that they would see faces in the exposures to be made, and before each target was presented the subjects were given a name to associate with each face they would see. The object was to learn the faces and their names. Finally, the two portions of the circle were put together, and then collateral conditions were manipulated to see whether the subjects could be predisposed to see one rather than the other of the two faces elicitable by the target. The subjects were told that when they saw *either* of two specified faces of the four they would be rewarded by 2 or 4 cents, and that each time they saw either of the other two of the four faces they would be deprived of 2 or 4 cents. In each trial, the subjects were told how much they had won or lost, and in accord with this they were to take from a pile of pennies the right amount, or put back into the pile what was owed.

Five subjects were used, and all of them acquired the same set or bias in favor of seeing the rewarded faces for the first 16 presentations, after which the perceptual process underwent what the authors called a process of consolidation. This process depended upon factors within the perceivers other than those controlled by the initial reward-and-punishment experiences. A control subject also acquired a set for two faces in the pretraining period.

Rock and Fleck (221) obtained negative results in their experiments with reward and punishment with figure-ground stimuli. They found that their two-face components had a novel appearance when put together.

As is usual, when two different investigations of the same matter turn out oppositely, we have to suspect differences in method of instruction, material used and/or differences in the subjects themselves. Actually, it is differences in subjects that is one of the chief concerns of the social psychologist, and we are prone to give some weight to such a possibility here. The fact that Schafer and Murphy obtained the positive results they did under the conditions, as best we can understand them, leads us to the conclusion that rewards and punishments do play a role in perception, such as in determining what will be seen as figure and what will be seen as ground. Often what is ground and what is figure are taken to be largely controlled by structural factors. We know that this is not so in all cases. There are those in which there is ambiguity, as in the targets of the experiments just cited. Schafer and Murphy have shown that organismic contributions are crucial in determining figure and ground in such cases. Not only reward and punishment but autistic factors are influential.

Lindzey and Rogalsky (164) presented twenty representative and six stereotyped photographs to 685 subjects. The subjects were asked to distinguish between the Jewish and non-Jewish persons represented in the photographs. That is, they were to tell which were and which were not Jews, and in addition were to indicate their confidence in the judgments they made. The subjects were also asked to fill out an Allport-Kramer Prejudice Scale.

The results were as follows. Five hypotheses which the authors held were substantiated at the 5 percent level of confidence: (1) the higher in prejudice (HP), as indicated by the Allport-Kramer scale, were more accurate in identifying the Jew and non-Jews; (2) the HP's labeled more faces Jews than did the less-prejudiced persons (LP's); (3) HP's indicated more self-confidence in their judgments; (4) the HP's were more accurate in identifying the stereotyped Jew and non-Jew faces; (5) HP's were more confident in judging the stereotyped Jew and non-Jew faces.

One hypothesis the authors held had to be rejected; namely, that HP's report use of more "cues" describing Jew and non-Jew faces.

In their findings, the authors were able to abstract four additional positive items that are relevant here: (1) judges of high accuracy (HA) were more confident than those with lower accuracy; (2) those high in anti-Semitic prejudice reported less equal-status contact with Jews than those lower in prejudice; (3) HA's were also more accurate in judging stereotyped faces; (4) the mean accuracy of identifying the faces was significantly above chance.

Here we have a not too unusual type of social experimentation. Obviously, one of the basic and crucial processes required of the subjects is visual perception. They had to look at pictures of faces in a discriminatory way, that is, in a way so as to make a two-category choice (judgment). The trouble with this investigation, as an example of social perception, is that it included far more than perception. It is an experiment in judgment, the utilization of a number of perceptions (immediate sensory responses) and certain other factors we have already mentioned in other connections. The subjects were obviously not curtailed in the time taken to make each of the separate choices. They could not only perceive but pause long enough to "think" about the faces as they were presented to them. Hence, the division of the faces into two categories, Jewish and non-Jewish, was very likely not solely a matter of perception.

We included this investigation here as an example of the kind of studies that are often spoken of as those in social perception. It is not safe to put such studies in this category without explicit qualifications. We do not know that perception itself was such a dominant factor in the choice responses that we can overlook the influences of other factors. For purposes of studying perception, the same investigation could have been differently conducted, and would have qualified. Let us say that the visual targets had been presented tachistoscopically, and that the responses had had to be made within some limited span of time; they then could have been called "immediate responses," and thus perceptual ones. The question is, Would the end results have been the same, or different? We do not know. But until the two opposing ways of conducting the study are tried out, we shall certainly not be at liberty to say that the nonimmediate response is for all ordinary purposes the same as the immediate or perceptual one.

Be all this as it may, we can be sure that a *certain class* of distinctions made by the subjects is perceptual, and that this was necessary before any judgmental choices could be made. That is, the subjects could not just as well have been kept from seeing the pictures in making the choices which they did.

Disturbing Stimuli and Two Orders of Response

Postman and Bruner (211) produced a very frustrating situation for a group of subjects. In it, subjects were given a series of three-word sentences by means of a modified Dodge tachistoscope. The subjects were to report "what they saw, or what they thought they saw." This request is a typically phrased one, owing to the tendency of the naïve subject to omit descriptions of perceived items with which considerable doubt is associated. It will be recalled, in this connection, that we earlier discussed the attribute of relative certainty in the perceiving process.

Each of the sentences was presented for various durations, some so brief that scarcely anything at all was seen, others long enough so that the three words were comprehended. Stated in other terms, each sentence was presented once for a duration of .03 second shorter than "threshold," once for .02 sec. shorter, twice for .01 sec. longer. Steps of .01 sec. in duration were added trial by trial until all three words were recognized.

The procedure for the first 9 sentences out of the total 18 was the same for both the control group and the experimental group. At the completion of this part of the investigation, the experimental group was put into a perceptually frustrating situation. In other words, the subjects were called upon to do the impossible and were badgered in various ways by the experimenters as the study progressed from this point.

A black-and-white reproduction of a highly complex painting was shown the members of this group. The subjects were instructed that they were going to be shown something that they were to describe very fully. The instructions were delivered in a very serious tone. The picture was exposed at a low illumination for only .01 second. None of the subjects could make anything out of the exposure except to discern a few vague contours and shadows. Remarks were made by the experimenters calculated to embarrass and belittle the observers for not being able to see something definite and detailed. During the 10 or 12 trials the picture was shown, even the health of each subject's eyes as well as the state of his mind were brought into question.

Control subjects were shown the same picture, but under favorable circumstances, including a 30-second exposure. During this time these subjects were given the same task as the experimental group.

The performances of the two groups were compared in terms of what was called threshold performances. If one word was perceived correctly out of the three, a one-word threshold was said to have been reached; if two words, a two-word threshold; if three, then a three-word threshold.

The control group improved, but the experimental group did not. Not only did it not improve but the sort of words it perceived from the material presented had some very illuminating characteristics. The words perceived pertained to the needs and curious circumstances in which the subjects found themselves.

McCleary and Lazarus (179) made a study that is highly significant in a number of ways. They used ten five-letter nonsense words. For one-half of them, an unpleasant effect was brought about by accompanying the one-second presentations of the words with an electric shock. This evoked, among other results, a galvanic skin response, a symptom of autonomic disturbance. Following the establishment of a conditioned response to the five words, all the words were shown tachistoscopically for durations ranging from extremely short to those just about long enough to recognize the words. The galvanic skin response was measured in each case between the time of presentation and the verbal report of what had been seen. Using only words that were correctly perceived (ones reported at subthreshold durations), it was found that the skin response was greater for the words previously accompanied by electric shock than for those not so accompanied. This is to say that even though the words' exposures were too brief to permit correct verbalizations (perhaps any sort of a perceptual response, from the conventional standpoint), they elicited the autonomic responses previously conditioned. This showed that although the presentation times were too brief for conscious discriminations, they were sufficient for another sort of discriminative response. Since the response has all the other characteristics necessary to fit our definition, we shall have to call it a type of perceptual response. The most significant finding of the study (if it can be taken at face value), of course, is that unconscious discrimination in the organism can occur, and involves a less energetic impingement than a conscious discrimination of the same sort.

McGinnies (182) used a list of 18 words that were presented one at a time tachistoscopically to 16 subjects, equally divided as to sex. The words were presented for increasing durations, step by step, until they were recognized. In each trial, the subject reported as to what he thought the word was. Eleven words were neutral, and seven were critical. The latter were socially disapproved words, for example, whore, raped, bitch.

Galvanic skin response was recorded in each trial. Duration thresholds for recognition of the critical words were greater than for the neutral ones. The galvanic skin reponses to the words before they were fully recognized were greater for the critical than for the neutral words. The "misperceptions" (or misjudgments?) for the critical words were less similar to the "right perceptions" than for the neutral words.

Here we have another example of much the same thing as in the previous investigation. It is as though a form of recognition occurs below what is called the recognition threshold, but it is of such a sort that possibly overt evasion can result. Really, what we are talking about here is a lie-detector test. Whereas overt *evasion* in verbal behavior can occur, it cannot occur in the autonomic responses, such as the galvanic skin reaction. Might there not be a very different way of instructing the subject, and as a result less discrepancy between autonomic and verbal end results show up? Might not new instructions be given after the regular thresholds for critical and neutral words were determined, and the autonomic responses for such terms be recorded? These instructions would warn the subjects that they were not going to get by with evasions. They could be instructed to come right out with what they perceived the words to be just as soon as they could possibly hazard a guess. It might well be expected that some change in thresholds for critical words would show up. Under ordinary circumstances we should expect that subjects would requie more "evidence" that a word is a nasty word before reporting what is is than would be the case for reporting "guesses" on neutral words. At least, we must rule out the "reluctance to report," or reluctance to hazard a guess on "tabooed material," as a factor before we can be fully sure of some of the assertions that have been made in interpreting the three experiments just cited.

The studies are open to speculations and criticisms, such as have just been made, by reason of the investigator's not having been quite as rigorous as the situation demanded in seeing to it that response was prompt. The needed form of investigation in these situations is a combination of a tachistoscopic and a reaction-time experiment. It will be recalled that the classical *word association test* was one in which recording time of response was crucial; for if, for any reason, evasion was attempted, it took longer to formulate a substitute response than to respond "honestly," that is, with the first word that came to mind. This difference became apparent at once and was interpreted as an evasion (a substitution).

HYPOTHETICAL CONSTRUCTS REGARDING RESPONSE

Social psychology that purports to be dealing with perception is well stocked with speculation regarding the nature of perception itself and with the mechanisms underlying it. There are several criticisms to be mentioned regarding these speculations. (1) Not all of either the experiments or the criticisms deal either exclusively with perception, or with perception at all. This is true even though the material is brought into discussions of perception as though it were pertinent. As an example, such terms as judgment and cognition are used, sometimes more or less interchangeably with perception. This confuses the issue at hand, and thus almost stalls the argument, as far as those who define perception as immediate response are concerned. (2) Hypothetical constructs seem to have been made too freely and in many cases represent how easy it is for those who believe something to believe that it is real. It is likely, however, that many of the intuitions of social psychologists are very insightful; i.e., could be substantiated were the appropriate experimental operations performed. (3) There is a tendency to couch many of the descriptions of mechanisms supposed to be at work either in ego or else in perceptual terms rather than in terms of processes basic to them. It is not realized that perception cannot be explained or accounted for in terms of itself. This practice is but a special example of explaining by "cues," discussed in earlier chapters. In some cases, the explanations of perception have, in effect, called for a little perceiver within the observer to make decisions prior to the final act that is described as perception. (4) Perception, while not properly distinguished from judging and other processes, is restricted to the experiential and so-called sensory reactions and is not defined so as to include overt behavior. It is not clearly understood that motor processes may express the organism's relation to its surrounds. The conventional view seems to imply that "thinking" or "perceiving" comes first and then action. It is as if overt action is not a *mode* of perception, but only a secondary expression of it. Our view is that action may *embody* all the perception that there is in some cases. At other moments perception is a highly conscious state, possibly with little or no overt sign of what is going on.

The foregoing criticisms are those which if observed would help very greatly not only in putting the study of social perception on a solid basis but in advancing it beyond the point at which we currently find certain other areas of perception.

Among the many terms that have been coined, or given a unique treatment in the area of social response, are those of *selection, accentuation,* and *fixation.* They have been invented by certain authors and then taken up by others. What is meant by selection may vary, but at least in some cases it refers to the lowering of thresholds for "objects of distinct personal reference to the individual." Accentuation has to do with the appearance of objects as brighter, larger, and so on, than would be expected in the classical matching experiment. Fixation is the term given to the persistence and preferential retention of certain modes of perceptual response. The attribution of these three forms of behavior to needs and personality mechanisms makes up considerable of what is said about perception, judgment, and cognition by the social psychologists.

A host of other terms have arisen in connection with the idea of perception being selective and accentuational. For example, there are such terms as dominance, normalization, assimilation, vigilance, primitivation, compromise formation, schematization, hierarchy of thresholds, and degrees of personal relevance, value resonance, selective sensitization, not to mention others, all of which have been meant to have some technical meaning. One of these is *perceptual defense.* Other terms that go with it are preperception and subception. The first is merely a term that has been used by critics in describing the implications of the idea of perceptual defense. The second (subception) is a term that was seriously used by McCleary and Lazarus (*179*) in accounting for the kind of results they obtained. In their investigation they obtained discriminatory galvanic skin responses to words with shorter exposures than were required for conscious recognition of the words themselves. McGinnies (*182*) describes such things as conditioned avoidance. Whereas there is no objection to having terms to indicate processes that occur within the organism and underlie the perceptual end result, it is important to know in what category these processes are supposed to take place. Are they neural or are they going to be in terms of still other hypothetical entities whose existence is as much in need of establishment as the processes to be explained? The tendency to build premise upon premise, each of which is equally hypothetical, is all too often a practice that is used in the more subtle areas of psychology.

Perceptual defense implies some sort of discrimination that precedes the discrimination that we call perception. To be on the defense, in the ordinary meaning of the term, is first to be able to determine what is threatening and what is not; and then, as a second step, to do whatever is required—as, for instance, in the case of reacting to words—to reject the threatening ones perceptually, or to treat them differently. Bruner and Postman (43, 44) are among those who are aware of the implication that two steps may be necessary and that the mechanism carrying out the first step is about equivalent to having a little man within the perceiver himself. They state the matter in a dramatic way, saying that the experiments "suggest to the guileless investigator the image of the superego peering through a Judas eye, scanning incoming percepts in order to decide which shall be permitted into consciousness."

Various suggestions have been offered to solve the problem. Klein and Schlesinger (140) have suggested that "suppressor areas" in the cortex activated by autonomic innervation might have something to do with selection in sensory outcomes. Murphy and Hochberg (191) suggest that the veridical aspect of percept formation with reference to externality is handled by the exteroceptive system. The authors suggest that in such cases the nonveridical or autistic aspects of the ultimate perception may be contributed by afferent impulses from the proprioceptors. This is a concept that can be put to test to a greater or smaller degree and bears experimental investigation. We might suggest that it is with interoception or proprioception and not with exteroception that one's feelings of satisfaction, ease, comfort, etc., are most intimately connected. Accordingly, there might be some connection between tension experience and interoception, and not between it and exteroception. The term tension is applied not only to feelings of concrete bodily tension but also to more diffuse experiences that relate even to one's orientation in social situations. It might be that the two uses of the term refer to a common denominator which is actually some process in relation to exteroception. Thus, whenever tension is involved it is always an interoceptively mediated affair. At times, the interoceptive components in the total activity may outweigh the exteroceptive ones, even in dealing with externality, and the perceptual outcome would be expected to be more particularly "evaluative" of the individual's orientation to the stimulus than is usually the case.

A functional distinction between the exteroceptive and the interoceptive seems to be related to what Werner and Wapner (257) are trying to get at in their sensory-tonic field theory of perception. We live in our muscles and any perceptual theory must take them into account, even in dealing with experiences of externality, just as it does the nervous system.

Bruner and colleagues (41, 43) have more to say about perceptual defense and the matter which some call subception. They suppose that the subject begins to recognize the generic characteristics of the stimulus, prior to complete recognition. In certain defensive perceptions, the subject often negates the nature of the actual stimulus in his response. This, they say, looks like a paradox at first. In order that the subject repress or negate a stimulus, it would seem that he must first recognize it for what it is. Bruner (41) and Postman believe that this paradox can be obliterated if we do not restrict the definition of recognition to a single type of report, namely, a veridical one, and if we do not insist that all responses about which we talk depend upon prior recognition. Now let us see how these cautions are to work. The authors say that to a stimulus there can be tripped off a constellation of response tendencies, among which veridical responding is only one. Others may be tripped off as well, and be very effectual in leading to other responses. Each of the possible tendencies is said to have its own threshold. This is determined both by the stimulus and the directive state of the organism. The directive state is otherwise labeled as the differential availability of the responses in the organism's total repertory. To make this idea work, they believe, the threshold of affective avoidance is often lower than for veridical report, although it may be the other way around in some cases. When so, "correct" recognition must take place prior to affective response.

We add an illustration here that seems relevant. It is not greatly different than the elements that were involved in Bruner and Postman's (43) incongruity investigation; it is only simpler.

The example is this. If a blank card is used for a target in a dark room and is the only part of the visual field that is visible, the experimenter may ask the subject how *far away* the object appears to be. He will get an answer. But we can later find that the answer has had some connection with how large the object was taken to be. The task of the subject might instead have been that of looking to see how *large* the seen object appeared to be. In this case, we could have found, by subsequent operations, that the perceived size had some connection with the distance at which the object was taken to be. *One* of the factors seems to be involved as a premise for the final outcome, and the *other* factor is the perception, or final outcome itself. We can say, then, that the *task at hand* is one of the factors that determines the way the internal activity ingredients are involved in relation to each other. The task at hand, as represented within the organism, determines which will be premise and which will be conclusion. This task demand, of course, is represented to a large degree in what Bruner (41) and his colleagues call the directive state of the individual at the moment.

Bruner and Postman (43) assume that recognition requires a process of interconnection between an incoming "stimulus" and a "trace." The matter, they say, can be stated in stimulus-response terms by saying that an incoming stimulus, in order to evoke a recognition response, must develop a connection with some response mechanism. The next assumption is that not all traces are equally "available" to the development of the connection with response processes. Deprivation, punishment, disuse, and the past history of the organism might be factors leading to this relative unavailability. They also include need states and states of expectancy in accounting for availability.

Bruner and Postman say that when a stimulus is in line with the prevailing state of the organism, it is recognized more readily. Put into our language, it would be said that all impingements are dealt with by the organism in ways dependent upon what is occurring in the organism at the instant. Some impingements will be quite ineffective in evoking perceptual response. Some impingements will be reacted to without delay (that is, with minimal latency); others will be slowly reacted to. Some impingements can be utilized in the internal ongoing process and will evoke perceptions of familiar objects; whereas in the great majority of other instances, the impingements would not evoke such perceptions at all. Hence, we have two problems: the quickness of response and the kind of response. If the internal state of the organism is "not favorable," a much more intense or long-lasting impingement will be required to evoke any response.

We all agree with Bruner and colleagues that from start to finish there is something hierarchical about the processes that are involved in developing what comes out as an experiential perception or as an overt act of recognition or choice. Just so long as we hold to envisaging these factors in other than perceptual terms, and thus keep away from language that should be confined to describing the perceptions themselves, we are on the proper path. The terms which we shall have to utilize are those that, although they may not as yet be used by neurophysiologists, will ultimately fit into their understandings.

There are still other experiments that are related to the question of subception, although they do not throw light on the mechanisms at work. Wispé and Drambarean (266) obtained word-perception thresholds for terms related to biological needs (hunger and thirst, etc.). They found that words connected with these needs were recognized at a lower threshold after a period of deprivation than otherwise. The deprivation did not carry its effect indefinitely. Twenty-four hours did not seem to be any more effective than ten hours. These authors interpreted their findings in terms of the hypothesis theory of Bruner and Postman and the stimulus-response learning theory. Hypothesis theory is that assumption that all perceptual and cognitive processes take on the form of hypotheses set up by the organism or evoked at the time. Hypotheses seem to be more or less ready-made orientations so structured as to require further experience to validate or disprove. The failure of the further experience to fit the hypothesis results in unclear object structuring or other unclear features of perception. Hypotheses change and the testing process goes on. This is something like the statistical averaging process assumed by the Ames transactional theory of perception (page 16). Word responses signifying personal acts instrumental to need satisfaction were found to decrease by the end of the ten-hour period, and to increase with 24 hours of deprivation. McClelland and Atkinson (*180*) interpreted their findings as showing that responses related to instrumental acts for need satisfaction increased as need increased.

An investigation was carried out by Bricker and Chapanis (*34*) in which they used guessed responses to nonsense words presented tachistoscopically. After the first two wrong guesses, fewer trials than needed by chance were found to be required to perceive the words "correctly." They used a very simple and convincing interpretation for their findings. It was merely that what is incorrectly perceived under the conditions of the experiment conveys some information. They state that information conveyed prior to recognition comes from partial aspects within the stimulus target. They thus attempted to by-pass the notion of subception, although it is not easily understood as to how they thought this was accomplished.

Certain other writers also reject the notion of subception. Perhaps the term itself does not sound suitable. Howes (*122*) declares that with certain fairly reasonable assumptions such data as those of McCleary and Lazarus (*179*) can be predicted better on the basis of *probability theory* than by subception. We have indicated that subception does not need to mean just one thing. It is a term that has to do with a set of processes, whatever they are, that goes on prior to the emergence of the end result we call perception. It is simply a way of labeling the antecedent processes rather than couching them in personalistic or psychoanalytic terms, and looking to processes on some level of functioning different than perception for the roles required to provide the end result. Undoubtedly chance plays a role, chance here being but a fortuitous concatenation of circumstances. Surely, however, there is more to it than mere fortuitousness. When one uses probability theory to explain something, he had better inspect his assumptions to see the nature of the *loading* they contain. The loading may contain the same elements that were rejected in the theory that probability is supposed to supplant.

Bruner (*41*) and Postman have resorted to the concept of adaptation level, a mechanism postulated by Helson (*112, 113*) to account for perceptual end results that are found in classical psychophysical experiments. Bruner and Postman make the use of adaptation level only a matter of words. They simply talk about the adaptation level for valued objects being higher than for others. To be able to say this, they involve the concept of a "trace system." This system that accounts for memory is supposed to operate on the adaptation principle. Thus in perceiving, or let us say judging, a valued object, the stimulus is "assimilated to the higher adaptation level" and as a result the object appears large. First of all, we must here be careful of what we are attributing to the stimulus and what to the perception, so as to avoid the caution we have on other occasions mentioned—namely, explaining perception in terms of itself. This caution can scarcely be offered too many times. Second, the phrase "assimilated to the higher level" does not mean much either as a concrete description or as a testable hypothesis.

Duncker (*68*) performed a study in which a leaf-shaped target made of green felt was exposed to his subjects in spectral illumination. The long wave length, or "red," end of the spectrum was used. The leaf target was matched with a comparison target so that they looked alike in color. Then a very differently shaped target seen as a donkey was cut out of the same green felt, and shown to the subjects in the same illumination as the leaf target. This target was matched for color and the match was found to be different. There are various reasons why this match might call for a different green than the first target, but let us suppose that all the necessary precautions had been observed; it showed that the leaf was seen as greener than the donkey. Bruner and Postman state this as "an assimilation to the adaptation level for the color of a green leaf, an adaptative level built up in course of the experience of the human species with green leaves." Does using adaptation level add any understanding to the matter here? Can we find what green it is that is the adaptation level, i.e., the green that is the green of the leaf? It would seem that actual operational use of the concept of adaptation level is confined to experimental situations in which the adapting conditions are known and measurable.

PERCEPTION AND SUGGESTION

At the beginning of this chapter, we mentioned that one form of social perception might well be the perception that occurs under social conditions. In other words, perception might operate differently when other people are around than when they are absent. Although it might be difficult to be sure what effect is being dealt with, it is something that is worth knowing about. Of course, effects in such situations are assigned to distraction, or changes in the character of attention, or suggestion. Experiments can be set up so as to let the effect of the proximity of others to operate, or else they can be set up so as to give the subject moment-to-moment indications of how others are actually behaving. In the latter case, the process that is customarily said to be operating is *suggestion*, although this does not constitute an explanation.

For some reason or other not much work that would be useful to us on this topic is available. The nearest to it, for example, is the work of Sherif (226) on the autokinetic phenomenon. This phenomenon has been mentioned previously on several occasions. It is obvious that in such a phenomenon there is the utmost ambiguity. Even when the observer is making his observations alone, he is not sure at all instants whether there is any movement of the light he sees or just in what direction or at what rate the movement is taking place. It is obvious, then, that there is little in the stimulus that can guide the observer. The main ingredients for the perception lie in the observer himself.

Sherif used this ambiguous situation to compare the performances of individuals working alone and in groups. The groups consisted in three subjects working together. The subjects reported upon the number of inches they saw the spot move. In each case, when the subjects worked alone, they differed significantly in the amount of movement perceived. When they worked in groups and were aware of one another's behavior, the amounts of movement were less extreme. Those who saw the most movement when working alone saw less when working with others. The same thing happened with subjects who saw the least movement. They, too, moved toward the mean. We have to wonder exactly how the subjects performed and how their perceptions were recorded. The reports could have been those of genuine perceptions or they could have been something else.

INDIVIDUAL DIFFERENCES—SOCIAL OR BIOLOGICAL?

Among the individual differences that have been found in perception are those that Witkin and colleagues (269) found in their extensive work on the perception of the vertical and horizontal. The first of the several tests in which sex differences in perception were found was the rod-and-frame experiment. In it a luminous frame was seen by the subject as a surround for a luminous rod which the subject was required to set so as to represent the true gravitational vertical or the true horizontal. The subject was either in an upright position or was supported in a leaning position 28 degrees from the vertical. The subjects almost always adjusted the rod away from the true vertical toward the tilt of the frame. The women, however, tended to tilt the rod to an even greater extent than the men. This was the case both when the subjects were upright and when they were tilted. It was concluded that women tend to be influenced more by the visual field than the gravitational field.

The tilting-room-tilting-chair test was the second set of conditions into which the subjects were put and in which the men and women differed in their responses. In this test, both the chair in which the subject was seated and the room within which the chair was placed were rotatable around a common axis. This axis permitted tilting the subject to the right or to the left as he faced forward. Both the chair and the room could be rotated out of the true vertical, or one or the other could be rotated alone. Likewise, the two could be rotated various amounts in opposite directions. When the subject's chair and the room were tilted and he was required to reset one or the other to the true vertical, the following occurred. In the parts of the study in which the room had to be made upright, most subjects were influenced in the visual direction of the field—that is, in accordance with the appearance to them of what they saw. The vertical of the tilted room tended to be the true vertical to them. Actually, the adjustment represented a compromise between the vertical of the room and the true gravitational vertical. In general, the women accepted the room's vertical as the true vertical at more extreme tilts than did the men.

In those portions of the study in which the subject (with the eyes closed) was required to bring his body to the true upright, it was found that most subjects did pretty well in aligning themselves with the true vertical. No sex differences were apparent here. When a tilted visual field was present, the result was much different. Subjects generally had to tilt themselves away from the beginning position toward the tilt of the room in order to perceive themselves as truly upright. The women, here again, were more extreme than the men. The results here indicate that in the perception of the surrounding field and of body position, women tend to be more strongly influenced by the visual field that is acting at the moment. This is to say that they are less able to distinguish between body position and field position.

The third test that Witkin and colleagues report upon is the rotating-room test. In this test the room in which the subject was enclosed was rotated, and he was also tilted. The subjects had to readjust room and chair so that they would be in the true upright position. Most subjects had to return their bodies and the room in the direction opposite to the displacement so as to perceive them in the upright position. The women had to make less of this return adjustment than the men. If the men and women had their eyes closed when this adjustment was being made, they came out with substantially the same results, but not so with eyes open. The women tended to align their bodies with what was visually upright rather than with what was gravitationally upright. In all the cases in which the men and women differed, the women were more influenced by visual than by postural factors.

The next test to be described was the *auditory-visual conflict test*. The instrumentation for this was so designed that the sound of the voice of the experimenter could be shifted to the right or to the left as the experimenter remained directly in front of the subject. The subjects were to indicate when the sound of the voice no longer seemed to come from the experimenter. With eyes open, both sexes allowed the displacement to be considerable before they lost the sound to the center position. Here again men and women differed. On the average, the men permitted a 64 percent increase in the displacement, and the women permitted a 109 percent increase, over the displacement allowed with eyes closed.

The next test was called the *embedded-figures test*. In it, a hidden figure within a geometrical pattern was used as a visual target. Men on the average required significantly less time to recognize the hidden figure. Out of the 24 hidden-figure patterns, all but two were recognized in less time by the men. In the test as a whole, there were 88 failures by women as against 35 for men. Here, again, the structure of the field was utilized differently by the men and women.

In another type of test, the subjects were required to match two similar items, the one in shadow and the other not. This test was administered in two forms. In these tests the women showed a slight but not statistically significant difference in tendency to be more influenced by the field surrounding the targets than did the men.

In all the foregoing tests the women and the men differed. This would be called a sex difference. Our question is whether this is really biologically a sex difference or one that is socially derived from differences in the social environment of boys and girls. Many, many differences that have first been attributed to the biology of sex have turned out to be differences that have been derived through the process of living. In the present experiments we do not know what to attribute the differences to. We have included them here in the belief that they are probably a demonstration of socially derived differences. They might belong just as well in the chapter on the development of perception (Chapter 5).

CONCLUSION

To say the least, perception, the sensory response to stimulation, is modifiable. It is not known just what the specific principles are that underlie the flexibility of this kind of behavior. A great deal of speculation has been made in recent years regarding causation. This has been more intuitive and verbal than actually substantiated and usable in a scientific understanding. To have brought the perceptions that occur in definitely social contexts under investigation and to have demonstrated the fluidity of this kind of behavior have, nevertheless, been great contributions to psychology. Psychology has been reawakened to the significance of perception in everyday behavior, the kinds of contexts under which perception will commonly be studied from now on have been broadened, and the student of perception has been liberated from a kind of near-sightedness summed up in the quick use of the phrase "perception is stimulus-bound."

The transactional outlook on perception, which certainly is closely akin to the various outlooks expressed by definitely social psychologists, has expressed the idea of the purposeful character of perception, and should be thought of in connection with social studies.

Chapter 19

ANOMALIES OF PERCEPTION

Perception may be classified into two forms, the kind that occurs when sensory and central mechanisms are intact and undisturbed, and that which occurs when trauma or disorganization develops in the nervous system. The latter we shall call anomalous perception. It is this sort of perception with which we shall deal in this chapter. Concentration on the anomalies of perception leads us into many kinds of phenomena, most of which form the content of medical books. We shall touch the phenomena but lightly. Our attempt will be to point out that many items that are not too well classified as perceptual certainly possess a perceptual basis, or component at least, and should be dealt with accordingly.

There are several classes of anomalies. Among them are the *paresthesias, synesthesias,* and *aphasias.* Paresthesias are a group of unpleasant sensory experiences based upon some trauma or excitation in the central nervous system, ranging from distortion of the usual perception to outright pain. Synesthesia is the curious functioning of the nervous system whereby the experiences ordinarily evoked by one sense mechanism are evoked by another in the form of vivid imagery that functions as a carrier of abstract meanings. Aphasia is divided into several quite distinct kinds and consists in certain forms of inability to perform. Some aphasia is inability to recognize, and is called *agnosia.* Other forms are inability to act, such as the inability to write (*alexia*). All forms involve the inability to respond to stimulation. Since the ordinary ability to respond immediately (to perceive) is lost, we are concerned with that aspect of the trouble. Regardless of whatever else is involved, it can be said that aphasias involve language. It is in language responses that the more abstract relations of the individual and his surrounds, including other people, are involved.

THE PARESTHESIAS

The paresthesias are a group of unpleasant and abnormal sensory experiences, including pricking, tingling, creeping experiences, and feelings of numbness in a limb or other skin surface. The intensity of the experiences is not to be attributed solely to the strength of some impingement or to the state of excitability of the peripheral nervous system. Many times it is to be attributed to the extent to which central inhibitory processes are at work. Physiologists attribute hyperesthesia (excessively intense experiences) and the extreme pain characteristic of the acute stages of encephalitis and disturbances of the thalamic regions partly to the inoperation of ordinary cortical inhibitory control. The ways various people react to what would seem to be about the same painful diseases are attributed to the roles played by the higher regions of the brain.

A marked example of what we mean by portions of the central nervous system outside specific conducting tracts being involved in producing paresthesia is shown in cases in which lesions in the dorsal columns of the spinal cord involve great pain, even though no pain tracts are known to exist in these columns.

The absorption of chemicals through the skin may produce sensory disturbances when commonly not expected. Some chemicals, for example, reduce tactual sensitivity to various degrees up to the point of anesthesia. Among them are formaldehyde, phenol, metol, and hydroquinone. On the other hand, substances that induce local vasomotor changes and inflammation sometimes exaggerate the irritability of the nerve endings in the skin, inducing heightened sensitivity to contact and thermal conditions. Both hyperemia (excessive blood in a tissue) and inflammation (swelling) involve intense pain and distorted tactual experience.

Tingling is not supposed to be due to peripheral stimulation. Although itching is a normal result of certain kinds of light contact on the skin, it may also be produced, some believe, by mild stimulation of pain endings incidental to vascular changes in the skin. Intense itching, called pruritus, is associated with hyperemia and postinflammatory conditions. This is the basis for the common idea that when a skin injury finally begins to itch, it is getting well.

Paresthesia from Peripheral Nerve

The findings regarding mechanical block and obliteration of sensitivity, when describing the study of skin senses, are relevant here. It was here pointed out that in compression the large nerve fibers are affected first.

These carry kinesthetic and tactual impulses. The smaller fibers that are affected only later carry pain and temperature impulses. In contrast to mechanical blocks, chemicals and drugs affect the smaller fibers first, and thus the effect of the two sorts of agencies runs in opposite directions. The order of effect in one case is the reverse of the other.

Loss of blood supply by embolism, arterial spasm, or thrombosis, for example, induces asphyxiation just as would mechanical pressure. It thus induces losses in the several skin senses quite in the same order as those produced by pressure block. Touch and kinesthetic experiences are first to go. The common observation that one cannot well control limb movement while in a state of numbness may not be solely due to blocking of motor nerves, but may also be the difficulty brought about by inactivating the usual kinesthetic feedback that ordinarily is involved in guiding movements. Movement in a limb when partially "asleep" is a kind of awkward all-or-none affair. Another factor that points toward the involvement of kinesthesis is that the tingling, cramping experience is intensified by muscle movement, both active and passive.

Paresthesia from Dorsal-Root Ganglia

The dorsal-root ganglia lie just outside the spinal cord. They are the groupings of cell bodies of unipolar cells whose axons are branched, one branch entering the cord and the other extending toward the body periphery, such as the skin. The axons carry impulses from the periphery to the cord.

Sometimes infectious agents that involve the organism affect these ganglia. Shooting and piercing pains may arise from such invasions. The overall difficulty does not include motor paralysis, since only sensory fibers are involved. Herpes zoster (shingles) is one of the infections of this sort. The skin disturbance is the outward component of the trouble that occurs along the nerve paths affected.

In some cases, tumors develop and press upon the dorsal roots. These tumors and other hardened tissue may cause paroxysmal neuralgia, one form of which is known as tic douloureux (spasmodic facial neuralgia). When the eighth nerve (auditory nerve) is the one affected, paroxysmal dizziness, nausea, nystagmus, and deafness may result.

Lesions in the Dorsal Column of the Cord

One of the better-known afflictions arising from lesions in the dorsal column of the cord is tabes dorsalis. In this disease, experiences of tingling and numbness occur in the fingers and hands during the early stages. Loss in manual skill is also produced. Later on, the lower extremities become involved, and the victim's gait and step become variable. Finally, the experience of motion and position of the limbs is largely obliterated. The gait becomes definitely ataxic (uncoördinated) and one of the names for the affliction is locomotor ataxia.

Gray-Matter Lesions

The gray matter of the spinal cord is sometimes the seat of disturbance. One of the more common afflictions of this sort is syringomyelia. Perceptual losses in certain modalities and not others characterize certain stages of the trouble. In the beginning, the appreciations of pain and temperature all diminish. Muscular weakness may go with the sensory loss. If the lesion happens to involve only one side of the cord, loss of temperature experience on the same side of the body as the lesion results. Touch and kinesthesis are unaltered until later.

So long as the white matter (conducting paths) of the cord is left unaffected, the sensory and motor effects are restricted to the body segments represented by the levels of the cord affected. But the involvement of white matter will result in spasticity below the level of the cord lesion, and may involve the loss of sensory experience below this level also.

Centers in the lateral columns of the cord connected with the autonomic nervous system, when affected, may result in vasomotor disturbances. These may consist in either absence or excess of sweating. Trophic (nutritional) disturbances, evidenced in the development of ulcers and gangrene, may stem from the impoverishment of blood supply through the vasomotor changes. This involves the loss of the usual perceptions; it may lead to failure to avoid or to recognize body injuries, and these may cause further trouble.

Brain-Stem Disturbances

Lesions may occur at various places in the brain stem, due in some cases to hemmorhage. When the lesions involve the median portion of the stem, temperature and pain are lost, for it is this portion of the stem that carries the tracts for these modalities. In some midbrain lesions, the superficial skin areas may be completely insensitive, while the deeper tissues are responsive to pressure. In these cases, the temperature sense may still be active, and deep pressure and thermal stimuli induce experiences of discomfort and pain.

Thalamic Involvement

Lesions of the thalamus affect the general sensibilities. A lesion on one side of the thalamus may produce partial anesthesia on one side to moderate impingements for touch, pain, and temperature. At the same time, the stereognostic perceptions (those of shape and texture) mediated by the other side of the body are lost. The third effect is the recurrent seizures of sharp pains on the anesthetic side.

Oral Paresthesia

Some people complain of various unpleasant experiences located in the mouth and on the tongue. Since these are unusual and no pathology of oral tissue can be found, it would seem that these experiences could be classed as paresthesias. The experiences are those of pain, itching, burning, boring, dryness, stinging, and feelings of grittiness, most generally involving the tongue.

When these symptoms are reported and no tissue disturbance can be found to which to attribute them, they are definitely classed as parasthesias. Such parasthesias have been related to certain other facts: (1) the trouble is most frequent in menopausic women; (2) the symptoms are often persistent and declared intolerable; (3) the troubles seem to be related to dental troubles; and (4) prominent psychogenic facts are also found. In one report, 7 out of 35 patients linked the onset of their trouble with previous antibiotic inflammation of the mouth or tongue.

Impingement Deprivation

The question of the behavior of the individual under conditions in which as little impingement as possible is provided has recently aroused interest. Not a great deal of investigation has had time to be completed as yet; but since there are indications that the individual's perceptions undergo change, some mention of this line of interest and investigation is relevant in this chapter.

Authorities from time to time have postulated that the activity of the central nervous system is largely dependent upon peripheral inputs from the sense organs. This input from the kinesthetic receptors has been termed *backlash* by Freeman (78) in his discussions of the role of muscular tension, etc., in the economy of the individual. Various men have spoken of this kinesthetic input as a kind of *feedback* to guide the motor system in the performance of nicely timed and regulated movement.

Although a great deal of the peripheral input into the central nervous system from instant to instant is of the kinesthetic variety, other forms of input loom large. Prominent features of waking life are visual, auditory, and tactual perceptions, provided for by the appropriate sensory channels. The question centers on what would result if virtually all sensory input was precluded.

Workers in neurophysiology are impressed with the autochthonous (self-initiated, or "spontaneous") and ongoing character of activity in the central nervous system. Many of them look upon sensory inputs as something that the central activity incorporates into the processes ongoing at the time. Thus, activation of sense organs and the production of afferent inputs are not so much a matter of nudging and activating the central nervous system as of providing material for incorporation into and modification of central nervous activity. At the same time, there are experiments to show that, under very special conditions, the cortex can be "driven." All this is to say that there are two aspects to the matter. Neither should be overemphasized. Depriving the organism of sensory stimulation is no easy matter, and perhaps the best that can be done is to reduce the usual amount and stabilize the kind of input. It is to be borne in mind that to deprive an organism of stimulation is very different from sedating or anesthetizing it. In sedation and anesthesia, it is the organism that is changed. It is made less receptive, less modifiable, less able to incorporate effects from the outside. The whole pace is reduced and the whole character of internal activity is modified directly in anesthesia. In deprivation of impingement, the organism is left to be what it will be, and only what is given it is changed. The question then is, What will the organism be like when it is deprived?

There are two general sorts of deprivation: (1) deprivation in amount of impingement and (2) deprivation in variety. The whole level of stimulation might be reduced, at least in some modalities, but its character remains the same. In other cases, the sheer variations in the come-and-go of impingement might be obliterated. In this connection, the kinds of impingements that could not be well controlled might be masked by using some uniform input such as acoustic energy to preclude hearing ordinary noises and variations in sound.

It may be mentioned here that this whole trend of investigation is not as removed from the affairs of life as it may seem. Aviation is now such that the pilot is reduced, in many cases, to a visual minimum. That is, his visual field, in many cases, becomes a near homogeneity, and it is found that his visual apparatus is not prepared to meet the emergencies that sometimes arise. The pilot under these conditions acts as though quite near-sighted, and does not see other planes soon enough. Such results as these have led to at least one sort of impingement-deprivation study for very practical rather than purely theoretical reasons.

The first systematic study of the results of deprivation was conducted by Bexton, Heron, and Scott (22) at McGill. In this study, the emphasis was upon reduction in variability of sensory input. The subjects wore glasses that allowed the perception of light, but not of form. They were confined to a cubicle, in which the acoustic inputs were made uniform by a masking input. The subjects wore cardboard gauntlets extending from beyond the finger tips to the elbows. This was to minimize the amount and variation in tactual stimulation. The subjects were confined for periods of as long as five days.

Tests of cognitive ability disclosed impairments of performance, referred to as deterioration of the intellect. Auditory and visual as well as tactual hallucinations were also reported. The inability to sustain trains of thought was also reported. On termination of the confining conditions, difficulties in focusing the eyes, and the tendency to perceive scenes as two-dimensional rather than three-dimensional, were reported. Colors were said to be seen with more than usual saturation.

It must be kept in mind that the subjects were subjected to what ordinarily is not a too comfortable condition—a constant acoustic stimulus. It would not be strange at all to think that this factor was of considerable influence on the subjects, so that sensory deprivation occurred only in one way. It was deprivation of variation, but not a great deprivation in amount. Actually the masking stimulus could have functioned as excitant to some extent.

A more recent preliminary study being made at Princeton has been reported. In it, four male subjects (one at a time) were confined for only 48 hours. A floating room, 15 by 9 feet, which was light-tight and capable of reducing acoustic input by 80 decibels, was the major facility. Ear plugs were used, but movements were not restricted. The subjects had free access to a bed and a chair within a cubicle 4 by 9 feet inside the room just described. Cardboard gauntlets, such as in the McGill study, were worn. The subjects were removed from the cubicle for meals, and could see about the large room by means of a 15-watt red bulb. Goggles were worn when the subjects had to leave the room for toilet needs. No conversation was allowed except for the making of learning tests. These tests constituted the main checks on possible differences in performance produced by the confinement. It was found that, in comparison with a control group, the subjects showed improvement during confinement in learning adjective lists. Not only was this a finding probably in conflict with expectations from the McGill study, but none of the hallucinatory and other effects obtained in the McGill study were found.

It would seem that the amount and character of deprivation have a great deal to do with outcomes. The deprivation of movement might be expected to be one of the most potent features for bringing about the loss of personal orientation and allied effects. Studies of the general kind dealt with here are just beginning, and we hope to see a great deal more come from them in the future.

THE AGNOSIAS

Agnosia is a state in which ordinary stimuli fail to elicit the ordinary responses of recognition. Stimuli that ought to appear to the subject as familiar objects—people, for example—do not do so. Sometimes this failure is visual and sometimes auditory, and sometimes it is tactual. Bilateral destruction of the cortical projection area, or destruction of this area in the dominant hemisphere and interruption of the fibers leading from one hemisphere to the other, for example, produce "cortical blindness." In this case it is supposed that the very basis for vision is lost. Visual imagination, however, is supposed to be left. Some authors do not call this true visual agnosia, for it pertains to fundamental sensory reaction processes. Certain other lesions outside the cortical projection area give rise to lack of appreciation of depth or movement, color, lack of "optic attention," or the inability to group more than one or two objects at a time. The same authors may say that these deficits are not true agnosia, either. True agnosia is the lack of recognition of objects or the loss of visual imagery or memory. When the agnosia pertains to letters or words, it is generally called aphasia.

Of the agnosias there are several kinds: (1) visual agnosia, (2) auditory agnosia, (3) tactual agnosia, (4) agnosia for body parts, (5) agnosia for space and time, and (6) agnosia for time. Visual agnosia is, of course, the inability to respond to visual stimuli by recognizing objects. Very often these stimuli are of some specific class. Auditory agnosia, like visual, presupposes that the peripheral mechanism is intact. Destruction of the transverse temporal cortex may produce verbal agnosia, better known, perhaps, as sensory aphasia. Agnosia for music; for voice, inflection, pitch, or loudness; or for various other aspects of sound may occur.

Tactile agnosia is known also as astereognosis, or the inability to recognize a stimulus by its form, i.e., by the ordinary tactually obtained information. Agnosia for body parts is a very curious form of defect. In it the patient is unable to name, point to, or move, as directed by command, the fingers of his own hand and those of others. The patient may be totally unaware of this difficulty and perform skilled movements, although with a slight awkwardness.

Spatial agnosia is the kind in which the patient is unable to indicate right, left, up, down, behind, in front. Such persons are generally tested for memory for spatial relationships and ability to use maps. In agnosia for time, the patient cannot demonstrate ordinary judgment of the passage of time, or rhythm, and cannot deal with clock time.

The behavior of the agnosia victim is quite unlike that of the victim of apraxia. The apraxic gives evidence of recognition of a visual target, for example, but seems not to be able to perform ordinary response movements. In such cases, the investigator's distinctions become very subtle in describing and theorizing about behavior and about perception. Many times, for the out-and-out behaviorist, the evidences he would wish to take for his data would be scant or absent. If it is movement, and movement very simply interpreted, that is to be used, the data are not plentiful. Even in the normal patient, many times there is little to talk about if one does not allow himself to make guarded deductions from the movements exhibited. In the agnosia victim, even less progress in understanding behavior would be made without such deductions.

The following is a case of a 36-year-old man who presented certain perceptual difficulties as a result of a lesion in the left parietal lobe of the brain. He exhibited a loss of the appreciation of position, two-point discrimination, and tactual localization in the right limbs. There was also astereognosis, visual "inattention," a defect in the patient's ability to shave and dress as it pertained to his right side. At first he denied illness and denied the existence of his right arm and leg. No aphasia or agraphia was present and there was no difficulty in the recognition of usual visual targets and of directions in space. At first there was a transitory trouble in some of the higher processes, such as arithmetic calculations. His confusion of right and left consisted in talking of the examiner's limbs as though they were mirror images of his own.

Except for a small patch on one side of the right hand, tactual perception, pain, temperature, and vibration were normal. The main features of the patient's disorder were those arising from impaired perception of space from stimulation of the receptors on the right side of the body.

The patient could indicate with his left hand the center of lines and geometrical forms, copy diagrams and drawings, and estimate distances well. No displacement of axes and coördinates was manifested, as in certain other patients.

As was stated earlier, the patient initially denied the existence of his right arm and hand, and disabilities arising from their dysfunction. This, of course, was an unawareness of hemiplegia (paralysis of one side of the body) similar to that described by other authorities, and called anosagnosia by Babinski. One author showed that this is a regular feature of sensory loss based on a cortical lesion, though not necessarily extreme. This type of manifestation is often associated with the loss of part of a conceptual entity, the "body image."

The patient showed some difficulty in connection with dressing as related to his right side. Apraxia of dressing has been considered by some as a disorder of the body concept. While the patient finally could picture to himself his right limbs, he acted as though they did not exist and spoke as though nothing existed or no events occurred in space to his right. In keeping with this, he generally looked to his left, and made only rare and fleeting glances to his right.

When his attention was directed toward the right, his judgments about the visual field were as good as for the other side. Thus, in a way, it could be said that he was not disoriented in space. Although the patient's behavior might be interpreted by some to be "unconscious repression of the unpleasant fact of disability," there seems to be no reason to look upon it in this light.

THE APHASIAS

In the aphasias there is a partial or complete loss of the self-initiated ability of the individual to express ideas in speech or writing. This loss may result from lesions in a sensory or a motor area, or in the association fibers. If speech is lacking from a lesion in the motor area, the aphasia is called a *motor aphasia.*

In motor aphasia, it is believed, the person knows what he wishes to say but has great difficulty in getting it said. If, on the other hand, the loss stems from a lesion in a sensory area, it is called a *sensory aphasia.* In perception, we certainly are not interested in difficulties that could be attributed purely to the motor mechanisms of expression, even though perception is an expressive act of the organism's relation to the environment. We restrict ourselves to dealing with the so-called sensory or associational bases for aphasia. And there certainly are cases of this sort.

They are the cases in which it appears that the patient cannot understand certain spoken words or sounds, or cannot understand certain written or printed language symbols. These difficulties are called *word blindness* and *word deafness* respectively.

In sensory aphasia, the difficulty is supposedly one of recognition and therefore would seem to be the very one described as agnosia. However, when the difficulty involves language, it is classed as an aphasia. The following case will illustrate the matter.

Dattner, Davis, and Smith (67) report a case of subcortical visual verbal agnosia. The patient was a man, 50 years old, who was hit by a bus. The patient's condition, several months after the injury, was as follows. He was well composed, coöperative, calm, and normally interested in the testing procedure which he was undergoing. He seemed well oriented in every way, and was able to travel long distances throughout metropolitan New York to keep appointments with his examiners, at which he always appeared on time. He manifested no difficulty in understanding the examiners in anything they said or asked him. He was able to express himself orally without grasping for words or perseverating. He could identify all familiar stimuli; thus he possessed ordinary object experiences. He could describe the use of the objects involved. He likewise could interpret pictures in magazines shown him. He could recognize and copy geometrical figures. He could identify symbols, such as for a dollar and a pound. He could write and read digits, and properly report the meaning of a number composed of seven or eight digits. He was able to solve simple arithmetic problems, either in his head or by means of pencil and paper. He could spell long unusual words orally, and could write them correctly. He could visualize the routes one would have to follow to reach a given destination.

He did have a right-sided hemianopia (blindness in the one half of the visual field), but in spite of this he could divide a line into equal halves. He did not overlook the right half of geometric figures shown to him.

The patient's essential trouble was his almost total inability to read words or sentences. Even single letters were generally of no significance. Once in a while, however, a letter could be recognized by tracing it with the finger or by head movements. He did recognize his name in either print or script. He could copy letters or words, but this did not enable him to read them. He could write either by demand or on his own initiative, but could not read a few minutes later what he had written.

Curiously, the only other difficulty that his physicians found was the designation of the color of spectral targets at the long wave end of the spectrum. He would call them "slightly reddish—not really red."

In the common way of looking at this patient, his sensory difficulties were his hemianopia and his inability to see red when long-wave-length radiation was involved. The patient's inability to read letters and words would be looked upon as a reading (comprehension) difficulty and thus not strictly sensory. This inability would be considered not to involve the visual pathway. Nevertheless, according to our way of defining perception, the inability to comprehend written letters and words is a perceptual loss. Whether the inability to see red is due to some trouble in the optic pathway is not totally certain. We should suspect that his response to the spectral target was a way of involving the concept of redness, at least, and that the patient was saying, in effect, "I know what red is, but this is not quite a legitimate sample." The hemianopia, the inability to see anything in the right half of the visual field, although customarily called a sensory loss, was certainly based in the central nervous system. We see no reason for dividing the patient's losses in ability into perceptual and nonperceptual.

OTHER DIFFICULTIES

The Aura of Migraine

In many instances the attack of the form of headache that is known as migraine is antidated by a set of experiences which are called the *aura*. The aura often is the expression of flashing lights of various colors and patterns. These, of course, are not produced by visual stimuli and may occur only in one half of the visual field. Transient hemianopia, i.e., blindness in one half of the visual field, may also follow. Occasionally, the blindness may involve the central part of the field instead.

Other forms of aura are not unknown. Auditory, gustatory, and cutaneous experiences sometimes make up the aura. Evidences point toward a vascular basis for migraine and the aura that precedes it. Certain portions of the central nervous system may characteristically be involved for certain people.

Vertigo

Among the various anomalies or unusual forms of perception that would seem to belong in this chapter are *vertigo*, dizziness, general spatial disorientation, and motion sickness. These terms are neither synonyms nor are they mutually exclusive. Strict dizziness of the sort that one experiences when he is mechanically disturbed, as by rotation, is one example of the general trouble we are referring to. In this case one or both of two symptoms are outstanding. They are that the very space about one is unstable. Objects whirl about him. He may feel as though he is falling through space, although he believes he has his feet on the ground or is otherwise being supported.

Many times the experience that is being alluded to is one that is more diffuse, amorphous, and thus less definable than dizziness. Nausea, curious muscular tension, headache, oculomotor incoördination, a curious metallic taste in the mouth, are some of the curious features of the syndrome known as motion sickness.

It has become customary to call many of the expressions of the trouble either vertigo or motion sickness. If any distinction between the terms is made, the term vertigo would tend more likely to be used if there is some component of spatial uneasiness or disorientation. The term motion sickness, though covering the whole gamut of symptoms, would tend more especially to be used when nausea, headache, sweating, pallor, and so on are more pronounced.

The truth of the matter is that labeling the states that fall into this broad category is as yet somewhat unclear and lacking in standardization. Our concern, of course, lies in the perceptual behavior of the individual, and the conditions we are discussing here certainly do exemplify disturbed perceptual performance.

Griffith (97), who made a study of dizziness by using careful introspective techniques in connection with rotation of subjects on a Baranay chair, came to the conclusion that this complex of sensory experiences generally called dizziness is largely based on the unusual tensions and pressures imposed on body tissues. Visceral organs are subjected to various uncommon pulls and pressures when the individual is subjected to certain accelerations. The tactual and kinesthetic perceptions arising from them form a general background of uneasiness, incipient nausea, and other factors, which with the vestibular component go to make up the very distressing experience called dizziness. The visual modality is able to compensate for some of the trouble when the visual mechanism itself is not stimulated in a too unusual way at the same time.

All dizziness and vertigo are not based on extreme forms of sensory stimulation. Some may be almost purely psychogenic. Other cases may develop as psychic disturbances from trivial somatic origins.

Freud identified a kind of vertigo, which he called the vertigo of anxiety neuroses. He said it was not a rotating vertigo, meaning likely that it did not arise from body rotation. He pointed out that it was a condition similar to the vertigo of the paralysis of the ocular muscles, rather than originating from trouble in the vestibular mechanism. This vertigo is expressed in a kind of uneasiness involving sensory experiences of an undulating or tipping floor, and of a curious heaviness of the limbs.

Lopez-Ibor (165) states that in about 53 percent of the cases in which a nonphysical factor sets off the neurosis, vertigo is one of the complaints. Vertigo seems to be one symptom of anxiety neurosis, which is not the simple psychic difficulty that it is often supposed to be. It has three symptomatic aspects according to Lopez-Ibor. (1) The mental plane, which clusters around the anxiety and phobias. (2) The neurological plane, in which the symptoms of headache and vertigo are found. In this plane are also the "alterations of body scheme," paresthesias, tremors, and various algias (aches and pains). The more frequent algias are often located in the back of the head under the shoulder blades. (3) The visceral plane, in which there are disturbances of the digestive, vascular, and other mechanisms. Symptomatology characteristically presents two features: the phasic and the interchangeability of symptoms as the phasic alternates or progresses.

Of the neurological aspects, the symptom of vertigo is the most prominent. The subject feels as though about to fall; that his legs will give way, or that the surface he is standing on tilts or is moving or giving way.

The following is a case of a patient who experienced vertigo when he found himself in an open space. In the patient's twenties, he began to have an experience of emptiness when in an open space, such as in a public square. In order to keep from falling, the patient would seek the support of the walls of the buildings around the square. After a few years, the patient was able to travel about normally and otherwise lead a normal life. At the death of the patient's father, the trouble reappeared, but was restricted to occasions when away from home, either in other cities or in open fields. The experience shifted from dizziness to anxiety.

The following is another case. The patient was a man 45 years old who suffered from dizziness particularly when walking. He finally developed a feeling of numbness in the face, which at times would become very red. He was unable to walk with his head erect, and had to tip it to watch the floor. Neurological examinations were all negative. There was, however, a slight hypoesthesia (reduced sensitivity to contact in the numb area). Were it not for the negative neurological findings, the symptoms might have suggested an irritation of some of the cranial nerves that have to do with the face and the vestibular organ.

If we reëxamine Lopez-Ibor's classification given above, we might conclude that symptoms such as vertigo either have such a basis or merely simulate those symptoms that have.

Cortical Ablations

Up to this point, we have been dealing with anomalous perception, in which cases the character, that is, much of the qualitative aspect of perception, is changed. We have information of another sort that might well be included in this chapter. It is exemplified in experiments on pa-

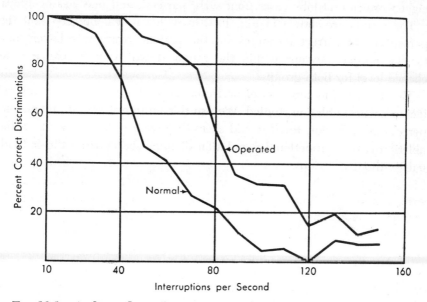

FIG. 19.1. Auditory flutter fusion in patients with cortical ablations (L. F. Chapman, D. Symmes, and W. C. Halstead, Auditory flutter fusion in patients with cortical oblations, *J. Comp. Physiol. Psychol.* [1955], 48: 421–425, Fig. I).

tients with known brain damage or with surgical ablations of the cerebral cortex. Such patients are compared with normal people in certain standardized experimental situations to see how they differ. In some cases, the same patients are tested both before and following operations upon their brains, as in the case of tumor removals.

A good example of the comparison between patients with cortical ablations and normals is reported in the work of Chapman, Symmes, and Halstead (58). The work to be reported here is but one of the many studies on the differences between normals and various types of brain-surgery cases that have been carried out in Halstead's laboratory over the past two or more decades. The workers just mentioned made a comparison between patients with cortical ablations and normals in auditory flutter. It will be recalled that auditory flutter and the conditions that produce it were described in Chapter 13.

Twenty-five patients were compared with 25 normals. The patient group comprised those individuals with a surgical lesion in one of the major lobes and sufficiently free from intellectual and personality deterioration to comprehend the task and to coöperate. Their ages ranged between 12 and 36 years. Twelve were anterior temporal lobe cases, eight were frontal lobe cases, four were parietal, and one was occipital.

The results are shown in Fig. 19.1, in which it will be seen that the percentage of correct responses for the patient group was lower than for the normals, except within the range at which performance is at chance level for both groups.

The degree of impairment of performance was constant for the several loci of cortical ablation studied. We use this as an example of anomalous perceptual behavior, for it would seem that we are dealing with, in the ablation cases, a functional population distinguishable from the individuals without ablations.

Chapter 20

PERCEPTION IN EVERYDAY LIFE

In the foregoing chapters, perception has been dealt with in a more or less technical fashion. It has been defined and set apart from other processes or aspects of behavior, and the various sense modalities have been taken one at a time and analyzed as one would do in the laboratory. At this point, it is appropriate to examine some everyday situations to see how perception actually is involved in them.

Everyday living consists in many kinds of situations, in none of which is perceptual response absent. The following ones will serve as examples: (1) looking down from high places, (2) attending movies, (3) visiting art galleries, (4) shopping at food stores, (5) browsing in a dress-goods shop, (6) driving a car on icy streets or roads, (7) becoming quite tired, (8) attending dances, (9) eating too much, (10) job hunting, (11) taking school examinations, (12) attending symphony concerts, (13) deciding how rooms will be lighted.

THE VIEW FROM A HIGH PLACE

For some people, going up into tall buildings is routine. For others, it is uncommon. In either case, to find oneself out on a balcony from which one can look directly down to the street may be rare. For many, such an occasion provokes uneasiness. To say the least, the distance to the street looks great, and the idea of falling becomes imminent. Here we have a specific nonlaboratory example of space perception. The very same distances involved on the horizontal and in the downward vertical do not seem the same in many respects. The downward look involves a definite kinesthetic component that is absent in the horizontal. The viewer tenses himself to keep from falling. A number of other features of the two perceptions also differ.

It is important to note that the apparent distance to the street becomes modified with extended experience. The author had his laboratories on the eighth floor of a building, and after he worked there for a while the distance to the street seemed much less that it did originally. The downward view to the street became very similar to the view from the usual second-story window at home.

It would seem that a reduction in the phenomenal distance, when looking down, is one of the things that makes a steeplejack or a trapeze aerialist different from the average person. It certainly must not seem nearly so far to the ground from where they perform as it would for another person, if taken to the same height. It is probable that one of the features of this reduced visual distance is the reduction in muscular tension represented in counteracting the imaginary falling experience. The steeplejack's downward view becomes dynamically more like the view of the average person in the horizontal direction.

People differ widely with reference to this fear of falling and the perceived distance downward. Some of it is possibly related to various other traceable components of personality.

ATTENDING THE MOTION-PICTURE THEATER

Attending movies is something fairly common for many people. It is generally the stars and the story that receive our attention in discussing them. But we wish to discuss the moviegoer.

It is true that people differ as to where they choose to sit to see the picture best. Some people go away down front and thus sit close to the screen. This makes the actors and other items in the visual target very large. The retinal images of these items are much exaggerated over what they ever are off the screen. People, as visual targets, would have to be giants to provide the viewers with such large retinal images. Images of this exaggerated size may tend to function the same as the images produced by field glasses or binoculars. That is, in being exaggerated, they would tend either to bring the actors even closer than represented by the metric distance to the screen or to make them appear *larger*. We suspect that what usually occurs in this case is the making of the actors closer than otherwise.

Other people sit midway toward the front, and still others choose rear seats. These three sorts of people must differ considerably in their space perception, and in what a visual situation is to them.

With some of the recent modes of presenting movies, the problem of viewing distance comes up anew. One of the features of the new presentation is the enhanced azimuth (horizontal width) of the screens. For anyone, at any distance, the new Cinemascope screen enhances the sizes of the retinal images considerably. It is known that some people who could sit one-third of the way down toward the front now find that they have to sit in the last row. Even there, some people are not now comfortable, or, at least, not until they can lose themselves in the story. What we have said regarding the persons who voluntarily used to select the first few rows is enhanced now with the wide-angle screens. It is hard to imagine how people can continue to sit so close to the screen. The fact that they still do raises a very fundamental problem that needs to be experimentally investigated.

As well as magnification of the retinal image and bringing the actors up perceptually closer to the viewer, the wide-angle screens tend to "encompass" the viewer. This encompassment was brought to its maximum with such arrangements as the Cinerama, in which the screen itself is not flat but tends to extend around the viewer. It gives him something to see out of the corner of his eye. Along with this, the loud-speaker placements provide acoustic stimulation from both sides of the viewer rather than from merely out toward the front somewhere.

The preliminary setups that preceded Cinerama used a number of projectors (as many as 11), each of which projected its own picture onto its own segment of the screen. The visual field then was one that extended greatly to the sides and above the viewer. This sort of an arrangement put the picture far around and also above the viewer. Since he was very greatly encompassed by it, it gave the scene a perfectly convincing three-dimensional effect. To look around him and above him, the viewer had to move his head quite extensively. This required the same motor components of behavior as the three-dimensional domain in which the viewer lives every day.

Thus far, we have been merely classifying people as to where in the theater they must sit to feel most comfortable visually. For a further understanding of this variance in people, we must take into account certain factors of physiological optics. Some people are near-sighted, some normal-sighted, and others far-sighted. The near-sighted people are those who must be close to visual targets in order to see them satisfactorily. Far-sighted people must be at a distance to see targets satisfactorily. What do eyeglasses do for these people? Near-sighted people need lenses that refract radiation so as to simulate its direction as it comes from near targets, when actually it comes from distant targets.

Far-sighted people need glasses that make visual targets at given distances function as though they were farther away than they metrically are. If one wears glasses that are not very "strong," he may change the apparent distances of the actors and pictorial scenes by removing his glasses. If he is a myope (near-sighted), he can make the scene recede somewhat. If he is a hyperope (far-sighted), he will make the scene come closer by removing his glasses. The changing of the apparent distance of objects is an important fact, although it is generally overlooked in stating what glasses do. It is generally the blurring or the clearing-up of what is seen that is spoken of.

Understanding that people differ greatly in the refractive characteristic of their eyes provides us with one factor in explaining why it is that they may choose to sit at various distances from the screen in a motion-picture theater.

Watching the movies is a kind of activity that involves the sensory (perceptual) mechanism of the individual in many ways. The timing of the individual frames of the film must lie within certain limits. Anyone comparing the film of the early twenties with the more recent films and the way they are projected will well discover this. The communication brought about by the pictures is accomplished differently today than it was yesterday. Then it was by pantomime, for hearing was not involved. Encompassment, the factor we have been describing, was absent in the early presentations. In early days, the motion-picture theaters were often simply renovated long and narrow stores, possibly 100 by 125 feet deep and only 15 to 20 feet wide. Sound effects were produced by talking machines (phonographs), pianos, or organs, the latter being able to develop considerable momentum of feeling and mood.

It must be realized that everything that is done by a scenario writer, a director, and an exhibitor, as well as those who design the technical equipment and install it, must be calculated to take the most appropriate advantage of the laws of human perception. This is the case whether or not those who are involved realize they are dealing with perceptual mechanisms. Failure to comprehend that what they do must be appropriate for psychobiological characteristics of their spectators or audiences diminishes their success by reducing what is ordinarily called the "appeal" of motion pictures. The factors that regulate appeal have more to do with perception than is realized.

VISITING AN ART GALLERY

Visiting an art gallery is a good example of a situation in which visual perception and its many possible personalistic factors come into play.

We turn to Mr. R for a description of certain factors that are commonly involved in a visit to an art gallery. Mr. R happens to be an individual who appreciates both classical and contemporary art forms. His description has to do not only with his own perceptual behavior but more specifically with those of others much less sophisticated than himself:

"Let us watch a typical viewer of a *modern* painting. What is it that he experiences? He is in a bit of confusion. He feels he does not know how to identify that at which he is looking. He could be led to describe the painting as some smears, blotches, or patches of color. But that sort of a description would not satisfy him. He is oriented to expect that what he is looking at is something more than that."

Mr. R notes that one of the very first remarks which an average viewer of a painting will make, upon viewing an abstract painting, is one or the other of the following: What is this? What is this meant to be? What is this a picture of? Such remarks, of course, indicate that the viewer is trying to derive familiar meaning in what he sees. This is the essential factor involved in perceiving, as was stated many times in previous chapters. What the typical person perceives in an art gallery is often very unsatisfactory to him, and he, of course, implies by this that the trouble lies in the painting. Paintings to him have little other use than to be representational of well-known objects or situations. So long as this is his attitude, remarks such as those cited above are bound to be made when he looks at certain modern paintings. To say the least, such paintings are ambiguous, and there is little tolerance for what, to the viewer, has that characteristic. Dissatisfaction is bound to continue.

There is one outstanding difference between the way our man behaves toward a painting and the way he reacts to "objects in Nature." To man-made constructions, the perceiver imputes purpose and design, which he assumes should be understandable. Since this is the case, what he looks at that is made by man is open to criticism. If the same spatial pattern of color that he sees in the painting was part of the design on a boa constrictor's back, it would be perceived with a different kind of attitude. If seen as a pretty color, it would simply be pretty color. Pure sensory delight might well be the result, but this does not seem to be so easy with reference to man-made arrangements.

Again, we do not know what has preceded our man's viewing of the painting. He may well have heard something about other people's expressions of distaste for modern paintings. He may have brought to the occasion the idea that paintings are to be beautiful. More than likely, the painting will not meet the perceiver's criteria of beauty, and hence it fails.

We may find that our man is color-blind. This is to say that he is not sensitive to minute variations in the spectral target and cannot see the many colors that others can see. This would, to some extent, preclude from the very start the possible enjoyment that might otherwise eventuate.

In modern abstract paintings, the viewer sees little, if any, third dimension, for in certain paintings the impression of third dimension is avoided. The perceived design lies in almost a single plane. Our man, knowingly or otherwise, is grasping for depth and for perspective. He likes some portions of what he sees to lie behind or farther away than other portions. Lacking this, he cannot feel himself into the composition so well, and thus rejects the painting.

On the other hand, some of the satisfaction that evolves from looking at paintings is quite prominently affective ("emotional"). Spectral stimuli in various combinations (compositions) may quite directly make an impact on the viewer. In such cases, the need for gaining conscious meaning is by-passed. Liberation from the persistent expectation that all color arrangements should be representational of common objects goes a long way toward the appreciation of many paintings. This is to some degree illustrated in the thrill which many people derive from certain colors and patterns in textiles prior to their being made into definite garments or decoration of homes.

Mr. R, as an example of a more sophisticated viewer, does not ask what a painting *is*, or what it is a picture of. Or, if it is a fairly "literalistic" landscape, he does not seek to determine exactly what specific scene the painting is a picture of. The very best landscapes may be symbolic of a country or a region, or may symbolize a mood instead of a place. This may be as true in the case of a color photograph as in the case of a painting. A visit to an art gallery is to Mr. R a perceptual adventure. He points out that the hungry sophisticate is hoping to find something quite new. The adventure consists in finding that something old is being said in a new and fresh way. But for the typical man, such adventures are more often found in sound than in sight. The typical person may get his satisfaction in hearing someone say, in a new way, something old. This is exemplified in the satisfactions that platitudes in speeches and sermons bring. Sounds much better symbolize something beyond themselves than do sights, particularly if the sounds are words. Even the manner in which the words are spoken carries meaning. Visual forms are not nearly so effective as symbols, except for the person "sophisticated in art." This is one of the reasons why the ballet is not so universally appreciated as certain other sensory presentations. In ballet, too much symbolism is couched in visual form, and the typical person is not prepared to deal in abstract visual symbols.

SHOPPING AT A FOOD STORE

Shopping at a food store brings into play a number of the senses and with them the endless number of meanings that go with foods, food aversions, cleanliness, appetites, cravings, the way foods are packaged, the way they are displayed, the food choices the other shoppers are making as is evidenced in what is in their carts. We see some people stocking up on many forms of meat, some loading up with starchy foods, some making sure not to forget their cigarettes, and some catering to the whims of the children. Whatever else we see, when we go to large markets, we see endless varieties of foods, and we see many kinds of people. We may or may not empathize with all of them, for some are always in the way. The stimuli we receive not only evoke space perceptions, and the more usually considered sensory reactions, but other types of immediate reactions as well. We get the feeling that all humanity must eat, or that most people do not need to be coaxed to eat, or that too much time is spent in deciding what to eat, in shopping for it, and in preparing it.

The items just enumerated are likely to be thought of as ideational rather than perceptual. It can be said, nevertheless, that all of them arise immediately from what is said, heard, smelled, or otherwise perceived, from instant to instant, in the half-hour that one spends in a food store. The variety of perceptions is endless and each of them involves memories, concepts, and attitudes. These, in many cases, are thought of without giving due credit to perceptual mechanisms and processes, but they are nevertheless dependent upon or are perceptual processes themselves.

BROWSING IN A DRESS-GOODS SHOP

Nowadays the selling of fabrics has come to the point of involving separate stores rather than only certain counters in stores. In these new stores, there are literally hundreds of patterns of fabrics: heavy, coarse, rough, smooth, and sheer. Fabrics for all sorts of purposes—sportswear, housewear, afternoon teas, dinner parties, dances, schoolwear. There are textiles for furniture, draperies, curtains. New colors and designs never before seen stand out at every glance. Iridescent sheers, pastel shades, full-bodied hues—everything to activate the senses. Every fabric seen calls up imagery of how it would look in some practical situation. One pictures how this material would look for a suit to travel in, or how some other material would look with the carpet in the living room, or how stunning Patricia would look in the material just pointed out as we passed the last display section. The whole shop is busy with color, and with it the thrilling jangle of ideas that emerge directly as each new item comes into view. Here, we have visual perception in a riot. One can actually come out of such a shop almost exhausted; but happily so, for he or she has been through a delightfully engaging experience. Nothing more needs to be said here, except to reaffirm the idea that we live in our sensory experiences, and that we as scientists should not overlook, in our study, the laws they involve.

DRIVING ON ICY PAVEMENTS

Driving a car involves, among other things, considerable kinesthesis. When one first learns to drive as a young person, it is not uncommon to feel as though the car is taking him "where it wants to go." Later, however, the driver feels that the car is a part of him. He steers it, leans, sways, and, kinesthetically and posturally, anticipates every move of the car, even cringing as it approaches a bump in the road. This same dynamic unity between car and experienced driver is exemplified by a bicycle and its rider, or a horse and its rider. The same lack of unity exists in all three cases in the beginning stages of learning to drive or ride.

Various occasions arise to disconcert the driver of a car. A sudden gust of wind, or a strong but variable wind, may deceive the driver. He is unable to tell what it is that is putting the car partially out of control. It may appear, at first, that the steering mechanism is suddenly faulty.

The worst condition of all for driving, obviously, is icy pavements, for it is then that nothing the driver does is sure to turn out right. The fact that the usual end results do not accrue from a given muscle movement in steering, or the same kinesthetic feedback does not eventuate from a move intended to change the car's direction, becomes very distressing and provocative of helplessness. The driver develops considerable postural rigidity, and this does not add to his success.

While all of the feelings that result from driving on icy pavement are well known and quite obvious from the sheer physical characteristics of the situation, certain of the same feelings may arise in much less extreme form even on dry pavement. There are times when one may feel as though the car is sliding. This is quite certain to arise in some cases on a wet pavement, when actually the car is not sliding. The only way to reassure oneself is to slow down and try sudden applications of the brake to see if the pavement is actually slippery. This "illusion" of slipperiness tends to arise more often when the person is tired from long hours of driving and when nightfall is coming on and one cannot see so well. In semidarkness, one cannot visually reassure himself, from instant to instant, that the pavement is not wet and slippery.

To say the least, a complex of perceptual factors is at stake in the driving of a car under all conditions, and in the ones mentioned the necessary stimuli are not always present to enable skillful performance. Sensory feedback of one sort or another is lacking. On ice, it is the literal lack of control due to slipperiness itself. At other times, the lack is in visual and allied factors. At such times the performer is subject to what is ordinarily called *suggestion;* that is, he is in such a condition that a slight and otherwise ineffective impingement factor may be crucial in deciding the perceptual outcome.

BECOMING TIRED

Fatigue is thought of in energistic terms. People consider it a kind of energy exhaustion—a body condition that comes about on account of exertion. Hence little consideration is given the actual perceptual components that are involved when tiredness appears.

It is our purpose here to point out that the experience of fatigue involves many kinds of *perceptions,* and that it never occurs without them. What we are "tired" of is the kind of experiences we are having at the moment. These experiences refer to our activity at the time (that is, our task and what it is perceived to demand) and to the way we feel bodily. The task is perceived to be demanding something of us which we are not now able to accomplish or are not able to continue to accomplish. The failure which we perceive may have to do with the social futility involved in continuing, or in the realization that we are making mistakes, or that the activity is very uncomfortable bodily. We just do not believe we can go on, and this is based on the complex of perceptions about ourselves in relation to the external situation we are in. We note that we have slowed down, or that we have become jittery, or that we cannot hold attention on the necessary items, or that we ache, or that we cannot see so well as usual, or that still other things are wrong. A crucial component in fatigue is the perceptual component. When certain drugs are given to dull the perceptual activities, their participation in self-appraisal is precluded, and fatigue is not experienced even though performance deteriorates. This is also clearly true, for example, in the case of acute anoxia, where perceptual reactions are dulled.

ATTENDING A DANCE

Dancing is generally thought of in terms of its social and entertainment factors, but we wish to take a look at it from the standpoint of the perceptual experiences it evokes in people. We are concerned with what dancing, by reason of the various kinds of stimuli it provides, means to the person while he is engaged in it.

We are having Mr. K report upon some of the experiences which dancing evokes in him. He is a fairly good dancer, but he is not always so sure of himself that a poor partner cannot disconcert him. He asserts that dancing is fun, but that it can be very uncomfortable if he gets a partner who cannot follow him well.

The most interesting things about dancing, aside from the music with its rhythm, the beautiful gowns the women wear, and all the things that meet the eye, are the experiences which women evoke when one dances with them. Although the experiences are largely kinesthetic, they are embellished with content that is extensively symbolic. It is our contention that one cannot well divorce the experiences of touch and movement, for example, from the meanings they immediately arouse.

People are one thing as dealt with visually, something else when we hear their voices, and a third thing when we come into bodily contact with them, as in dancing. Speaking of bodily contact, we may use as an introductive example the act of shaking hands. People differ radically in how they seem to us as they are disclosed in their handgrasps and handshakes. Some people present limp arms and fragile, wobbly hands; others' hands are wet and sweaty. Both of these types make contact rather repellent for many persons. Some people make the grasp of one's hand so firm and the shake so minimal that little awkwardness is involved. Others try pumping one's arm rapidly and with curious jerks. In this case, two people seldom get in phase in the process. This is extremely awkward and evokes mingled feelings of disgust and amusement.

Dancing is one of those few occasions in which general bodily contact is tolerated, and this is by reason of the conventionalized way it occurs. Certain properties provide for what otherwise would be unimaginably distasteful and intolerable from the perceptual standpoint. If there is a lack of certain degrees of skill, it is kinesthetically very distasteful, even so.

While supposedly dancing is a social art wherein two people attend to the experiences music and movement provide, in so being it is much more than that. It is an additional way in which two people mutually or perhaps unwittingly make known their personalities to each other through such sensory channels as touch and kinesthesis. The man has no real idea of how he seems to the woman, of course, and the woman is likewise limited in how she seems to a man. We possess no clear perceptual mechanism for determining this very thing. One may learn by means of certain responses as to the degree of acceptability, but through direct experience, or even imagery, one cannot perceive himself as others perceive him. This lack is richly substituted for in the many forms of perceptual contact that disclose the other person. Both dancers surely transmit much of their own personalities through the sensory features of dancing. Some dancers are sluggish, cumbersome, slow, often out of step with their partners and with the music. Some are alert. Some men lead well and are easy to follow. Some women follow well and are easy to lead. Stating these facts is nothing new unless we contemplate what they mean beyond themselves. Hesitancy in dancing may mean hesitancy in other things. Willingness on the part of the woman to follow may mean coöperativeness in other affairs. If this and other similar things are so, then it can be said that much more pervasive characteristics of personality are disclosed in the motor behavior of dancing than we often talk about. Through tactual and kinesthetic perception a whole field of possibilities regarding the other person is opened up.

Dancing involves some of the same functional features as in playing with the ouija board. It will be recalled here that each partner accuses the other of moving the board; when these claims and counterclaims are thrashed out, the partners may come to the conclusion that neither is responsible for its motion. The matter becomes mystical. In dancing, neither of the two persons is fully aware of all the little characteristics of timing and movement that are transmitted to the other. The ouija board and dancing situations are somewhat different, however, because in dancing male leading is conventional. It is to be expected, and, to the extent that it is carried out, the next sensitive factor lies in how well a second person follows. Thus there are two factors involved in the woman's part: her willingness and her skill in following. At times it seems as though it is her willingness rather than her skill that is at stake. The woman can detect something about the man's self-assurance, decisiveness, and many other things. The man can detect many things about the woman, which he, perhaps for want of more analytical terms, would call femininity.

Blended with the kinesthetic and tactual is the olfactory—the kind of perfume that is worn. Is it too strong; is it heavy? Does it seem to fit? Does it, in any case, have symbolic significance to those who smell it, that is, various memories, or kinds of imagery? It is a strange fact, but nevertheless true, that some men do not seem to be able to smell the perfume their own wives use, but are able to smell the perfume worn by other women.

There are many other features of one's dancing partner that could be enumerated; but all of them, just like those already mentioned, have to do with the senses and perceptual behavior, the instant-to-instant mutual reactions, of the dancers and what they mean in the broader social situation. Dancing is obviously a good situation to illustrate the fact that perceptual and ideational activities in humans are pretty well intertwined and interwoven, if not fully blended. Dullness of the perceptions, whether strictly mechanical or having to do with the social amenities, is a pretty big handicap and deficiency in a ballroom situation.

Mr. K's assertions could go on for some time, but we shall relate only one more experience before we terminate our description of perceptual behavior in ballroom dancing. Mr. K said that on one or two occasions he and his partner exchanged roles. He took on the role of the dancer being led, and his female partner took on the role of the male in leading the dancing. Unique and unexpected results followed from the first trial. Actually, it was, in a way, one of the unique experiences in his life. The uniqueness consisted in the feeling of being wafted across the dance floor as if on air. The action was a wonderfully smooth one in which some supporting structure carried him along to the rhythm of the music. The undulations of this supporting structure (the human arm) were a very curious experience.

EATING TOO MUCH

The condition that results when one goes on a picnic or attends a dinner party at a friend's or relative's home is often describable as a person's having eaten too much.

Many people are not sure just what the bodily feelings of genuine hunger are. In textbooks, stomach contractions are described as a definite factor involved in the condition of hunger, but little has been done to depict the experiential features that are involved in hunger. With long-

borne food deprivation the whole complex which the person experiences
must be hunger. Very definite and unique imaginal experiences arise
and they are centered about food and eating.

Despite the lack of definiteness in regard to hunger experiences, it is
not at all uncommon for people to know quite clearly what overeating
feels like. One can say, first of all, that the experience certainly has to
do with details of bodily feeling. One may feel a tightness in the head,
a sluggishness in muscles, a fullness in the abdomen, a lack of breath, a
drowsiness, a tang of nausea now and then, an aversion to food. All of
these and many more analytical perceptions may be involved. They are
tinged with feelings and attitudes about food and self. Guilt feelings or
resolutions not to repeat this again may develop with some degree of
clearness.

HUNTING A JOB

In trying to find a new job, the interview situation is one in which perceptions are not only prominent but may also undergo change as they
refer to people and other items in the overall situation.

The perceptions that loom large in a job-hunting situation have to do
with little evidences of one's own abilities and the characteristics of jobs,
employers, and working conditions. Let us take an illustrative case. Joan R
was looking for a job the summer following graduation from college. She
had been only a fair student and was not sure what she wanted to do or
what she really could do in the workaday world. She lived in a town of
about 25,000 people and had occasion to know, by sight, a number of
the more or less prominent men in it. She could have identified many
of them away from home, that is, in strange contexts. This familiarity with
how they looked is one of the items with which we wish to deal a little
later. Joan had also been acquainted with a number of items of rumor
pro and con about the town's leading figures. Hence, it could be said that
she had coupled the personal appearance of the well-known men with
their reputations and supposed personalities. When she would see one
of these men, naturally, what had been said about the man would be
recalled. Hence, certain men *looked like* certain kinds of people—some
mean, some grasping, some playboys, some successful, some good family
men, some brilliant, and others of other sorts.

On the day in question, Joan went to interview Mr. H for a position
as his secretary. She knew that she had had little experience as a background for such a position. The woman who had served Mr. H in this

capacity was an older person. Nevertheless, Joan thought she would try for the job.

While waiting in the outer office, Joan asked herself why she had ever come into this office for the interview. The manners and various characteristics she perceived in the receptionist seemed to her to be so perfect, and so much above her own, that she wondered why Mr. H was not choosing her for his secretary. The receptionist seemed so unperturbed about many of the things that would seem like distractions that Joan was really amazed. She perceived the whole office situation as one that was foreign to her kind of living up to now. There seemed to be a discipline required that she doubted she would be capable of living up to. Her hands began to sweat. She wondered whether her perturbation and feeling of inadequacy were apparent to others around her. She wondered how she could be at her best when she went in to see Mr. H. The office seemed noisy. Each of the little events, as they came and went, was perceived as demonstrating her unfitness for working in such a place. She felt so much out of place that she was about to make an excuse to leave. Then she remembered a remark that one of her stepmother's relatives had made about her. This immediately angered her again and recast her mood, and she began to feel somewhat better. The whole office, glance by glance, began to seem like the place for the demonstration of her capabilities.

Soon she was in Mr. H's office talking to him, and listening to what he had to say. In the midst of this she realized how changed several things had become. She had changed while waiting to see Mr. H, and a part of this change was the way that things about her were perceived. Now she saw that Mr. H looked very different in his present role than he had seemed on other occasions. She had heard that he was a little hard to please, but what she was hearing him say, and the way he was saying it, convinced her that her fears in this respect were ungrounded. His whole face looked different to her than it ever did. His voice was not what she expected either.

TAKING A SCHOOL EXAMINATION

One of the many situations in which perception plays a highly varied role is in the taking of an examination. Very frequently examinations are spoken of in terms of how well the examinee *understands* the questions. Having the matter put in terms of understanding seems to leave perception out of the matter. This is not so, for in the first place "understanding" is a matter of perceiving what is meant by the questions. Perception thus is involved in what is immediately apprehended. Some of the examination questions may be "misperceived"; that is, what the examinee perceives to be meant is different than what the examiner requires. For example, in the case of the ordinary true-false type of examination, a given statement may be taken very differently than was meant by the examiner. The examiner did not perceive, in the combination of words he used, something that might be very obvious to a number of other people.

Under the stress of taking an examination, acoustic impingements that never were very effective in gaining attention or distracting the individual may become quite disturbing. Even the room illumination may be too low to satisfy the examinee. The perception of time is likely to change, and what is one or two hours may for some seem much longer, or for many others seem all too short. The room may seem too warm, or too stuffy. This may be the case even though the ventilating system is doing a fair job of changing the air. Worst of all, in some cases, examinees' minds "go blank." This, of course, is nothing but a special case of perception—a case of being unable to perceive in the usual fashion. It is sometimes called blocking.

ATTENDING A SYMPHONY CONCERT

Giving attention to extended periods of musical rendition is a unique kind of performance, not only on account of its rarity, but because it is a case of being sensitive from instant to instant to complex variations in a single stimulus modality. It is not acoustic stimulation one instant, photic the next, and so on. The stimuli to which attention is paid belong to what is reacted to as a close-knit continuity. The preoccupation with this single dimension of stimulation provides either for the very maximum impact on the person or for going to sleep. Acoustic impingements evoke an extreme amount and variety of symbolism. The listener may be taken over by elaborate imagery, each succeeding impingement carrying it on further and further. This is to say, orchestral sounds tend to mean a great many things, not only concrete but in mood and visual imagery.

Different people have been trained to expect different things from music. This is particularly true with respect to the various generations of individuals. The young expect one thing, and the old expect something very different. We do not know whether to assign this to age or to training and chance. We are accustomed to calling these differences of *taste*, but taste functions through the vehicle of perception.

THE LIGHTING OF A ROOM

By the lighting of a room we mean its visual appearance as determined by the general level and specific distribution of photic radiation used. In addition, it includes the spectral distribution of the radiation. Thus the experience of color as well as intensity are generally involved. One can scarcely deal with radiation without consideration of its spectral composition as well as intensity. Once color effects as dependent upon the illumination spectrum are considered, the reflective characteristics of the room surfaces in producing color are relevant.

If rooms do not contain enough radiation, they are not only dark but are inadequate for certain kinds of human activity. Since the proper levels are not obtained by merely stumbling onto them, the consideration of threshold and suprathreshold levels for various tasks has occupied the attention of certain investigators for a number of years.

Above and beyond the consideration of appropriate radiation levels, the matter of aesthetics and the creation of moods and of general personal comfort enter in. A room can be so patterned in the distribution of visual stimulation, or in the spectral combinations used, as to be irritating, or very soothing and restful. Some study of the relation between the spectral composition of illumination and mood has been made, but as yet not too much can be definitely said in this direction. Personal taste, for example, is a highly variable factor that comingles with whatever generalizations one otherwise might make regarding what colors to use, or not to use, for various purposes. This is because perception is a highly alterable affair. Conditioning for or against a given visual situation can so easily occur.

A good example of the perceived effect of a room is shown in a certain cafeteria. In it one sees only solid, stark hues. The walls are large unbroken areas of deep green and orange reds. The surfaces are slightly glossy. They look cold, and excite restlessness. Some of the patrons are conscious of the effects just implied, including the feeling of hurry. Other patrons must be entirely unaware of them.

One evening, the author was sitting in this cafeteria with a companion. All other patrons had gone, and the place was empty except for several waitresses who were sitting around a distant table sipping coffee and chatting. This group, seen out of the cafeteria context, that is, in isolation, would have been perceived as a picture of ease and relaxation. But the uneasiness associated with the garish walls and the cold metal furnishings of the large room was most obvious. Thus, visually, the author was face to face with two conflicting sets of stimulus conditions. The scene struck him rather forcefully as he stared back and forth at the "picture of leisure" embodied in the group of coffee drinkers and the factors making for the restlessness involved in the room colors. It was actually a startling perceptual contrast. The two factors did not go together at all, and if the scene were to be the subject of a painting it would be judged internally most incongruent.

Chapter 21

CONCLUSIONS

We have come now to the end of our presentation of perception. Its scope has been elementary, and therefore many topics that would have been of importance in a more penetrating treatment of the subject have been intentionally omitted. It is believed that if the reader well grasps the ideas and principles that have been included, he will have made a good beginning on the subject.

This concluding chapter is meant to bring together briefly some of the main ideas either expressed or implied in the material in the preceding chapters. These chapters, themselves, have been a kind of stocktaking of perception. The present conclusions will be a culmination of it.

The conclusions to which we wish to call attention fall into six categories or topics. The first of these had to do with the choosing of a basis for defining perception. The second pertains to the further structuring of perception. The third deals with perception as a part of scientific psychology. The fourth refers to the use of perception in clinical psychology. The fifth refers to the use of perception findings and principles in the allied professions, such as optometry, ophthalmology, and other specialties in medicine. The sixth deals with the possibility of further exploitation of perceptual principles in everyday living. The conclusions in each category will be very briefly stated, and later most of them will be discussed more fully.

The following conclusions belong in the first category:

1. No systematic and comprehensive statement of perception is to be found in the literature. The material we have is the result of accretion rather than logical formulation backed by experimentation. Hence, students beginning an acquaintance with perception as a subject must not expect to be presented with a well-organized, not to say finished, product.

2. It has been the task of the present text to decide, among the array

of alternatives, just what perception is. To do this, a stand had to be taken with regard to the relation between experience, behavior, and the world the physicist describes, namely, the energistic world that is the subject of the basic sciences of physics and chemistry.

3. Once perceptual activity was set apart from the energistic world in its descriptive characteristics, the next step was to distinguish between immediate response to or interaction with stimulus events and behavior only more remotely related to such events. It is obvious, then, that what constitutes perception is arrived at by definition rather than by blind, though precise, experimentation.

4. Our basic, definitive procedure has led to one further characteristic required of behavior in order that it be considered perceptual. It must be discriminatory, else it falls below the level of being perceptual.

The second category includes the following:

1. Perception, in any system of psychology, must be distinguished from the other-named analytical features of behavior, such as thought, memory, judgment.

2. Perception must be dealt with as stemming from the organism as a whole. It is the function of the highest-order processes and thus an expression of the person, or, as more commonly put, of personality.

3. Whereas perceptual behavior is generally dealt with in a highly analytical fashion in which each sense modality is structured separately, a large segment of our understanding of perception and of personalistic behavior must come from the study of the interrelation of the sense modalities, or, better still, of certain broad functions in which several senses participate. Some of these are, for example, the maintenance of posture, space perception, the appreciation of foods, appreciation of time.

4. The organism is related to its surrounds in ways of its own making. It develops symbolic relations to the world around it, and these are not rigidly spelled out, as would be implied if perception was only "stimulus-bound."

5. While it is implied in (4) that perception is modifiable, it is fruitful to state this explicitly, to be on the lookout for ways in which this occurs, and to discover principles by which it takes place. This is the true goal of the study of learning.

6. Perception expresses the continuity and ongoingness of the organism. This in its highest form is called purpose; at lower levels it may be given other names.

7. Perception, in representing the direct contact of the organism with

its surrounds, is more basic than any form of behavior that may be called derivative.

The third category has to do with the study of perception in experimental psychology. Accordingly, some of the conclusions are as follows:

1. A number of features of perception have been postulated and have become well-known theories regarding perception. Each of them addresses itself to a single aspect of perception rather than to accounting for perception as an entirety. Most of the features seem quite tenable, but several things are yet necessary. They need to be examined in the light of whether all the separate theories are necessary to form an adequate description of perception. They need to be recast so as to be in line with some systematic view, and they need to be tested further.

2. Certain features, exclusive of those dealt with in the perceptual theories just mentioned, remain to be included in the systematic formulations on a par with the ideas involved in the theories.

3. Certain requirements of experimentation, not hitherto clearly recognized and consistently followed, need to be adhered to so as to obtain results that will, as directly as possible, yield data concerning perception.

The fourth type of conclusion is the following:

1. The behavior which we call deviant or anomalous is often based upon anomalous perception.

2. A full recognition of this would require that those dealing with abnormal behavior—that is, clinical psychologists—would study perception and build their systems of understanding and therapy upon insights into its nature.

The fifth class of conclusions pertains to those having to do with the understanding of perception as a contributor to the healing arts aside from clinical psychology. The solution of many problems in optometry and ophthalmology, for instance, rests upon an understanding of the nature of perception—the fact that sensory problems do not exclusively stem from anomalous sense organs but also depend upon the perceptual employment of sense organs, normal and/or defective ones alike.

The sixth and final class of conclusions concerns the further use of perception in everyday life.

1. Our culture could profitably exploit the pleasurable possibilities of several of the sense modalities that find only restricted use.

2. The average person could well add to his comfort and well-being by understanding some of the facts and principles dealt with in the previous chapters.

PERCEPTION NOT COMPREHENSIVELY DESCRIBED

Nowhere in the literature can we find in concise and adequate form a well-rounded account of what perception is, what its characteristics are, and/or how it relates to other aspects of behavior. In fact, an adequate account does not even appear in scattered fragments. Most of the workers in the area of perception have been preoccupied with refining some quantitative detail, or investigating some single aspect of behavior, and have not devoted themselves to rounding out a statement of perception. Not all workers will agree in defining perception and many will find it difficult to settle on any definition.

We point this out not to criticize but rather to warn the reader as to what to expect, or to guide him in his outlook. It is to be hoped that embryonic psychologists will not relax in contentment as if the work of describing and defining perception was already accomplished for them by workers who have gone before. We have come to a new era, one in which more attention is likely to be paid to formulations of ideas about perception as a behavior function than has been done for some time.

A STUDY REGARDING FUNDAMENTAL AXIOMS

Among the general run of scientists and their followers, there is somewhat of an abhorrence against making explicit choices among metaphysical alternatives in formulating their systems of thought. They prefer to leave this feature of their stand with regard to Nature as amorphous as possible, assuming that so long as nothing is put into words nothing metaphysical is really involved in their thinking. One often hears the caution to avoid metaphysics and epistemology. On the one hand, it is easy to see why this caution is given. There are so many ramifications and alternatives that to enter the domain of metaphysics is to run the risk of getting into an insoluble maze, in a realm where, obviously, nothing is absolute. On the other hand, it surely must be known by every seasoned scientist that one can start out in no other way than by making either tacit or explicit assumptions called axioms. These are propositions one takes for granted, not through absolute proof but by choice. They represent one's best judgment, and to begin with axioms is to begin in philosophy.

The choice we have taken in writing this text has been one that is commonly enough implied in scattered statements of a great many people—scientists and others, alike. It is, therefore, not original and unique in this respect. It is unique enough in another respect. We have tried to hold to the implications of these statements as consistently and persistently as possible. The view to which we refer posits two separate domains: the domain of the physicist, in which the items are manifestations of something called energy, and the domain of human experiences —the perceptual and conceptual domain. In attempting to deal with perception in a consistent and effective way, we have found this distinction necessary. Not to do so would leave us simply to expressing everything in a purely common-sense way. It is obvious that to confine oneself to the common-sense way of thinking and verbally expressing things is both an easier and more familiar procedure. We can see little use for talking as the man on the street when this does not meet the problems that must be faced.

DEFINABILITY OF PERCEPTION

That perception is definable is another conclusion. To use the word and save any of its ordinary meaning, the most logical and useful primary procedure is to divide human activity into two vast categories. The first is the behavior that follows closely upon stimulation, a behavior that is immediately available for response to the come-and-go of impingements upon it. The second category includes all activity that succeeds the first —the aftermath and sequel to perceptual response. That the dividing line between the two categories may seem bothersome to many does not preclude attempting the distinction. Once the distinction is made, the nature of immediate response can be delineated. Part of this delineation is by definition and part by experimentation. It is by definition, for example, that perception can be said to be discriminatory.

NEED TO DISTINGUISH PERCEPTION

We have inherited a number of categories of behavior, such as perceiving, thinking, willing, emoting, learning, remembering, feeling. Any fully developed system of psychology must either define these items or else tell why any of them that are not defined can be omitted from the system. It is not incumbent upon all systematizers to use all the terms that are inherited. It is only necessary that a system actually deal with all examples of behavior. Most systems or partial systems of psychology retain all of the classical terms. We have gone no farther in this text than to indicate that learning and thinking, for example, are retained, and that perception therefore must be distinguished from these categories.

PERCEPTION AND THE WHOLE ORGANISM

It has been emphasized throughout the text that perception is not an isolated reaction of a restricted tissue system. It is a reaction in which several body systems participate under the direction of the central nervous system. This has been said so often that it would seem both quite obvious and even trite. But despite this, there is one central fact that seems to have escaped many psychologists. It is the realization that studying perception is a potential means of studying personality. Personality is an expression of perception. It is because this has escaped most people that the matter is pointed out. Personality is studied these days primarily in two ways: either as a group of traits or as a little-analyzed something that varies in a few described ways, such as in amount of frustration, as it interacts with outward circumstances. In such a mode of study, attention centers around a much-restricted set of concepts, e.g., frustration, fixation.

In stating that perceptual behavior stems from the organism as a whole, it is implied that perception might well be studied along a different dimension than is usual. That is, perception might well be studied more often in terms of the interrelations between the senso modalities. The need for this is illustrated in the study of such matters as space perception, postural responses and the maintenance of equilibrium, taste experiences, hunger, and thirst. None of this involves only a single sense modality, although they are unitary functions and ones most often experienced as unitary.

PERCEPTION AND REFLEXES

There are two closely allied aspects of behavior that have generally been involved in its classification. One is its *motor* automaticity, and the other is its absolute relation to the stimulus. If one "automatically" *sees* a tree every time the same target is presented, it is not customary to call the response a reflex. But if one "automatically" (i.e., quickly and without forethought) makes the same *motor response* to some stimulus presentation, it is customarily called a reflex, if it cannot be shown to have been learned. Thus, in the thinking of the day, reflexes are considered to be a specified set of activities apart from all others. We have indicated that they are logically a form of perceptual response when it can be shown that they are not only immediate responses but also discriminatory.

Some forms of response have appeared so consistently upon the presentation of a given stimulus that they seem to have come to be stimulus-bound. From this it has been deduced, at least tacitly, that to account for the reaction, one need only consider the stimulus and the nature of the sense organ. This, admittedly, provides a certain degree of accuracy in prediction, but it is the kind of understanding that is involved in the motorman's answer to the passenger's question of what makes the streetcar run. To this question the motorman in the story said that it was the handle he turned that made the car run. We can see the statistical connection between the two, but we still look for another sort of answer. It involves a description of the underlying mechanism.

In the case of perception, the insightful account might reveal, in principle, why the response did not follow the stimulus in those few cases in which it did not. For example, seeing a certain color is considered a reaction that is stimulus-bound, but it is known that one does not always see the same color as a result of the repeated presentation of the same stimulus. The stimulus is a big factor, but not the only factor.

SYMBOLIC NATURE OF PERCEPTION

All immediate response to stimulation carries in it much that is not "inherent." These responses, even though some of them may be reflexes, are carried out in ways that imply "meaning." That is to say, they imply "realization" of harm, not only something that has developed through long ages of evolution, but something ("meaning") that has developed through learning in the individual organism. It is all too easy for us to minimize the contribution of early learning in the individual, and to talk about the rigidity of relation between stimulus and response. The idea that response is stimulus-bound seems to stem from this minimization and from a feeling that "things could not be otherwise." All too little testing has ever been made of how different response could actually become under essentially different learning conditions.

Response seems to have reference to matters not literally existent, and thus not directly operative at the time. That a conditioned response is as it is, is dependent upon what has been made to occur in a nervous system. Yet to look upon such a response and to know its antecedents is to be willing to admit that time and space are "bound" by such behavior.

The behavior, in referring to what is not directly operative, is symbolic, according to one meaning of the term.

PERCEPTION AN APPROACH TO LEARNING

In studying learning, the units of concern are "responses." These responses are often perceptual since they are observable immediate reactions to conditions either accidently, incidentally, or intentionally imposed by the experimenter. So long as the significance of these responses as interactions to the imposed circumstances is by-passed, the understanding of learning is aborted. It is difficult if not impossible to see how the experimenter can avoid imputing some sort of significance or meaning to the animal's overt reactions. To avoid imputing or postulating some sort of significance should not be the ideal of experimentation. The aim should rather be the development of a self-consistent comprehensive account of the learning organism's behavior. If this account does a more adequate job of providing an explanation for behavior in general than other accounts, it is the one to be adhered to until a still more consistent and comprehensive one makes its appearance. We believe that to understand perception is one of the primary steps in providing an account of the learning process.

PERCEPTION AND ORGANISMIC CONTINUITY

In order to account for behavior, we must posit some sort of connectedness in what the organism does from moment to moment. This attribute we call connectedness may be called continuity, and continuity implies directionality. The connectedness with which we deal is not the pieced-together sort of behavior that would be the case if all that determined moment-to-moment responses were the external stimulus conditions. There are conditions existing within the organism that do not tally with or run apace with the conditions that externally come and go. The highest-order continuity and directionality are often called *purpose*. We need not always deal with continuity that carries with it a conscious aspect. Hence, according to customary usage, we possibly are not always dealing with purpose. Even though we are not, we find ourselves pretty much at one with what seems to be the general intent of the transactionalists in dealing with the continuity of the organism and its contribution to the interactions ("transaction") of the moment.

PERCEPTION AS BASIC

As has been stated again and again, perception represents the direct contact of the organism with the events or forces around it, and in being this it certainly is, in one way, the very basis for all other forms of activity. It has been easy for many to focus consideration in the other direction and say that perception is a product of "past experience." To do so is not to misstate the matter, for certainly perception is a developmental product. But the behavior that the organism is prepared to manifest as the immediate reactions to the instant-to-instant come-and-go of impingements upon it has a significance that the more remote reactions of thinking, for example, do not have. The immediate behavior is certainly foundational. Even if one considers only consciousness, it will be found that there is an absoluteness and an effectiveness to what is experienced as the "here and now," in contrast to what is imagined, or remembered "out of space and time." Response to the "here and now" is more compelling than other forms of activity. For example, how does one escape the gravitational field, or the thermal aspect of one's surrounds?

PERCEPTION THEORIES

In Chapter 1, certain prominent perception theories were given. They show that a number of separate properties of perception have been given consideration from time to time, but each without much regard to the others. While these theories represent attempts to deal with separate prime aspects of perception, they are stated in ways that do not make them parts of a single comprehensive outlook. Some of them were meant to supplant others rather than to complement them. The first step in making something unitary out of them would be to examine them to determine to what problems or broad aspects of behavior they address themselves. Accordingly, it would seem, they fall into four classes. They address themselves to one or the other of four general problems. The first problem is that of specifying internal structure of perception. The others are the organism's relation to its surrounds, the body mechanisms involved, and the purpose or other feature of the organism's activity that perception serves.

In the first category, it is possible to place the core-context theory; in the second, the texture-gradient, the adaptation-level, and the topological field theories. In the third category, we could place the cybernetics, the cell-assembly, the motor-adjustment, and the sensory-tonic field theories.

In the last, we could put the probabilistic, the transactional, the direc-tive-state, and the hypothesis theories. It scarcely does justice to some of these theories to place them in a single category; but if one judges the prime objective in the minds of the theorizers, the location of the theories becomes somewhat more restricted. For example, the cell-assembly theory, though placed in the category relating body mechanisms to the perceptual outcome, may in a way belong also in the category describing the internal structure of the perception. Likewise, although the transac-tional and probabilistic theories are placed in the category dealing with the organism's purposes and directionality, they might well also belong in the category having to do with the organism's relations to its surrounds.

It can be said, then, that with reference to problem one, the core-context theory offers no acceptable statement. With reference to category two, the texture-gradient and adaptation-level theories do offer some-thing very substantial and acceptable. They do specify principles relating the organism to its surrounds. They are mutually exclusive in so doing. The probabilistic and the transactional theories, insofar as they pertain to this category, also make certain acceptable statements; namely, that there is something probabilistic about the relation of the organism to its environment. However, since Brunswik's basic axioms fail to make the needed distinctions between the energy and perception domains, the referents in his statement of probability are not acceptable in its literal form. Topological field theory fails to do anything with the physicist's energistic domain and therefore by-passes a fundamental issue, thus fail-ing to be usable as an integral part of a system that might contain most of the theories we are reviewing.

The motor-adjustment and sensory-tonic field theories each recognize a separate aspect of body activity that should be incorporated into a com-prehensive theory of perception.

In dealing with behavior from the organism's standpoint, there are the four theories already mentioned: the probabilistic, the transactional, the directive-state, and the hypothesis theories. It would seem that certain features of each of them could be extracted and combined to give a more comprehensive statement of what is involved in perceptual behavior, viewed from the standpoint of the organ's continuity and contribution.

Throughout, the integrator of the theories would have to be careful to see that all statements and implications were in line with a single set of primary assumptions or axioms, as, for example, those having to do with such matters as the distinction between the energistic and the perceptual domains.

What this text has called the relational properties of perception would add to the features that need to be expressed in an overall perceptual theory—for example, that perception is symbolic, that perceptual behavior implies classification of stimuli, that perception is interpretative, and that it is field-determined.

REQUIREMENTS OF PERCEPTUAL EXPERIMENTATION

The material that has been set forth in the preceding chapters leads toward the conclusion that a sharpening of experimentation is called for in areas of so-called perception.

1. There must be a turning away from clustering together the ideas of estimation, judging, expressing an attitude, etc., under the heading of perception. Obviously, perceiving is somehow involved in all such processes, but in various and unknown ways. The mere involvement of perception does not allow one to call the overall process perception. Ways must be sought to control time, not only of presentation but that involved in responding, so as not to be studying judging, for example, rather than perceiving.

2. Terminology must be developed to dispel the present verbal ambiguity between what is stimulus and what is response. Avoiding the use of the same words for both is the very first step in this direction.

3. In cases in which judgments rather than perceptions must unavoidably be our experimental data, we must find ways of determining the relation between perceiving and judging so as to know how certain judgments stand for perceptions.

PERCEPTION AND ANOMALOUS BEHAVIOR

Another appropriate conclusion from the study of perception is that much of what we now recognize as anomalous behavior is or is based upon anomalous perceptual processes.

A very large interest in psychology today is a professional one— clinical psychology. In this field, abnormal or anomalous behavior is the object of study and correction. In the present manner of doing this, there is an implicit if not a directly expressed assumption that human difficulties are to be understood exclusively as social phenomena. As a consequence of this general outlook, the study of behavior is undertaken by immediate entrance into the investigation of social phenomena without a real attempt to understand underlying psychobiological mechanisms.

Great numbers of psychologists have no interest in behavior aside from that which they can talk about by means of a limited vocabulary containing such words as frustration and aggression. It is understandable why such ultimate specialization would occur. Psychologists need to understand, nevertheless, that largely untapped possibilities for studying the behavior in which they are ultimately interested await them in the study of perception and the organism's direct contact with its surrounds. Very much more needs to be done in studying the sensory behavior of the abnormal—the study of his space perception, his taste, and his other sensory preferences and aversions. We need to know the structure of each person's perceptual world in order to do what we need to do for him.

PSYCHOLOGY AND THE HEALING ARTS

Medicine, dentistry, optometry, osteopathy, and so on are often called the healing arts. Psychology, in the form of clinical psychology, is developing as another healing art. In the preceding section, the further development of clinical psychology was suggested by way of the study of the sensory processes, a hitherto much-neglected possibility. Our purpose in this section is to express the conclusion that psychology potentially has much to offer certain of the other healing arts. All of the findings of experimental psychology are not to be contained within its borders, or even within the confines of clinical psychology. Experimental psychology is rightfully a basic science, which means that its findings are contributing to all science.

To illustrate what we are suggesting here, the profession of optometry is a case in point. Professional optometry has come to conceive its task as one of providing visual skills to young and old. The focus of attention in this profession has left the eye and has reached the whole person as he operates in a space world.

The prescribing of eyeglasses is a necessary but incidental part of the whole task of providing proper vision. Professions providing this comprehensive care train *visual skills* in their patients, for they realize that vision is a learned achievement. Psychology was naturally the original discipline whose task it was to understand sensory processes and perception. For some time now, there has been a scarcity of workers for providing the understanding of perception and learning that the professions need. The professional men, conceiving their task to provide visual training, have had to play the role of scientists as well as therapists in order to find out what they need to know. Psychology must begin to realize to what extent this has been the case during the past couple of decades. With the clear realization that the professions lack the knowledge of perception and learning which they need, psychology should surely renew its efforts in psychosensory research.

SENSORY APPRECIATION IN EVERYDAY LIFE

Our society represents but one of the many possibilities of utilizing man's nature. A person may exercise his sensory capacities in certain ways, but in others he may not. Either he will be grossly misunderstood, or he will be considered vulgar and immoral.

A study of perception—that is, the possibilities of the sense modalities —leads us to believe that there are various favorable potentialities of perception that have not been exploited. Although the individual is allowed to explore taste possibilities by putting substances in his mouth, he is not expected to put the substances near his nose, for this is taken to be an act of suspicion rather than appreciation. Hence, it is socially tabooed. One may actively smell flowers or brandy, but not potatoes or cheese. One is not supposed to tell his host, for example, that his home smells nice, but he may tell him that it looks nice. To place this limitation on what one may do robs us of certain pleasures we might otherwise experience.

In vulgar expression, however, almost anything which one does not like is, these days, said to stink. Thus, while one portion of society holds tight rein on certain matters of sensory expression, another portion overdoes the matter by seizing upon a facet of sensory experience and stereotyping (universally idiomizing) it.

Another case in which daily practice represents limitation in sensory (or sensuous) possibilities occurs in vision. Few persons have developed the ability (let us say, art) of exploring their surrounds for items that may bring sheer sensuous pleasure. What they see must have the characteristics of familiar objects. They do not seem to be greatly impressed by seeing colors and textures as such. Vision seems to be primarily a means of reaching for, manipulating, and/or avoiding objects. It is, of course, conventional to declare that a sunset is beautiful, but there are hosts of other possibilities which we pass over daily with no attention paid and no appreciation given whatsoever.

The typical man does not understand his kinesthetic sense in a way that will lead to its maximum appreciation. Note the vast difference between the effects which children obtain on a merry-go-round, and every other device at an amusement park, and the effects obtained by adults. By the time that most people reach early adulthood, they do not like to ride on swings. The discomfort they experience is real, but how much of it is a conditioned affair, and thus an avoidable feature of living? May not a society move in the opposite direction?

It is probable that the person who gets great enjoyment out of his senses—that is, gets pleasure out of the sheer sensuous impact of his surrounds—is in pretty good mental health.

REFERENCES

1. Abraham, O., Zur psychologischen Akustik von Wellenlänge und Schweringungszahl, *Zf. f. Sinnesphysiol.* (1920), *51*:121–152.
2. Alexander, S. J.; Cotzin, M.; Hill, C. J., Jr.; Ricciuti, E. A.; and Wendt, G. R., The effect of variation of time intervals between accelerations upon sickness rates, *J. Psychol.* (1945), *19*:49–62.
3. Alexander, S. J.; Cotzin, M.; Klee, J. B.; and Wendt, G. R., The effect upon sickness rates of waves of various frequencies but identical acceleration, *J. Exper. Psychol.* (1947), *37*:440–448.
4. Allport, F., *Theories of Perception and the Concept of Structure*, Wiley, 1955.
5. Ames, A., Jr., Reconsideration of the origin and nature of perception, in S. Ratner (ed.), *Vision and Action*, Rutgers University Press, 1953.
6. Ammons, C. H.; Worchel, P.; and Dallenbach, K. M., "Facial vision," the perception of obstacles out of doors by blindfolded and blindfolded-deafened subjects, *Am. J. Psychol.* (1953), *66*:519–553.
7. Ashley, W. R.; Harper, R. S.; and Runyan, D. L., The perceived size of coins in normal and hypnotically induced income states, *Am. J. Psychol.* (1951), *64*:564–572.
8. Bartlett, F. C., *Remembering: A Study in Experimental and Social Psychology*, Cambridge University Press, 1932.
9. Bartley, S. H., The basis of flicker in the visual field surrounding the test object, *J. Exper. Psychol.* (1936), *19*:342–350.
10. Bartley, S. H., The relation of retinal illumination to the experience of movement, *J. Exper. Psychol.* (1936), *19*:476–485.
11. Bartley, S. H., A central mechanism in brightness enhancement, *Proc. Soc. Exper. Biol. Med.* (1938), *38*:535–536.
12. Bartley, S. H., *Vision: A Study of Its Basis*, Van Nostrand, 1941.
13. Bartley, S. H., Visual sensation and its dependence on the neurophysiology of the optic pathway, *Biol. Symp.* (1942), *7*:87–106.
14. Bartley, S. H., The perception of size or distance based on tactile and kinesthetic data, *J. Psychol.* (1953), *36*:401–408.
15. Bartley, S. H., and Miller, J. W., Some circumstances surrounding apparent movement in the line of regard, *J. Psychol.* (1954), *38*:453–456.
16. Bartley, S. H., and Seibel, J. L., A further study of entoptic stray light, *J. Psychol.* (1954), *38*:313–319.
17. Bartley, S. H., and Wilkinson, F. W., Certain factors in producing com-

plexity of response to a single pulse of light, *J. Psychol.* (1953), *35*:299–306.

18. Beebe-Center, J. G., Standards for use of the gust scale, *J. Psychol.* (1949), *28*:411–419.

19. Beebe-Center, J. G., and Waddell, D., A general psychological scale of taste, *J. Psychol.* (1948), *26*:517–524.

20. Békésy, G. von, Zur theorie des Hörens, *Physik. Zf.* (1929), *30*:721–745.

21. Benjamin, H. B.; Wagner, M.; Ihrig, H. K.; and Zeit, W., Hypothermia by internal cooling, *Science* (1956), *123*:1128–1129.

22. Bexton, W. R.; Heron, W.; and Scott, R. H., Effects of decreased variation in the sensory environment, *Canad. J. Psychol.* (1954), *8*:70–76.

23. Bishop, G. H., Responses to electrical stimulation of single sensory units of skin, *J. Neurophysiol.* (1943), *6*:361–382.

24. Bishop, G. H., The peripheral unit for pain, *J. Neurophysiol.* (1944), *7*:71–80.

25. Bishop, G. H., Neural mechanisms of cutaneous sense, *Physiol. Rev.* (1946), *26*:77–102.

26. Bishop, G. H., Relation of pain sensory threshold to form of mechanical stimulator, *J. Neurophysiol.* (1949), *12*:51–57.

27. Blakely, W., The discrimination of short empty temporal intervals, Ph.D., diss., *University of Illinois*, 1933.

28. Blanton, M. G., The behavior of the human infant during the first thirty days of life, *Psychol. Rev.* (1917), *24*:456–483.

29. Boring, E. G., *The Physical Dimensions of Consciousness*, Appleton-Century, 1933.

30. Boring, E. G., The moon illusion, *Am. J. Physics* (1943), *11*:55–60.

31. Boring, E. G.; Langfeld, H.; and Weld, H. P., *Foundations of Psychology*, Wiley, 1948.

32. Boring, E. G., and Stevens, S. S., The nature of tonal brightness, *Proc. Nat. Acad. Sci.* (1936), *22*:514–521.

33. Bornstein, W. S., Cortical representation of taste in man and monkey, *Yale J. Biol. Med.* (1940), *13*:133–156.

34. Bricker, P. D., and Chapanis, A., Do incorrectly perceived tachistoscopic stimuli convey some information? *Psychol. Rev.* (1953), *60*:181–188.

35. Brogden, W. J., Tests of sensory pre-conditioning with human subjects, *J. Exper. Psychol.* (1952), *31*:505–517.

36. Brown, J. F., The thresholds for visual movement, *Psychol. Forsch.* (1931), *14*:249–268.

37. Brown, J. F., and Voth, A. C., The path of seen movement as a function of the vector-field, *Am. J. Psychol.* (1937), *49*:543–563.

38. Brown, J. S., and Jenkins, W. O., An analysis of human motor abilities related to design of equipment and a suggested program of research, in P. M. Fitts (ed.), *Psychological Research on Equipment Design*, Government Printing Office, 1947, 35–63.

39. Brown, J. S.; Knauft, E. B.; and Rosenbaum, G., The accuracy of positioning reactions as a function of their direction and extent, *Am. J. Psychol.* (1948), *61*:167–182.

40. Brozek, J.; Guetzkow, H.; and Baldwin, M. V., A quantitative study of perception and association in semi-starvation, *J. Personal.* (1950–1951), *19*:245–264.

41. Bruner, J. S., Personality dynamics and the process of perceiving, in Blake and Ramsey (eds.), *Perception: An Approach to Personality,* Ronald Press, 1951.

42. Bruner, J. S., and Goodman, C. C., Value and need as organizing factors in perception, *J. Abnorm. Soc. Psychol.* (1947), *42*:33–44.

43. Bruner, J. S., and Postman, L., Emotional selectivity in perception and reaction, *J. Personal.* (1947), *16*:69–77.

44. Bruner, J. S., and Postman, L., Symbolic value as an organizing factor in perception, *J. Soc. Psychol.* (1948), *27*:203–208.

45. Brunswik, E., Thing constancy as measured by correlation coefficients, *Psychol. Rev.* (1940), *47*:69–78.

46. Brunswik, E., *Systematic and Representative Design of Psychological Experiments,* University of California Press, 1947, Series 304.

47. Bürck, W.; Kotowski, P.; and Lichte, H., Der Aufbau des Tonhöhenbewusstseins, *Elek. Nachr.-Techn.* (1935), *12*:326–333.

48. Burtt, H., Auditory illusions of movement: a preliminary study, *J. Exper. Psychol.* (1917), *2*:63–75.

49. Burtt, H. E., Tactual illusions of movement, *J. Exper. Psychol.* (1917), *2*:371–385.

50. Byall, R. S., Interpretation of the Van Orden Star, *Visual Training at Work* (1955), *4*:21–28 (Optometric Extension Program, Duncan, Okla.).

51. Canestrini, S., Über des Sinnesleben des Neugeborenen, *Mon. Neural. Psychiat.,* No. 5, Springer (Berlin), 1913.

52. Cantril, H., The nature of social perception, *Trans. N.Y. Acad. Sci.* (1948), *10*:142–153.

53. Carmichael, L., An experimental study in the pre-natal guinea-pig of the origin and development of reflexes and patterns of behavior in relation to the stimulation of specific receptor areas during the period of active foetal life, *Genet. Psychol. Mono.* (1934), *16*:337–491.

54. Carmichael, L., The experimental embryology of the mind, *Psychol. Bull.* (1941), *38*:1–28.

55. Carmichael, L., The onset and early development of behavior, in L. Carmichael (ed.), *Manual of Child Psychology,* Wiley, 1946.

56. Carr, H. A., *An Introduction to Space Perception,* Longmans, 1935.

57. Carter, L., and Schooler, E., Value, need, and other factors in perception, *Psychol. Rev.* (1949), *56*:200–208.

58. Chapman, L. F.; Symmes, D.; and Halstead, W. C., Auditory flutter fusion in patients with cortical ablations, *J. Comp. Physiol. Psychol.* (1955), *48*:421–425.

59. Child, I., and Wendt, G. R., The temporal course of the influence of visual stimulation upon the auditory threshold, *J. Exper. Psychol.* (1938), *23*:109–127.

60. Clark, D.; Hough, H.; and Wolff, H. G., Experimental studies on headache, *Arch. Neurol. & Psychiat.* (1936), *35*:1054–1069.

61. Committee on Colorimetry, Optical Society of America, *Science of Color,* Crowell, 1953.
62. Cotyzin, M., and Dallenbach, K. M., "Facial vision," the role of pitch and loudness in the perception of obstacles by the blind, *Am. J. Psychol.* (1950), 63:485–515.
63. Cramer, T., Über die Beziehung des Zwischenmediums zu den Transformations und Kontrasterscheinungen, *Zf. f. Sinnesphysiol.* (1923), 54: 215–242.
64. Cutsforth, T. D., *The Blind in School and Society,* American Foundation for the Blind, 1951.
65. Dallenbach, K. M., The temperature spots and end organs, *Am. J. Psychol.* (1927), 39:402–427.
66. Dallenbach, K. M., A method of marking the skin, *Am. J. Psychol.* (1931), 43:287.
67. Dattner, B.; Davis, V. T.; and Smith, C. E., A case of subcortical verbal agnosia, *J. Nerv. & Ment. Dis.* (1952), *116*:808–811.
68. Duncker, K., The influence of past experience upon perceptual properties, *Am. J. Psychol.* (1939), 52:255–265.
69. Edgington, E. S., Kinesthetically guided movements of head and arm, *J. Psychol.* (1953), 36:51–57.
70. Edgington, E. S., A tactual-kinesthetic curvature illusion, *J. Psychol.* (1956), 41:271–272.
71. Ellson, D. G., Hallucinations produced by sensory conditioning, *J. Exper. Psychol.* (1941), 28:1–20.
72. Evans, R. M., *An Introduction to Color,* Wiley, 1948.
73. Findley, A. E., Further studies of Henning's system of olfactory qualities, *Am. J. Psychol.* (1924), 35:436–445.
74. Fisher, B. M., The relationship of size of surrounding field to visual acuity in the fovea, *J. Exper. Psychol.* (1938), *23*:215–238.
75. Fisher, S. C., The process of generalizing abstraction, and its product, the general concept, *Psychol. Monog.* (1916), *21*:5–213.
76. Fitts, P. M., A study of location discrimination ability, in P. M. Fitts (ed.), *Psychological Research on Equipment Design,* Government Printing Office, 1947, 202–217.
77. Fletcher, H., Loudness, pitch and timbre of musical tones and their relation to the intensity, the frequency and the overtone structure, *J. Acous. Soc. Am.* (1934), 6:59–69.
78. Freeman, G. L., *The Energetics of Human Behavior,* Cornell University Press, 1948.
79. Fry, G. A., and Bartley, S. H., The brilliance of an object seen binocularly, *Am. J. Ophthal.* (1933), *16*:687–693.
80. Fry, G. A., and Bartley, S. H., The effect of one border in the visual field upon the threshold of another, *Am. J. Physiol.* (1935), *112*:414–421.
81. Fry, G. A., and Cobb, P. W., A new method for determining the blurredness of the retinal image, *Trans. Acad. Ophthal. & Otolaryng.* (1935).
82. Geldard, F. A., *The Human Senses,* Wiley, 1953.

83. Gesell, A.; Ilg, F. L.; and Bullis, G. E., *Vision, Its Development in Infant and Child*, Hoeber, 1949.

84. Gibson, J. J., The reproduction of visually perceived forms, *J. Exper. Psychol.* (1929), *12*:1–39.

85. Gibson, J. J., Adaptation, after-effect, and contrast in the perception of curved lines, *J. Exper. Psychol.* (1933), *16*:1–31.

86. Gibson, J. J., *The Perception of the Visual World*, Houghton Mifflin, 1950.

87. Gibson, J. J., The perception of visual surfaces, *Am. J. Psychol.* (1950), *63*:367–384.

88. Goldscheider, A., *Untersuchungen über den Muskelsinn:* I, Über die Bewegungsempfindung; II, Über die Empfindung der Schwere und des Widerstandes (in Goldscheider, *Gesammelte Abhandlungen*), Barth (Leipzig), 1898.

89. Graham, C. H., An investigation of binocular summation: I, the fovea, *J. Gen. Psychol.* (1930), *3*:494–510.

90. Graham, C. H., Psychophysics and behavior, *J. Gen. Psychol.* (1942), *10*:299–310.

91. Graham, C. H., Visual perception, in S. S. Stevens (ed.), *Handbook of Experimental Psychology*, Wiley, 1951.

92. Graham, C. H.; Baker, K. E.; Hecht, M.; and Lloyd, V. V., Factors influencing thresholds for monocular movement parallax, *J. Exper. Psychol.* (1948), *38*:205–223.

93. Graham, C. H., and Bartlett, N. R., The relation of size of stimulus and intensity in the human eye: II, Intensity thresholds for red and violet light, *J. Exper. Psychol.* (1939), *24*:574–587.

94. Graham, C. H.; Brown, R. H.; and Mote, F. A., Jr., The relation of size of stimulus and intensity in the human eye: I, Intensity thresholds for white light, *J. Exper. Psychol.* (1939), *24*:555–573.

95. Graham, C. H., and Cook, C., Visual acuity as a function of intensity and exposure time, *Am. J. Psychol.* (1937), *49*:654–661.

96. Graybiel, A.; Kerr, W. A.; and Bartley, S. H., Stimulus thresholds of the semicircular canals as a function of angular acceleration, *Am. J. Psychol.* (1948), *61*:21–36.

97. Griffith, C. R., An experimental study of dizziness, *J. Exper. Psychol.* (1920), *3*:89–125.

98. Guilford, J. P., The effective value of color as a function of hue, tint, and chroma., *J. Exper. Psychol.* (1934), *17*:342–370.

99. Guilford, M. P., and Lovewell, E. M., Touch spots and the intensity of the stimulus, *J. Gen. Psychol.* (1936), *15*:149–159.

100. Haan, E. L., and Bartley, S. H., The apparent orientation of a luminous figure in darkness, *Am. J. Psychol.* (1954), *67*:500–508.

101. Hahn, H., and Günther, Über de Reize und die Reizbedingungen des Geschmackssinnes, *Pflüg. Arch. ges. Psysiol.* (1932), *231*:48–67.

102. Hahn, H.; Kuckulies, G.; and Taeger, H., Ein systematische Untersuchung der Geschmackschwellen, *Zf. f. Sinnesphysiol.* (1938), *67*:259–306.

103. Hardy, J. D., and Soderstrom, C. F., Heat loss from the nude body and peripheral blood flow at temperatures from 22° C. to 35° C., *J. Nutrition* (1938), *16*:493–510.

104. Hartmann, G. E., Changes in visual acuity through simultaneous stimulation of other sense organs, *J. Exper. Psychol.* (1933), *16*:393–407.

105. Hastorf, A. H., The influence of suggestion on the relationship between stimulus size and perceived distance, *J. Psychol.* (1950), *29*:195–217.

106. Hazzard, F. W., A descriptive account of odors, *J. Exper. Psychol.* (1930), *13*:297–331.

107. Hebb, D. O., *The Organization of Behavior,* Wiley, 1949.

108. Hecht, S.; Haig, C.; and Chase, A. M., The influence of light adaptation on subsequent dark adaptation of the eye, *J. Gen. Physiol.* (1937), *20*: 831–850.

109. Hecht, S., and Mintz, E. U., The visibility of single lines at various illuminations and the retinal basis of visual resolution, *J. Gen. Physiol.* (1939), *22*:593–612.

110. Heinbecker, P., and Bishop, G. H., The mechanism of painful sensation, *Proc. Assoc. Res. Nerv. & Ment. Dis.* (1934), *15*:226–238.

111. Heinbecker, P.; Bishop, G. H.; and O'Leary, J., Analysis of sensation in terms of the nerve impulse, *Arch. Neurol. & Psychiat.* (1934), *31*:34–53.

112. Helson, H., Adaptation-level as a basis for a quantitative theory of frames of reference, *Psychol. Rev.* (1948), *55*:297–313.

113. Helson, H., *Theoretical Foundations of Psychology,* Van Nostrand, 1951.

114. Helson, H., and Fehrer, E., Role of form in perception, *Am. J. Psychol.* (1932), *44*:37–102.

115. Helson, H., and King, S. M., The tau effect: an example of psychological relativity, *J. Exper. Psychol.* (1931), *14*:202–217.

116. Henning, H., Die Qualitatenreihe des Geschmacks, *Zf. f. Psychol.* (1916), *74*:203–219.

117. Hermann, J., Gesamterlebnisse bei Geruchen, *Neue psychol. Stud.* (1926), *1*:473–506.

118. Hilgard, E. R., The role of learning in perception, in Blake and Ramsey (eds.), *Perception: An Approach to Personality,* Ronald Press, 1951.

119. Holway, A. H., and Boring, E. G., The moon illusion and the angle of regard, *Am. J. Psychol.* (1940), *53*:109–116.

120. Holway, A. H., and Boring, E. G., The apparent size of the moon as a function of the angle of regard, *Am. J. Psychol.* (1940), *53*:537–553.

121. Holway, A. H., and Boring, E. G., Determinants of apparent visual size with distance variant, *Am. J. Psychol.* (1941), *54*:21–37.

122. Howes, D., A statistical theory of the phenomenon of subception, *Psychol. Rev.* (1954), *61*:98–110.

123. Hulin, W. S., The effect on tactual localization of movement during stimulation, *J. Exper. Psychol.* (1935), *18*:97–105.

124. Hunter, I. M. L., Tactile-kinesthetic perception of straightness in blind and sighted humans, *Quart. J. Psychol.* (1954), *6*:149–154.

125. Ittelson, W. H., The constancies in perceptual theory, *Psychol. Rev.* (1951), *58*:285–294.

126. Ittelson, W. H., *The Ames Demonstrations in Perception,* Princeton University Press, 1952.

127. Ittelson, W. H., and Cantril, H., *Perception: A Transactional Approach,* Doubleday, 1954.

128. James, William, *Principles of Psychology,* Holt, 1892.

129. Jenkins, W. L., Studies in thermal sensitivity, *J. Exper. Psychol.* (1938), 23:411–416.

130. Jenkins, W. L., Somesthesis, in S. S. Stevens (ed.), *Handbook of Experimental Psychology,* Wiley, 1951.

131. Johnson, D. M., *Essentials of Psychology,* McGraw-Hill, 1948.

132. Judd, D. B., Basic correlates of the visual stimulus, in S. S. Stevens (ed.), *Handbook of Experimental Psychology,* Wiley, 1951.

133. Judd, D. B., and Kelly, K. L., Method of designating colors, *J. Res. Nat. Bur. Stand.* (1939), 23:355–385.

134. Kardos, L., Ding und Schatten, *Zf. f. Psychol.* (1934), Supp., 23:184.

135. Karwoski, T. F., and Odbert, H. S., Color-music, *Psych. Mono.* (1938), 50, No. 2.

136. Karwoski, T. F.; Odbert, H. S.; and Osgood, C. E., Studies in synesthesic thinking: II, The role of form in visual responses to music, *J. Gen. Psychol.* (1942), 26:199–222.

137. Katz, D., *The World of Color,* Kegan Paul, Trench, Trubner, 1935.

138. Katz, D., and Révész, G., Experimentelle Studien zur vergelichenden Psychologie, Versuche mit Huhnern, *Zf. f. angl. Psychol.* (1951), 18:307–320.

139. Klein, G. S., and Schlesinger, H., Where is the perceiver in perceptual theory? *J. Personal.* (1949), 18:32–47.

140. Klein, G. S.; Schlesinger, H. J.; and Meister, D., The effect of personal values on perception: an experimental critique, *Psychol. Rev.* (1951), 58.96–112.

141. Kloehn, N. W., and Brogden, W. J., The alkaline taste, *Am. J. Psychol.* (1948), 61:90–93.

142. Köhler, W., and Emery, D. A., Figural after-effects in the third dimension of visual space, *Am. J. Psychol.* (1947), 60:159–201.

143. Köhler, W., and Wallach, H., Figural after-effects: an investigation of visual processes, *Proc. Am. Philos. Soc.* (1944), 88:269–357.

144. Koffka, K., Some problems of space perception, in Carl Murchison (ed.), *Psychologies of 1930,* Clark University Press, 1930, 161–187.

145. Koffka, K., *Gestalt Psychology,* Harcourt, Brace, 1935.

146. Koffka, K., and Harrower, M., *Color and Organization,* Smith College Studies in Psychology, No. 3, 1932.

147. Korte, A., Kinematoscopische Untersuchungen, *Zf. f. Psychol.* (1915), 72:193–206.

148. Kravkov, S. V., Critical frequency of flicker and indirect stimuli, *Comptes Rendus* (1939), 22:64–66.

149. Kreezer, G., The neurological level of the factors underlying time-errors, *Am. J. Psychol.* (1938), 51:18–43.

150. Ladd, G. T., and Woodworth, R. S., *Elements of Physiological Psychology,* Scribner, 1911.

151. Laidlaw, R. W., and Hamilton, M. A., A study of thresholds in perception of passive movement among normal control subjects, *Am. J. Psychol.* (1937), 49:469–475.

152. Lambert, W. W.; Solomon, R. L.; and Watson, P. D., Reinforcement and extinction as factors in size estimation, *J. Exper. Psychol.* (1949), 39: 637–641.

153. Lashley, K. S., *Brain Mechanisms and Intelligence,* University of Chicago Press, 1929.

154. Lashley, K. S., The problem of cerebral organization in vision, *Biol. Symposia* (1942), 7:301–322.

155. Lawrence, M., *Studies in Human Behavior,* Princeton University Press, 1949.

156. Leeper, R., A study of a neglected portion of the field of learning—the development of sensory organization, *J. Genet. Psychol.* (1935), 46:41–75.

157. Leibowitz, H.; Mitchell, E.; and Angrist, N., Exposure duration in the perception of shape, *Science* (1954), 120:400.

158. Leibowitz, H.; Myers, N. A.; and Chinetti, P., The role of simultaneous contrast in brightness constancy, *J. Exper. Psychol.* (1955), 50:15–18.

159. Leibowitz, H., and Walker, L. C., Effect of field size and luminance on binocular summation of suprathreshold stimuli, *J. Op. Soc. Am.* (1956), 46:171–172.

160. Lemberger, F., Psychologische Untersuchungen über den Geschmach von Zucker und Saccharin, *Arch. Ges. Physiol.* (1908), 123:293–311.

161. Levine, R.; Chein, I.; and Murphy, G., The relation of the intensity of a need to the amount of perceptual distortion, *J. Psychol.* (1942), 13:283–293.

162. Lewis, D. R., Psychological scales of taste, *J. Psychol.* (1948), 26:437–446.

163. Licklider, J. R. C., Basic correlates of the auditory stimulus, in S. S. Stevens (ed.), *Handbook of Experimental Psychology,* Wiley, 1951.

164. Lindzey, G., and Rogolsky, S., Prejudice and identification of minority group membership, *J. Abnorm. Soc. Psychol.* (1950), 45:37–53.

165. Lopez-Ibor, J. J., Agoraphobia vertigo with consideration of the nature of Mênière syndrome, *J. Nerv. & Ment. Dis.* (1952), 116:794–807.

166. Lowenstein, E., and Dallenbach, K. M., The critical temperature for heat and for burning heat, *Am. J. Psychol.* (1930), 42:423–429.

167. Luckiesh, M., *Light, Vision and Seeing,* Van Nostrand, 1944.

168. Ludvigh, E. J., The visibility of moving objects, *Science* (1948), 108:63.

169. Ludvigh, E. J., and Miller, J. W., *A Study of Dynamic Visual Acuity,* Joint Project Report No. 1, Kresge Eye Institute Contract Nonr 586 (00), ONR Project Designation No. 142–023, BuMed Project NM 001067.01.01, 1953.

170. MacDonald, M. K., An experimental study of Henning's prism of olfactory qualities, *Am. J. Psychol.* (1922), 33:535–553.

171. MacLeod, R. B., An experimental investigation of brightness constancy, *Arch. Psychol.* (1932), 135:102.

172. MacLeod, R. B., Brightness constancy in unrecognized shadows, *J. Exper. Psychol.* (1940), 27:1–22.

173. Maerz, A., and Paul, M. R., A Dictionary of Color, McGraw-Hill, 1930.

174. Manas, L., Cheiroscopic drawing: target modification for maximum training benefits, Am. J. Optom. (1956), 33:113–117.

175. Mann, C. W., and Berry, N. H., The Perception of the Postural Vertical: II, Visual Factors, Joint Report No. 5, Tulane University and U.S.N. School of Aviation Medicine, Pensacola, Fla., 1949.

176. Mann, C. W., and Dauterive, J. H., Jr., The Perception of the Postural Vertical: I, The Modification of Non-labyrinthine Cues, Joint Report No. 4, Tulane University and U.S.N. School of Aviation Medicine, Pensacola, Fla., 1949.

177. Mathieson, A., Apparent movement in auditory perception, Psychol. Mono., Univ. of Iowa Studies Psychol. (1931), 14:74–131.

178. Maxfield, J. P., Some physical factors affecting illusion in sound motion pictures, J. Acoust. Soc. Am. (1931), 3:69–80.

179. McCleary, R. A., and Lazarus, R. S., Autonomic discrimination without awareness, J. Personal. (1949), 18:171–179.

180. McClelland, D. C., and Atkinson, J. W., The projective expression of needs, J. Psychol. (1948), 25:205–221.

181. McCulloch, W., and Pitts, W., The statistical organization of nervous activity, J. Am. Statist. Assoc. (1948), 4:91–99.

182. McGinnies, E., Emotionality and perceptual defense, Psychol. Rev. (1949), 56:244–251.

183. Miller, G. A., and Taylor, W. G., The perception of repeated bursts of noise, J. Acoust. Soc. Am. (1948), 20:171–182.

184. Miller, J. W., and Bartley, S. H., A study of object shape as influenced by instrumental magnification, J. Gen. Psychol. (1954), 50:141–146.

185. Miller, J. W., and Ludvigh, E. J., Dynamic Visual Acuity When the Required Pursuit Movement of the Eye Is in a Vertical Plane, Report No. 2, Bureau of Medicine and Surgery, U.S.N., Project No. NM 001075.01.02, 1953.

186. Miller, W. R., Light sensitivity and form perception in dark adaptation, J. Op. Soc. Am. (1953), 43:560–566.

187. Montagu, M. F. A., The sensory influences of the skin, Texas Rpt. Med. & Biol. (1953), 11:291–301.

188. Müller, G. E., and Schumann, F. Über die psychologischen Grundlagen der Vergleichung gehabener Gewichte, Pflüg. Arch. ges. Phys. (1889), 45:37.

189. Munn, N. L., Psychology: The Fundamentals of Human Adjustment, 2nd ed., Houghton Mifflin, 1951.

190. Munsell Book of Color, Munsell Color Co., Inc., 1942.

191. Murphy, G., and Hochberg, J., Perceptual development; some tentative hypotheses, Psychol. Rev. (1951), 58:332–349.

192. Nafe, J. P., Pressure, pain, and temperature senses, in C. Murchison (ed.), A Handbook of General Experimental Psychology, Clark University Press, 1938.

193. Nafe, J. P., and Wagoner, K. S., The experience of warmth, cold and heat, J. Psychol. (1936), 2:421–431.

194. Nafe, J. P., and Wagoner, K. S., The effect of thermal stimulation upon

dilation and constriction of the blood vessels of the skin of a contralateral hand, *J. Psychol.* (1936), *2*:461–477.

195. Nafe, J. P., and Wagoner, K. S., The nature of pressure adaptation, *J. Gen. Psychol.* (1941), *25*:323–351.

196. Nelson, T. M., and Bartley, S. H., The perception of form in an unstructured field, *J. Gen. Psychol.* (1956), *54*:57–63.

197. Newman, E. B., Versuche über das Gamma-Phänomen, *Psychol. Forsch.* (1934), *19*:102–121.

198. Newman, E. B., Hearing, in E. G. Boring, H. Langfeld, and H. P. Weld (eds.), *Foundations of Psychology*, Wiley, 1948.

199. Newman, E. B.; Volkmann, J.; and Stevens, S. S., On the method of bisection and its relation to a loudness scale, *Am. J. Psychol.* (1937), *49*: 134–137.

200. Nissen, H. W., Phylogenetic comparison, in S. S. Stevens (ed.), *Handbook of Experimental Psychology*, Wiley, 1951.

201. Nissen, H. W., Phylogenetic development, in S. S. Stevens (ed.), *Handbook of Experimental Psychology*, Wiley, 1951.

202. Ogle, K. N., *Researches in Binocular Vision*, Saunders, 1950.

203. Ogle, K. N., and Ellerbrock, V. J., Cyclofusional movements, *Arch. Ophthal.* (1946), *36*:700–735.

204. Osgood, C. E., and Heyer, A. W., A new interpretation of figural aftereffects, *Psychol. Rev.* (1951), *59*:98–118.

205. Ostwald, W., *Color Science*, Winsor and Newton (London), Part I, 1931; Part II, 1933.

206. Passey, G. E., and Guedry, F. E., Jr., *The Perception of the Postural Vertical: III, Adaptation Effects in Four Planes*, Joint Report No. 6, Tulane University and U.S.N. School of Aviation Medicine, Pensacola, Fla., 1949.

207. Payne, B., and Davis, R. C., The role of muscular tension in the comparison of lifted weights, *J. Exper. Psychol.* (1940), *27*:227–242.

208. Penfield, W. G., A contribution to the mechanisms of intracranial pain, in C. A. Patten, A. M. Franz, and C. C. Hare (eds.), *Sensation: Its Mechanisms and Disturbances*, Williams & Wilkins, 1935, 399–436.

209. Pfaffmann, C., Taste and smell, in S. S. Stevens (ed.), *Handbook of Experimental Psychology*, Wiley, 1951.

210. Pillsbury, W. B., Does the sensation of movement originate in the joint? *Am. J. Psychol.* (1901), *12*:346–353.

211. Postman, L.; Bruner, J. S.; and McGinnies, E., Personal values as selective in perception, *J. Abnorm. Soc. Psychol.* (1948), *42*:142–154.

212. Pratt, K. C.; Nelson, A. K.; Sun, K. H., The behavior of the newborn infant, *Ohio State Univ. Studies, Contrib. Psychol.*, 1930, No. 10.

213. Preyer, W., *Specielle Physiologie des Embryo*, Grieben (Leipzig), 1885.

214. Proshansky, H., and Murphy, G., The effects of reward and punishment on perception, *J. Psychol.* (1942), *13*:295–305.

215. Purdy, D. M., Spectral hue as a function of intensity, *Am. J. Psychol.* (1931), *43*:541–559.

216. Reid, R. L., An illusion of movement complementary to the horizontal-vertical illusion, *Quart. J. Psychol.* (1954), *6*:107–111.

217. Renshaw, S., The errors of cutaneous localization and the effect of practice on the localizing movement in children and adults, *J. Genet. Psychol.* (1930), *38*:223–238.

218. Renshaw, S., and Wherry, R. J., Studies on cutaneous localization: III, The age of onset of ocular dominance, *J. Genet. Phychol.* (1931), *39*:493–496.

219. Renshaw, S.; Wherry, R. J.; and Newlin, J. C., Cutaneous localization in congenitally blind versus seeing children and adults, *J. Genet. Psychol.* (1930), *38*:239–248.

220. Révész, G., System der optischen und haptischen Raumtäuschungen, *Zf. f. Psychol.* (1934), *131*:296–375.

✓ 221. Rock, I., and Fleck, F. S., A re-examination of the effect of momentary reward and punishment on figure-ground perception, *J. Exper. Psychol.* (1950), *40*:766–776.

222. Schafer, R., and Murphy, G., The role of autism in a visual figure-ground relationship, *J. Exper. Psychol.* (1943), *32*:335–343.

223. Schur, E., Mondtäuschung und Segrosskonstanz, *Psychol. Forsch.* (1925), *7*:44–80.

224. Seashore, Carl, *Introduction to Psychology*, Macmillan, 1924.

225. Serrat, W. D., and Karwoski, T., An investigation of the effect of auditory stimulation on visual sensitivity, *J. Exper. Psychol.* (1936), *19*:604–611.

226. Sherif, M., A study in some social factors in perception, *Arch. Psychol.*, 1935, No. 187.

227. Sherman, M., Judgments of emotional responses from motion picture views and from actual observation, *J. Comp. Psychol.* (1927), *7*:265–284.

228. Shlaer, S., The relation between visual acuity and illumination, *J. Gen. Physiol.* (1937), *21*:165–188.

229. Skramlik, F. von, Über die Lokalization der Empfindung bei den niederen Sinnen, *Zf. f. Sinnesphysiol.* (1925), *56*:69–140.

230. Smith, D. E., and Hochberg, J. E., The effect of "punishment" (electric shock) on figure-ground perception, *J. Psychol.* (1954), *38*:83–87.

231. Smith, W.; Powell, E. K.; and Ross, S., Manifest anxiety and food aversions, *J. Abnorm. & Soc. Psychol.* (1955), *50*:101–104.

232. Stagner, R., and Karwoski, T., *Psychology*, McGraw-Hill, 1952.

233. Stavrianos, B. K., The relation of shape perception to explicit judgments of inclination, *Arch. Psychol.*, No. 296, 1945.

234. Steinhardt, J., Intensity discrimination in the human eye, *J. Gen. Physiol.* (1936), *20*:185–209.

235. Stevens, S. S., The attributes of tones, *Proc. Nat. Acad. Sci.* (1934), *20*:457–459.

236. Stevens, S. S., The volume and intensity of tones, *Am. J. Psychol.* (1934), *46*:397–408.

237. Stevens, S. S., Tonal density, *J. Exper. Psychol.* (1934), *17*:585–592.

238. Stevens, S. S., The relation of pitch to intensity, *J. Acous. Soc. Am.* (1935), *6*:150–154.

239. Stevens, S. S., A scale for the measurement of a psychological magnitude: loudness, *Psychol. Rev.* (1936), *43*:405–416.

240. Stevens, S. S., The measurement of loudness, *J. Acoust. Soc. Am.* (1955), 27:815–829.

241. Stevens, S. S., and Davis, H., *Hearing: Its Psychology and Physiology*, Wiley, 1938.

242. Stevens, S. S., and Newman, E. B., The localization of actual sources of sound, *Am. J. Psychol.* (1936), 48:297–306.

243. Stevens, S. S.; Volkmann, J.; and Newman, E. B., A scale for the measurement of the psychological magnitude of pitch, *J. Acoust. Soc. Am.* (1937), 8:185–190.

244. Stewart, G. W., and Hovda, O., in H. A. Carr, *An Introduction to Space Perception*, Longmans, 1935.

245. Supa, M.; Cotyzin, M.; and Dallenbach, K. M., "Facial vision," the perception of obstacles by the blind, *Am. J. Psychol.* (1944), 57:133–183.

246. Symmes, D.; Chapman, L. F.; and Halstead, W. C., Fusion of intermittent white mice, *J. Acoust. Soc. Am.* (1955), 27:470–473.

247. Thouless, R. H., Phenomenal regression to the real object, *Brit. J. Psychol.* (1931), Part I, 21:339–359; Part II, 22:1–30.

248. Vanderplas, J. M., and Blake, R. R., Selective sensitization in auditory perception, *J. Personal.* (1940), 18:252–266.

249. Vernon, M. D., *Visual Perception*, Cambridge University Press, 1937.

250. Vernon, M. D., *A Further Study of Visual Perception*, Cambridge University Press, 1952.

251. Vernon, J., and Hoffman, J., Effect of sensory deprivation on learning rate in human beings, *Science* (1956), 123:1074–1075.

252. Wallach, H., The role of head movements and vestibular and visual cues in sound localization, *J. Exper. Psychol.* (1940), 27:339–368.

253. Wallach, H.; Newman, E. B.; and Rosenzweig, M. R., The precedence effect in sound localization, *Am. J. Psychol.* (1949), 62:315–336.

254. Weitz, J., and Compton, B., A further stereoscopic study of figural aftereffects, *Am. J. Psychol.* (1950), 63:78–83.

255. Wendt, G. R., Vestibular functions, in S. S. Stevens (ed.), *Handbook of Experimental Psychology*, Wiley, 1951.

256. Werner, H., Studies in contour: I, Qualitative analyses, *Am. J. Psychol.* (1935), 47:40–64.

257. Werner, H., and Wapner, S., Toward a general theory of perception, *Psychol. Rev.* (1952), 59:324–338.

258. Wertheimer, M., Experimentelle Studien über das Sehen Bewegungen, *Zf. f. Psychol.* (1912), 61:161–265.

259. Wertheimer, M., Constant errors in the measurement of figural aftereffects, *Am. J. Psychol.* (1954), 67:543–550.

260. Wertheimer, M., and Wertheimer, N., A metabolic interpretation of individual difference in figural after-effects, *Psychol. Rev.* (1954), 61:279–280.

261. Wheeler, R. H., and Cutsforth, T. D., Synaesthesia, a form of perception, *Psychol. Rev.* (1922), 29:212–220.

262. Wheeler, R. H., and Cutsforth, T. D., The synaesthesia of a blind sub-

ject with comparative data from an asynesthetic blind subject, *Univ. Oregon, Pub.*, 1, No. 10, 1922.

263. Wilcox, W. W., The basis of the dependence of visual acuity on illumination, *Proc. Nat. Acad. Sci.* (1932), *18*:47–56.

264. Wing, C. W., Jr., and Passey, G. E., *The Perception of the Postural Vertical: XI, The Visual Vertical Under Conflicting Visual and Acceleratory Factors,* Joint Report, No. 20, Tulane University and U.S.N. School of Aviation Medicine, Pensacola, Fla., 1950.

265. Winslow, C.-E. A.; Herrington, L. P.; and Gagge, A. P., Relations between atmospheric conditions and sensations of pleasantness, *Am. J. Hygiene* (1937), *26*:103–115.

266. Wispé, L. G., and Drambarean, N. C., Physiological need, word frequency, and visual duration thresholds, *J. Exper. Psychol.* (1953), *46*: 25–31.

267. Witkin, H. A., and Asch, S. E., Studies in space orientation: III, Perception of the upright in absence of a visual field, *J. Exper. Psychol.* (1948), *38*:603–614.

268. Witkin, H. A., and Asch, S. E., Studies in space orientation: IV, Further experiments on perception of the upright with displaced visual fields, *J. Exper. Psychol.* (1948), *38*:762–782.

269. Witkin, H. A.; Lewis, H. B.; Hertzman, M.; Machover, K.; Meissner, P. P.; and Wapner, S., *Personality Through Perception,* Harper, 1954.

270. Woodrow, H., Behavior with respect to short temporal stimulus forms, *J. Exper. Psychol.* (1928), *11*:174.

271. Woodrow, H., Reproduction of temporal intervals, *J. Exper. Psychol.* (1930), *13*:473–499.

272. Woodrow, H., Individual differences in the reproduction of temporal intervals, *Am. J. Psychol.* (1933), *45*:271–281.

273. Woodrow, H., Time perception, in S. S. Stevens (ed.), *Handbook of Experimental Psychology,* Wiley, 1951.

274. Woodworth, R. S., and Schlossberg, H., *Experimental Psychology,* rev. ed., Holt, 1954.

275. Worchel, P., and Berry, J. H., The perception of obstacles by the deaf, *J. Exper. Psychol.* (1952), *43*:187–194.

276. Worchel, P., and Dallenbach, K. M., "Facial vision," perception of obstacles by the deaf-blind, *Am. J. Psychol.* (1947), *60*:502–553.

277. Zwaardemaker, H., *L'Odorat,* Doin (Paris), 1925.

Index of Names

Alexander, S. J., 331
Allport, F., 12, 18, 388, 392, 397
Ames, A., Jr., 17, 176, 216, 218
Ammons, C. H., 308
Angrist, N., 29
Aristotle, 356
Asch, S. E., 334, 335
Ashley, W. R., 393
Atkinson, J. W., 407
Aubert, H., 261

Babinski, J., 422
Baker, K. E., 262
Baldwin, M. V., 390
Bartlett, F. C., 94
Bartley, S. H., 121, 123, 124, 127, 128,
    129, 131, 132, 141, 142, 145, 147,
    191, 192, 193, 194, 195, 196, 239,
    251, 266, 268, 324, 329, 333, 365,
    367
Beebe-Center, J. G., 346, 347
Békésy, G. von, 283
Benjamin, H. B., 376
Berry, N. H., 334
Bexton, W. R., 417
Biedermann, H., 317
Bishop, G. H., 359, 363, 378
Blake, R. R., 392
Blakely, W., 70
Blanton, M. G., 79
Blix, M., 359
Boring, E. G., 11, 183, 287, 299
Bornstein, W. S., 344
Brewster, D., 231
Bricker, P. D., 407
Brogden, W. J., 65
Brown, J. F., 262
Brozek, J., 390
Bruner, J. S., 17, 18, 388, 392, 393, 394,
    399, 403, 404, 405, 406, 407, 408
Brunswik, E., 16, 34, 174

Bullis, G. E., 80, 81
Bürck, W., 282, 284
Buitt, H., 260, 272
Byall, R. S., 248

Carmichael, L., 79
Carter, L., 393
Chapanis, A., 407
Chapman, L. F., 295, 427
Chase, A. M., 110
Chein, I., 389, 390
Child, I., 64
Clason, 186
Clark, D., 382
Cobb, P. W., 141, 142, 146
Cotyzin, M., 308
Cotzin, M., 331
Cramer, T., 198, 199
Cutsforth, T. D., 65, 312

Dallenbach, K. M., 308, 358, 371
Dattner, B., 422
Dauterive, J. H., Jr., 334
Davis, H., 278, 282, 289
Davis, R. C., 90
Davis, V. T., 422
Donaldson, H. H., 359
Drambarean, N. C., 406
Duncker, K., 422

Edgington, E. S., 322
Ellerbrock, V., 288
Ellson, D. G., 88, 89
Euclid, 31, 32, 205
Evans, R. M., 155, 159

Fehrer, E., 92, 93
Findley, A. E., 350
Fisher, B., 140
Fisher, S., 53, 54
Fleck, F. S., 391, 397

475

Index of Subjects

DATE DUE

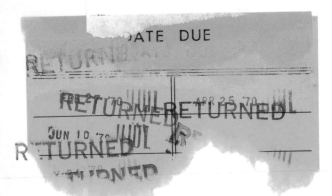